SCOTT FORESMAN · ADDISON WESLEY

Mathematics

Grade 2

Answer Key
for Reteaching, Practice, Enrichment and Problem Solving

PEARSON

Scott
Foresman

Editorial Offices: Glenview, Illinois • Parsippany, New Jersey • New York, New York

Sales Offices: Parsippany, New Jersey • Duluth, Georgia • Glenview, Illinois
Coppell, Texas • Ontario, California • Mesa, Arizona

ISBN: 0-328-04940-9

Name _____

R 1-1

Joining Groups to Add

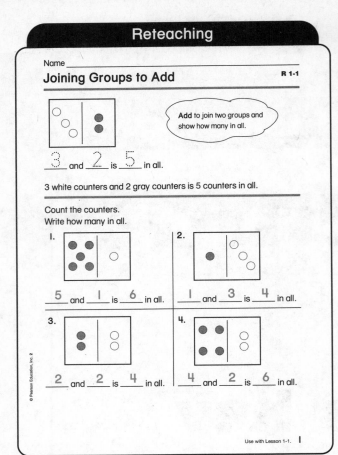

Add to join two groups and show how many in all.

___3___ and ___2___ is ___5___ in all.

3 white counters and 2 gray counters is 5 counters in all.

Count the counters.
Write how many in all.

1. ___5___ and ___1___ is ___6___ in all.

2. ___1___ and ___3___ is ___4___ in all.

3. ___2___ and ___2___ is ___4___ in all.

4. ___4___ and ___2___ is ___6___ in all.

Use with Lesson 1-1.

© Pearson Education, Inc. 2

Name _____

P 1-1

Joining Groups to Add

Count the fruit in the two groups.
Draw and write how many there are in all.

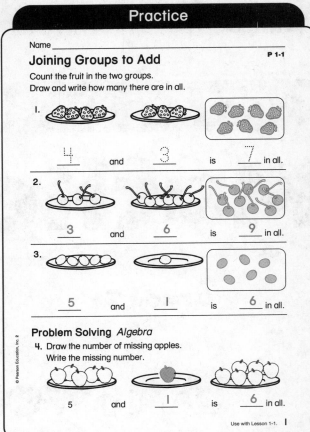

1. ___4___ and ___3___ is ___7___ in all.

2. ___3___ and ___6___ is ___9___ in all.

3. ___5___ and ___1___ is ___6___ in all.

Problem Solving *Algebra*

4. Draw the number of missing apples.
Write the missing number.

5 and ___1___ is ___6___ in all.

Use with Lesson 1-1.

© Pearson Education, Inc. 2

Name _____

E 1-1
NUMBER SENSE

Balloon Party

Write the numbers to show how many there are in all.
Use each number in a balloon only once.
You may use counters if you need to.

Order of addends may vary.

1.
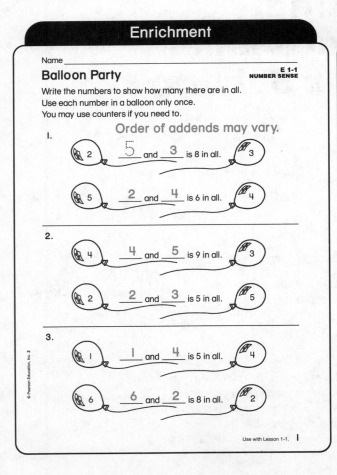

2 ___5___ and ___3___ is 8 in all. 3

5 ___2___ and ___4___ is 6 in all. 4

2.

4 ___4___ and ___5___ is 9 in all. 3

2 ___2___ and ___3___ is 5 in all. 5

3.

1 ___1___ and ___4___ is 5 in all. 4

6 ___6___ and ___2___ is 8 in all. 2

Use with Lesson 1-1.

© Pearson Education, Inc. 2

Name _____

PS 1-1

Joining Groups to Add

Draw the number of missing apples.
Write the missing numbers.

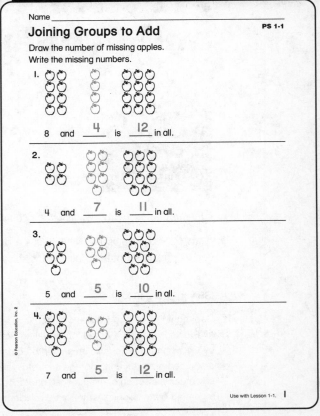

1. 8 and ___4___ is ___12___ in all.

2. 4 and ___7___ is ___11___ in all.

3. 5 and ___5___ is ___10___ in all.

4. 7 and ___5___ is ___12___ in all.

Use with Lesson 1-1.

© Pearson Education, Inc. 2

© Pearson Education, Inc. **2**

Name _____

Writing Addition Sentences
R 1-2

How many counters are there in all?

2 + 4 = 6
is called an
addition sentence.

Part	Part		Whole
2 and	4	is	6.
2 plus	4	equals	6.

2 + 4 = 6
addends   sum

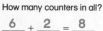

$\underline{2} + \underline{4} = \underline{6}$

Use counters and Workmat 1.
Write the addition sentence to solve the problem.

1.

How many counters in all?
$\underline{6} + \underline{2} = \underline{8}$

2.
How many counters in all?
$\underline{7} + \underline{3} = \underline{10}$

3.
How many counters in all?
$\underline{4} + \underline{5} = \underline{9}$

4.
How many counters in all?
$\underline{7} + \underline{5} = \underline{12}$

2 Use with Lesson 1-2.

© Pearson Education, Inc. 2

Name _____

Writing Addition Sentences
P 1-2

Write an addition sentence to solve the problem.

1. 5 boys are at the party.
6 girls are at the party.
How many children are
there in all?
$\underline{5} + \underline{6} = \underline{11}$ children

2. There are 6 blue hats.
There are 2 red hats.
How many hats are
there in all?
$\underline{6} + \underline{2} = \underline{8}$ hats

3. 4 children play a game.
5 children sing a song.
How many children are
there in all?
$\underline{4} + \underline{5} = \underline{9}$ children

4. 7 cups are on the table.
1 cup is on a shelf.
How many cups are
there in all?
$\underline{7} + \underline{1} = \underline{8}$ cups

5. There are 3 red ribbons.
There are 3 blue ribbons.
How many ribbons are
there in all?
$\underline{3} + \underline{3} = \underline{6}$ ribbons

6. There are 7 gifts for Suzi.
There are 0 gifts for David.
How many gifts are
there in all?
$\underline{7} + \underline{0} = \underline{7}$ gifts

Problem Solving Visual Thinking
Complete the addition sentence.

7. There are 7 balloons in all.
Color some balloons red.
Color some balloons blue.

_____ + _____ = _____ balloons Answers may vary.

2 Use with Lesson 1-2.

© Pearson Education, Inc. 2

Name _____

Apple Picking
E 1-2
VISUAL THINKING

Five friends went apple picking.

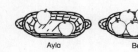

Lisa   Lee   Paco

Ayla   Ben

Write an addition sentence to solve each problem.

1. How many apples did
Lisa and Ayla pick in all?
$\underline{5} + \underline{2} = \underline{7}$ apples

2. How many apples did
Lee and Ben pick in all?
$\underline{4} + \underline{6} = \underline{10}$ apples

3. How many apples did
Paco and Lisa pick in all?
$\underline{3} + \underline{5} = \underline{8}$ apples

4. How many apples did
Ben and Ayla pick in all?
$\underline{6} + \underline{2} = \underline{8}$ apples

2 Use with Lesson 1-2.

© Pearson Education, Inc. 2

Name _____

Writing Addition Sentences
PS 1-2

Write an addition sentence to solve the problem.

1. There are 3 blue boats.
There are 7 red boats.
How many boats are
there in all?

$\underline{3} + \underline{7} = \underline{10}$ boats

2. 9 boys ride on the bus.
2 girls ride on the bus.
How many children
ride on the bus?

$\underline{9} + \underline{2} = \underline{11}$ children

3. There are 8 cars in all.
How many cars are
behind the fence?

$\underline{4} + \underline{4} = \underline{8}$ cars

$\underline{4}$ cars are behind the fence.

4. There are 12 pencils in all.
How many pencils are in
the pencil case?

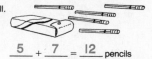

$\underline{5} + \underline{7} = \underline{12}$ pencils

$\underline{7}$ pencils are in the pencil case.

2 Use with Lesson 1-2.

© Pearson Education, Inc. 2

Name _____

PROBLEM-SOLVING STRATEGY   R 1-3

Write a Number Sentence

Read and Understand

6 cats are on the steps.
3 more cats join them.
How many cats are there in all?

Add to join groups.
The addition sentence
6 + 3 = 9 can be used
to solve the problem.

Plan and Solve

You need to find out how many cats there are in all.

_6_ and _3_ is _9_.

_6_ plus _3_ equals _9_.

_6_ + _3_ = _9_ cats.

Look Back and Check

Did you answer the question?

Write a number sentence to solve each problem.

1. 5 puppies are playing.
   3 puppies join them.
   How many puppies are
   there altogether?

   _5_ plus _3_ equals _8_.

   _5_ + _3_ = _8_

   There are _8_ puppies altogether.

Use with Lesson 1-3. **3**

Name _____

PROBLEM-SOLVING STRATEGY   P 1-3

Write a Number Sentence

Write a number sentence to solve the problem.

1. 6 goldfish are in one bowl.
   4 goldfish are in another bowl.
   How many goldfish are there altogether?

   _6_ ⊕ _4_ ⊜ _10_ goldfish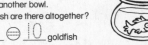

2. There are 3 mice in a cage.
   There are 4 mice in another cage.
   How many mice are there in all?

   _3_ ⊕ _4_ ⊜ _7_ mice

3. There are 2 frogs on a rock.
   There are 6 frogs in the water.
   How many frogs are there in all?

   _2_ ⊕ _6_ ⊜ _8_ frogs

4. 3 kittens are playing.
   8 kittens are sleeping.
   How many kittens are there in all?

   _3_ ⊕ _8_ ⊜ _11_ kittens

5. 5 butterflies are on a flower.
   4 butterflies are on another flower.
   How many butterflies are there in all?

   _5_ ⊕ _4_ ⊜ _9_ butterflies

Use with Lesson 1-3. **3**

Name _____

Time for Lunch   E 1-3
                                     DATA

The table shows how many children ordered
school lunches for one week.

School Lunches Ordered

	Monday	Tuesday	Wednesday	Thursday	Friday
Grade 1	2	3	4	6	3
Grade 2	5	4	7	1	8

Write a number sentence to solve each problem.

1. How many lunches did Grade 1 order on Monday?   _2_

   How many lunches did Grade 2 order on Monday?   _5_

   How many lunches were
   ordered in all on Monday?   _2 + 5 = 7_ lunches

2. How many lunches did Grade 1 order on Friday?   _3_

   How many lunches did Grade 2 order on Friday?   _8_

   How many lunches were
   ordered altogether on Friday?   _3 + 8 = 11_ lunches

3. How many lunches did Grade 2 order on Thursday?   _1_

   How many lunches did Grade 2 order on Friday?   _8_

   How many lunches were ordered
   in Grade 2 on these two days?   _1 + 8 = 9_ lunches

Use with Lesson 1-3. **3**

Name _____

PROBLEM-SOLVING STRATEGY   PS 1-3

Write a Number Sentence

5 horses are in a barn.
2 horses are in the field.
How many horses are
there altogether?

_5_ horses in the barn   _2_ horses in the field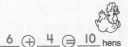

What do you need to find out? **How many horses**
there are altogether

_5_ ⊕ _2_ ⊜ _7_ horses

1. 3 pigs are in the pigpen.
   2 pigs are in the yard.
   How many pigs are there
   in all?

   _3_ ⊕ _2_ ⊜ _5_ pigs

2. 5 cows are in the field.
   3 cows are on the road.
   How many cows are
   there altogether?

   _5_ ⊕ _3_ ⊜ _8_ cows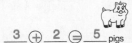

3. There are 6 hens in
   the yard. There are
   4 hens in the coop.
   How many hens are
   there in all?

   _6_ ⊕ _4_ ⊜ _10_ hens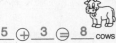

Using the page Have children **read** the story. To help them **understand**, ask children to identify the number of
animals and tell what the question is asking.

Use with Lesson 1-3. **3**

Name _____

Taking Away to Subtract

R 1-4

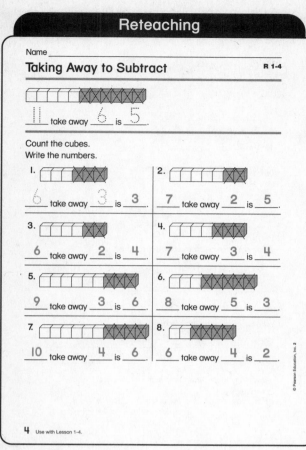

__11__ take away __6__ is __5__.

Count the cubes.
Write the numbers.

1. __6__ take away __3__ is __3__.

2. __7__ take away __2__ is __5__.

3. __6__ take away __2__ is __4__.

4. __7__ take away __3__ is __4__.

5. __9__ take away __3__ is __6__.

6. __8__ take away __5__ is __3__.

7. __10__ take away __4__ is __6__.

8. __6__ take away __4__ is __2__.

© Pearson Education, Inc. 2

4 Use with Lesson 1-4.

Name _____

Taking Away to Subtract

P 1-4

Write the numbers.

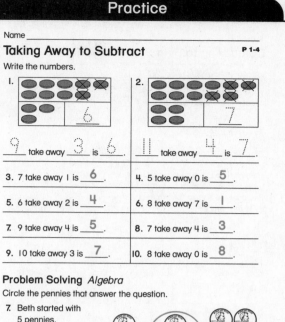

1. (box with 6) __9__ take away __3__ is __6__.

2. (box with 7) __11__ take away __4__ is __7__.

3. 7 take away 1 is __6__.

4. 5 take away 0 is __5__.

5. 6 take away 2 is __4__.

6. 8 take away 7 is __1__.

7. 9 take away 4 is __5__.

8. 7 take away 4 is __3__.

9. 10 take away 3 is __7__.

10. 8 take away 0 is __8__.

Problem Solving Algebra

Circle the pennies that answer the question.

7. Beth started with
5 pennies.
She lost 2 pennies.
How many pennies
does Beth now have?

© Pearson Education, Inc. 2

4 Use with Lesson 1-4.

Name _____

Making Fruit Salad

E 1-4
DECISION MAKING

Help Carla make fruit salad.
Decide how many pieces of each fruit you will use.
Cross out the pieces of fruit you do not use.
Write the numbers.

Answers may vary.

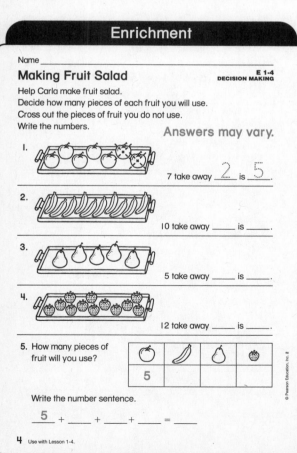

1. 7 take away __2__ is __5__.

2. 10 take away _____ is _____.

3. 5 take away _____ is _____.

4. 12 take away _____ is _____.

5. How many pieces of fruit will you use?

🍅	🍌	🍐	🍓
5			

Write the number sentence.

__5__ + _____ + _____ + _____ = _____

4 Use with Lesson 1-4.

© Pearson Education, Inc. 2

Name _____

Taking Away to Subtract

PS 1-4

Cross out some stars.
Write the numbers.

Answers will vary.
A sample answer is shown.

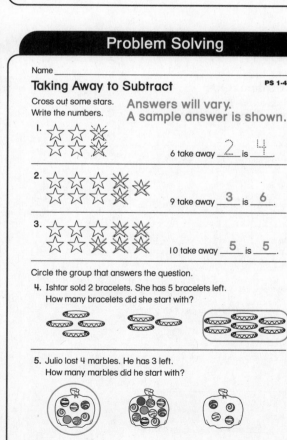

1. 6 take away __2__ is __4__.

2. 9 take away __3__ is __6__.

3. 10 take away __5__ is __5__.

Circle the group that answers the question.

4. Ishtar sold 2 bracelets. She has 5 bracelets left.
How many bracelets did she start with?

5. Julio lost 4 marbles. He has 3 left.
How many marbles did he start with?

4 Use with Lesson 1-4.

© Pearson Education, Inc. 2

Name _____

Comparing to Find How Many More   R 1-5

○ ○ ○ ○ ○

□ □ □

> To compare the number of circles and squares, match each circle with a square. There are 2 circles left over.

There are __5__ circles.

There are __3__ squares.

There are __2__ more circles than squares.

Compare the number of circles and squares.
Write the numbers.

1. ○ ○ ○ ○ ○
   □ □

   __6__ circles   __2__ squares

   __4__ more circles than squares.

2. ○ ○ ○ ○ ○
   □

   __5__ circles   __1__ square

   __4__ more circles than squares.

3. ○ ○ ○ ○ ○
   □ □ □ □ □

   __6__ circles   __5__ squares

   __1__ more circle than squares.

4. ○ ○ ○ ○
   □ □ □ □

   __4__ circles   __4__ squares

   __0__ more circles than squares.

Use with Lesson 1-5. 5

Name _____

Comparing to Find How Many More   P 1-5

Compare the number of objects in each group.
Write the numbers.

1. How many more white ducks are there?

   __8__ white ducks   __3__ gray ducks   __5__ more white ducks

2. How many more spotted bears are there?

   __5__ spotted bears   __3__ white bears   __2__ more spotted bears

Reasoning *Writing in Math*   Stories may vary.

3. Write a math story to go with the picture.

   Sample answer: 3 flowers are in the striped pot. 2 flowers are in the spotted pot.

   How many more flowers are in the striped pot?

   __3__ flowers − __2__ flowers = __1__ more flower in the striped pot

Use with Lesson 1-5. 5

Name _____

Counting Birds   E 1-5 DATA

Mrs. Johnson's class went bird watching.
The graph shows the birds they saw.

Birds We Saw

Bluejays	🐦 🐦 🐦 🐦 🐦 🐦
Robins	🐦 🐦 🐦 🐦 🐦 🐦 🐦 🐦
Cardinals	🐦 🐦 🐦
Sparrows	🐦 🐦 🐦 🐦 🐦

One 🐦 stands for 1 bird.

Use the graph to solve each problem.

1. How many more bluejays than cardinals are there?

   __6__ bluejays   __3__ cardinals   __3__ more bluejays

2. How many more robins than sparrows are there?

   __8__ robins   __5__ sparrows   __3__ more robins

3. How many more robins than cardinals are there?

   __8__ robins   __3__ cardinals   __5__ more robins

Use with Lesson 1-5. 5

Name _____

Comparing to Find How Many More   PS 1-5

Compare the number of animals in each group.
Write the numbers.

1. __5__ puppies   __3__ kittens
   __2__ more puppies

2. __4__ ducks   __2__ frogs
   __2__ more ducks

3. __4__ hens   __1__ pig
   __3__ more hens

Writing in Math

4. Write a math story with 5 birds and 3 turtles.

   Stories will vary.

Use with Lesson 1-5. 5

Name _____

Writing Subtraction Sentences

In a subtraction sentence, the answer is the **difference**.

6 take away 4 is 2.

6 minus 4 equals 2.

$\underline{6} - \underline{4} = \underline{2}$ puppies

Write the subtraction sentence to solve the problem.

1. There are 7 trucks.
   Take away 5 trucks.
   How many trucks are left?

   $\underline{7} - \underline{5} = \underline{2}$ trucks

2. There are 5 cats.
   Take away 2 cats.
   How many cats are left?

   $\underline{5} - \underline{2} = \underline{3}$ cats

3. There are 8 apples.
   Take away 6 apples.
   How many apples are left?

   $\underline{8} - \underline{6} = \underline{2}$ apples

6 Use with Lesson 1-6.

© Pearson Education, Inc. 2

Name _____

Writing Subtraction Sentences

Write the subtraction sentence to solve the problem.

1. There are 11 red flowers.
   There are 5 white flowers.
   How many more red
   flowers are there? $\underline{11} - \underline{5} = \underline{6}$ red flowers

2. 8 beetles are on a bush.
   2 beetles fly away.
   How many beetles are
   left on the bush?  $\underline{8} - \underline{2} = \underline{6}$ beetles

3. 10 bugs are in the sand.
   5 bugs are in the water.
   How many more bugs
   are in the sand? $\underline{10} - \underline{5} = \underline{5}$ bugs

4. James picks 7 roses.
   He gives 3 roses to Lee.
   How many roses does
   James have left? $\underline{7} - \underline{3} = \underline{4}$ roses

Problem Solving *Reasonableness*

Circle the answer to the question.

5. Mary has 10 flowers. She gives some to her mother.
   Which answer tells how many flowers Mary might have left?
   Explain.

   (4 flowers)   10 flowers   12 flowers

   Sample answer: If Mary gave some flowers
   away, she would have fewer than 10 flowers left.

6 Use with Lesson 1-6.

© Pearson Education, Inc. 2

Name _____

Disappearing Beads

Look at the crossed out beads.
Write a subtraction sentence.

1. $\underline{7} - \underline{5} = \underline{2}$

   $\underline{8} - \underline{4} = \underline{4}$

   $\underline{9} - \underline{3} = \underline{6}$

   $\underline{10} - \underline{2} = \underline{8}$

2. $\underline{6} - \underline{3} = \underline{3}$

   $\underline{8} - \underline{6} = \underline{2}$

   $\underline{10} - \underline{9} = \underline{1}$

   $\underline{12} - \underline{12} = \underline{0}$

6 Use with Lesson 1-6.

© Pearson Education, Inc. 2

Name _____

Writing Subtraction Sentences

Write a subtraction sentence to solve the problem.

1. There are 7 birds in a tree.
   4 birds fly away.
   How many birds are left?

   $\underline{7} - \underline{4} = \underline{3}$ birds

2. 5 kittens are in a basket.
   2 kittens jump out.
   How many kittens are left?

   $\underline{5} - \underline{2} = \underline{3}$ kittens

3. Billy sees 9 frogs on a log.
   Matt sees 3 frogs on a log.
   How many more frogs does
   Billy see?

   $\underline{9} - \underline{3} = \underline{6}$ frogs

Circle the answer to the question.

4. Neda has 7 coloring books.
   She gave some to Felix.
   Which answer tells how many
   coloring books Neda might have left?

   7 coloring books
   8 coloring books
   (4 coloring books)

6 Use with Lesson 1-6.

© Pearson Education, Inc. 2

Reteaching

Name _____

Choose an Operation

Which number sentence can be used to
solve the problem?

5 birds are in a tree.	7 frogs are on a log.
3 birds join them.	2 frogs hop away.
How many birds are there in all?	How many frogs are left?
(5 + 3 = 8) 8 − 3 = 5	5 + 2 = 7 (7 − 2 = 5)

Circle the number sentence that solves the problem.

1. 5 parrots are in a cage.
   4 parrots fly away.
   How many parrots are left?

   1 + 4 = 5   (5 − 4 = 1)

2. 6 kittens are in a box.
   1 kitten jumps in.
   How many kittens are
   there in all?

   (6 + 1 = 7)   7 − 1 = 6

Practice

Name _____

Choose an Operation

Circle **add** or **subtract**.
Then write the number sentence to solve the problem.

1. Sasha has 12 toy cars. She
   gives 6 of them to Michael.   add   (subtract)
   How many toy cars does
   Sasha have left?   12 ⊖ 6 ⊜ 6 toy cars

2. Sara has 7 crayons.
   Bobby gives her 1 more   (add)   subtract
   crayon. How many crayons
   does Sara have in all?   7 ⊕ 1 ⊜ 8 crayons

3. 8 children play a game.
   4 children go home.   add   (subtract)
   How many children are
   left playing the game?   8 ⊖ 4 ⊜ 4 children

4. 5 children play hopscotch.
   3 children play jump rope.   add   (subtract)
   How many more children
   play hopscotch?   5 ⊖ 3 ⊜ 2 children

Reasoning *Writing in Math*   Stories may vary.

5. Write a math story. Then write a number sentence to solve it.

   Sample answer: 9 books were on
   the table. Lisa took 4 books with her.
   How many books were left on the table?
   9 − 4 = 5 books

Enrichment

Name _____

Obey the Rules

Decide if you need to add to or subtract from the
number in the **In** column to get the number in the
Out column. Then circle one of the rules to the right
of the chart.

1.
In	Out
3	6
4	7
6	9

Add 1.
Subtract 2.
(Add 3.)

2.
In	Out
8	6
5	3
6	4

Add 2.
Subtract 1.
(Subtract 2.)

3.
In	Out
7	4
9	6
4	1

Add 2.
(Subtract 3.)
Add 3.

4.
In	Out
6	7
4	5
8	9

(Add 1.)
Subtract 2.
Subtract 1.

Write the rule.

5.
In	5	9	10
Out	4	8	9

The rule is _subtract 1_

Problem Solving

Name _____

Choose an Operation

Circle **add** or **subtract**.
Then write the number sentence to solve the problem.

Kim has 7 pencils.
Bobby has 3 pencils.
How many pencils do
they have in all?

Is this a joining story
or a separating story?

(add)   subtract   7 ⊕ 3 ⊜ 10 pencils

1. Pedro has 9 crayons.
   Kate has 4 crayons.
   How many more crayons
   does Pedro have?

   add   (subtract)   9 ⊖ 4 ⊜ 5 crayons

2. Doug has 6 stamps.
   Shawna has 2 stamps.
   How many stamps do
   they have in all?

   (add)   subtract   6 ⊕ 2 ⊜ 8 stamps

Using the page Have students *read* the guiding question. To help them *understand* what they
are being asked to do, have them identify the operation that must be used to solve the problem.

Name _____

Adding in Any Order

R 1-8

$5 + 2 = $ 7 $2 + 5 = $ 7

Same addends in a different order.

[5 + 2] = 7   [2 + 5] = 7 are **related addition facts**.

same sum

Write the numbers for each picture.

1.

$3 + 4 = $ 7 $4 + 3 = $ 7

2.

$6 + $ 1 $= $ 7 $1 + $ 6 $= $ 7

3.

2
+ 4
6

4
+ 2
6

Name _____

Adding in Any Order

P 1-8

Write the sum. Then write the related addition fact.

1. $2 + 4 = $ 6
   $4 + 2 = 6$

2. $7 + 1 = $ 8
   $1 + 7 = 8$

3. $9 + 2 = $ 11
   $2 + 9 = 11$

4. $5 + 3 = $ 8
   $3 + 5 = 8$

5.
6
+ 4
10

4
+ 6
10

6.
3
+ 4
7

4
+ 3
7

Problem Solving *Writing in Math*

Write a number sentence to solve the problem.

7. There are 4 birds in the nest. 3 birds join them.
   How many birds are there in all?

   4 (+) 3 (=) 7 birds

8. Change the order of the addends in the number sentence
   in Exercise 7. Write a story for this new number sentence.

   Stories will vary. _____

Name _____

Picture Match Up

E 1-8
VISUAL THINKING

Find the group of pictures in Box 1 and
Box 2 that have the same objects.
Write two addition sentences to show
how many there are in all.

Box 1	Box 2

1. ♡ 6 $+$ 2 $=$ 8   2 $+$ 6 $=$ 8

2. ❀ 4 $+$ 6 $=$ 10   6 $+$ 4 $=$ 10

3. ◇ 3 $+$ 5 $=$ 8   5 $+$ 3 $=$ 8

4. ☼ 2 $+$ 7 $=$ 9   7 $+$ 2 $=$ 9

5. ↗ 5 $+$ 1 $=$ 6   1 $+$ 5 $=$ 6

Name _____

Adding in Any Order

PS 1-8

Write the addition sentence.
Then write the related addition fact.

1. 5 $+$ 3 $=$ 8
   3 $+$ 5 $=$ 8

2. 3 $+$ 7 $=$ 10
   7 $+$ 3 $=$ 10

3. 6 $+$ 3 $=$ 9
   3 $+$ 6 $=$ 9

Writing in Math

4. Write the related addition fact.
   Then write a math story for
   one of the number sentences.

   $3 + 4 = $ 7
   4 $+$ 3 $=$ 7

   Stories will vary. _____

Name _____

Ways to Make 10

R 1-9

How many ways can you make 10?
Color the remaining cubes red.
Write the number sentence.

There is __1__ gray cube.

There are __9__ red cubes.

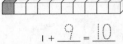

$1 + 9 = 10$

Find ways to make ten. Color the remaining cubes red.

1. $2 + 8 = 10$

2. $3 + 7 = 10$

3. $4 + 6 = 10$

Use two different colors. Color to show a way
to make ten. Write the number sentence.

Number sentences may vary.

4. ____ + ____ = ____

5. Look at the pattern.
Find the missing numbers.

$10 + 0 =$	**5**	$+ 5$	
$9 +$ **1**	$= 4 + 6$		
$8 + 2 =$	$3 +$ **7**		
$7 +$ **3**	$= 2 + 8$		
$6 +$ **4**	$= 1 + 9$		

Use with Lesson 1-9. **9**

Name _____

Ways to Make 10

P 1-9

Find different ways to make 10.
Complete each number sentence.

1. $5 + $ **5** $= 10$

2. **8** $+ 2 = 10$

3. $9 + $ **1** $= 10$

4. $10 = $ **3** $+ 7$

5. $4 + $ **6** $= 10$

6. $10 = 10 + $ **0**

Write five more ways to make 10. Use different
number sentences from those in Exercises 1–3.

7. **1** $+$ **9** $= 10$

8. **2** $+$ **8** $= 10$

9. **0** $+$ **10** $= 10$

10. **7** $+$ **3** $= 10$

11. **6** $+$ **4** $= 10$

Order of number sentences may vary.

Problem Solving *Mental Math*

Use mental math to find the missing numbers.
Look for the pattern in each chart.

12. Make 8

0	1	2	3	4
8	7	6	5	4

13. Make 6

0	1	2	3
6	5	4	3

Use with Lesson 1-9. **9**

Name _____

Finding 10

E 1-9
ALGEBRA

1. Find different ways to make 10.
Complete each number sentence.

$0 + $ **10** $= 10$

1 $+ 9 = 10$

$2 + $ **8** $= 10$

3 $+ 7 = 10$

$4 + $ **6** $= 10$

5 $+ 5 = 10$

2. Ring the pairs of numbers that make 10.
Use the number sentences above to help you.

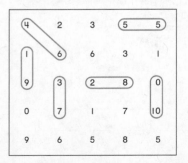

Use with Lesson 1-9. **9**

Name _____

Ways to Make 10

PS 1-9

Draw dots to make 10.
Then write a number sentence.

1.
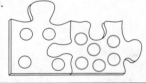

4 $+$ **6** $=$ **10**

2.

3 $+$ **7** $=$ **10**

3.

2 $+$ **8** $=$ **10**

4. Look at the pattern. Find the missing numbers.

$10 + 0 = $ **5** $+ 5$

$9 + 1 = 4 + $ **6**

$8 + 2 = $ **3** $+ 7$

Use with Lesson 1-9. **9**

Fact Families

Name _____

R 1-10

Fact families have the same three numbers.

Addition Facts

3 + 5 = 8

5 + 3 = 8

Subtraction Facts

8 − 5 = 3

8 − 3 = 5

These four related facts make up a **fact family**.

Complete each fact family.

1.

5 + 6 = 11

6 + 5 = 11

11 − 6 = 5

11 − 5 = 6

2.

3
+ 9
12

9
+ 3
12

12
− 9
3

12
− 3
9

10 Use with Lesson 1-10.

© Pearson Education, Inc. 2

Fact Families

Name _____

P 1-10

Complete each fact family.

1. 8 + 2 = 10
    2 + 8 = 10
    10 − 2 = 8
    10 − 8 = 2

2. 3 + 4 = 7
    4 + 3 = 7
    7 − 4 = 3
    7 − 3 = 4

Write your own fact families. **Answers may vary.**

3. ___ + ___ = ___
    ___ + ___ = ___
    ___ − ___ = ___
    ___ − ___ = ___

4.
3
+ 3
6

6
− 3
3

Problem Solving *Number Sense*

Circle all the answers that go with the problem.

5. There are 5 boys at the party.
    There are 6 girls at the party.
    How many children are at the party?
    (5 + 6)   6 − 5   (11 children)

6. 5 boys left the party.
    Now how many children are at the party?
    11 + 5   (11 − 5)   (6 children)

10 Use with Lesson 1-10.

© Pearson Education, Inc. 2

Lucky Facts

Name _____

E 1-10
NUMBER SENSE

Draw the missing dots.
Write a fact family for each.

1.

4 + 5 = 9

5 + 4 = 9

9 − 5 = 4

9 − 4 = 5

2.

5 + 2 = 7

2 + 5 = 7

7 − 2 = 5

7 − 5 = 2

3.

7 + 4 = 11

4 + 7 = 11

11 − 4 = 7

11 − 7 = 4

4.

2 + 6 = 8

6 + 2 = 8

8 − 6 = 2

8 − 2 = 6

10 Use with Lesson 1-10.

© Pearson Education, Inc. 2

Fact Families

Name _____

PS 1-10

What facts do these counters show?
Write the fact families.

1.

3 + 4 = 7   7 − 4 = 3

4 + 3 = 7   7 − 3 = 4

2.

5 + 4 = 9   9 − 4 = 5

4 + 5 = 9   9 − 5 = 4

3.

3 + 3 = 6   6 − 3 = 3

4. Asha has 6 markers. Cane gave her 3 more.
    How many markers does Asha have in all?

    6 ⊕ 3 ⊜ 9 markers

5. Cane asked for his 3 markers back.
    Now how many markers does Asha have?

    9 ⊖ 3 ⊜ 6 markers

10 Use with Lesson 1-10.

© Pearson Education, Inc. 2

© Pearson Education, Inc. **2**

Name _____

Finding the Missing Part

R 1-11

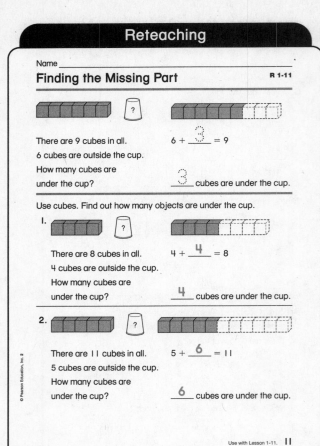

There are 9 cubes in all.
6 cubes are outside the cup.
How many cubes are
under the cup?

$6 + \underline{3} = 9$

$\underline{3}$ cubes are under the cup.

Use cubes. Find out how many objects are under the cup.

1.

There are 8 cubes in all.
4 cubes are outside the cup.
How many cubes are
under the cup?

$4 + \underline{4} = 8$

$\underline{4}$ cubes are under the cup.

2.

There are 11 cubes in all.
5 cubes are outside the cup.
How many cubes are
under the cup?

$5 + \underline{6} = 11$

$\underline{6}$ cubes are under the cup.

© Pearson Education, Inc. 2

Use with Lesson 1-11. 11

Name _____

Finding the Missing Part

P 1-11

Use counters.
Find out how many objects are in the bag.

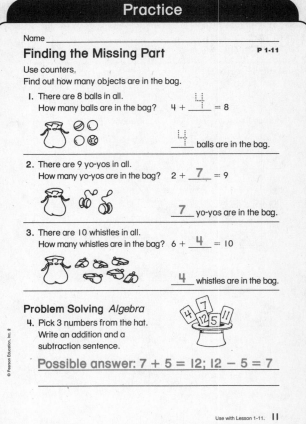

1. There are 8 balls in all.
How many balls are in the bag? $4 + \underline{4} = 8$

$\underline{4}$ balls are in the bag.

2. There are 9 yo-yos in all.
How many yo-yos are in the bag? $2 + \underline{7} = 9$

$\underline{7}$ yo-yos are in the bag.

3. There are 10 whistles in all.
How many whistles are in the bag? $6 + \underline{4} = 10$

$\underline{4}$ whistles are in the bag.

Problem Solving *Algebra*

4. Pick 3 numbers from the hat.
Write an addition and a
subtraction sentence.

Possible answer: $7 + 5 = 12$; $12 - 5 = 7$

© Pearson Education, Inc. 2

Use with Lesson 1-11. 11

Name _____

What's Missing?

E 1-11
ALGEBRA

Each problem has a missing part.
Fill in the missing numbers. Use counters or
draw pictures to help.

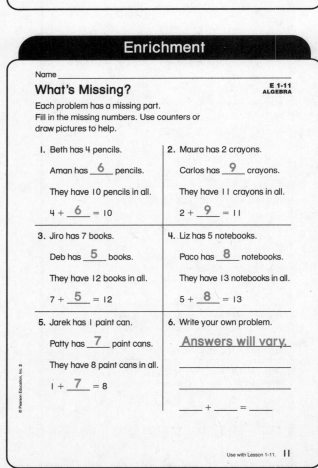

1. Beth has 4 pencils.

   Aman has $\underline{6}$ pencils.

   They have 10 pencils in all.

   $4 + \underline{6} = 10$

2. Maura has 2 crayons.

   Carlos has $\underline{9}$ crayons.

   They have 11 crayons in all.

   $2 + \underline{9} = 11$

3. Jiro has 7 books.

   Deb has $\underline{5}$ books.

   They have 12 books in all.

   $7 + \underline{5} = 12$

4. Liz has 5 notebooks.

   Paco has $\underline{8}$ notebooks.

   They have 13 notebooks in all.

   $5 + \underline{8} = 13$

5. Jarek has 1 paint can.

   Patty has $\underline{7}$ paint cans.

   They have 8 paint cans in all.

   $1 + \underline{7} = 8$

6. Write your own problem.

   Answers will vary.

   _____

   _____ + _____ = _____

© Pearson Education, Inc. 2

Use with Lesson 1-11. 11

Name _____

Finding the Missing Part

PS 1-11

Solve.

1. Sara and Joey have
11 postcards in all. Sara has
8 postcards. How many
postcards does Joey have?

$8 + \underline{3} = 11$

$\underline{3}$ postcards

2. Zoe and Luis pick 9 flowers
in all. Zoe picks 6 flowers.
How many flowers
does Luis pick?

$6 + \underline{3} = 9$

$\underline{3}$ flowers

3. Marta and Jimmy buy
10 apples. Marta buys
5 apples. How many
apples does Jimmy buy?

$5 + \underline{5} = 10$

$\underline{5}$ apples

4. Mario and Sue have
12 games in all. Mario has
4 games. How many
games does Sue have?

$4 + \underline{8} = 12$

$\underline{8}$ games

What number is the △ ?

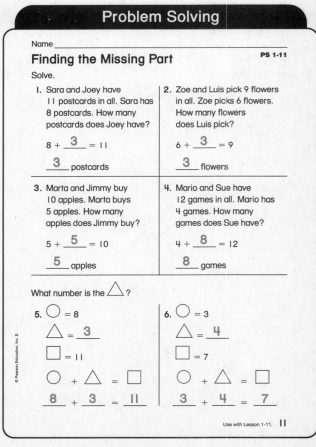

5. ○ = 8

△ = $\underline{3}$

□ = 11

○ + △ = □

$\underline{8} + \underline{3} = \underline{11}$

6. ○ = 3

△ = $\underline{4}$

□ = 7

○ + △ = □

$\underline{3} + \underline{4} = \underline{7}$

© Pearson Education, Inc. 2

Use with Lesson 1-11. 11

© Pearson Education, Inc. 2

Name _____

PROBLEM-SOLVING APPLICATIONS   R 1-12

Frogs and Toads

Circle the number sentence that solves the problem.

5 frogs are on a rock.	9 frogs are on a rock.
3 frogs join them.	4 frogs jump off.
How many frogs in all?	How many frogs are left?
Add to join groups.	**Subtract to separate groups or to compare.**

$\boxed{5 + 3 = 8}$ $5 - 3 = 2$ $9 + 4 = 13$ $\boxed{9 - 4 = 5}$

_8_ frogs in all.   _5_ frogs are left.

Circle the number sentence that solves the problem.

1. 10 toads are in a pond.
5 toads jump out.
How many toads are left?

$10 + 5 = 15$ $\boxed{10 - 5 = 5}$

_5_ toads are left.

2. 8 bugs are on a leaf.
5 bugs join them.
How many bugs in all?

$8 - 5 = 3$ $\boxed{8 + 5 = 13}$

_13_ bugs in all.

3. 6 lizards are on a log.
2 more lizards join them.
How many lizards in all?

$6 - 2 = 4$ $\boxed{6 + 2 = 8}$

_8_ lizards in all.

4. 7 birds are in a tree.
1 bird flies away.
How many birds are left?

$\boxed{7 - 1 = 6}$ $7 + 1 = 8$

_6_ birds are left.

12   Use with Lesson 1-12.

© Pearson Education, Inc. 2

Name _____

PROBLEM-SOLVING APPLICATIONS   P 1-12

Frogs and Toads

Solve the problems.

1. A frog eats 3 mealworms. A toad eats 7 mealworms.
How many more mealworms does the toad eat?

$7 - 3 =$ _4_ mealworms

2. There are 7 bullfrogs on a rock. 6 more bullfrogs join them.
How many bullfrogs in all are on the rock now?

_7_ ⊕ _6_ ⊜ _13_ bullfrogs

3. One American toad is 2 inches long. A second American toad
is 4 inches long. How long are the two toads together?

_2_ ⊕ _4_ ⊜ _6_ inches

Writing in Math

4. Write a number story about a frog who jumps
and then jumps again.

Sample answer:
The frog jumped 2 feet. The frog jumped
3 more feet. How far did the frog jump?
2 + 3 = 5 feet

5. Stan has 11 tree frogs. Joy has 4 tree frogs.
How many more tree frogs does Stan have?

_11_ ⊖ _4_ ⊜ _7_ tree frogs

12   Use with Lesson 1-12.

© Pearson Education, Inc. 2

Name _____

Find the Secret Number   E 1-12
REASONING

Read the clues to find the secret number.

1.

I am inside the path.
I am the sum of 2 other
numbers inside the path.

What number am I? _9_

2.

I am outside the path.
I am the difference of
2 numbers inside the path.
I am less than 5.

What number am I? _3_

3.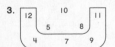

I am inside the path.
I am the sum of 2 other
numbers inside the path.

What number am I? _11_

4.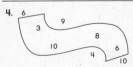

I am outside the path.
I am the difference of 2 other
numbers outside the path.
I am greater than 5.

What number am I? _6_

12   Use with Lesson 1-12.

© Pearson Education, Inc. 2

Name _____

PROBLEM-SOLVING APPLICATION   PS 1-12

Frogs and Toads

Write a number sentence to solve.

1. There are 6 frogs in a pond.
4 more frogs jump in the pond.
How many frogs are there now?

_6_ ⊕ _4_ ⊜ _10_ frogs

2. A bullfrog frog eats 9 bugs.
A cane frog eats 7 bugs.
How many more bugs does the bullfrog eat?

_9_ ⊖ _7_ ⊜ _2_ more bugs

3. There are 5 frogs near a tree.
3 frogs jump away from the tree.
How many frogs are left?

_5_ ⊖ _3_ ⊜ _2_ frogs

4. A toad jumps 10 inches. A frog jumps 8 inches.
How many more inches does the toad jump?

_10_ ⊖ _8_ ⊜ _2_ more inches

5. 3 toads are sitting on a log. 6 more toads come to join them.
How many toads are on the log now?

_3_ ⊕ _6_ ⊜ _9_ toads

Using the page To help children *plan* and *solve* each problem, have them underline words that are clues for addition or subtraction.

12   Use with Lesson 1-12.

© Pearson Education, Inc. 2

Reteaching

Name _____

Counting On   R 2-1

You can use the number line to count on.

> To add, **count on** 1, 2, or 3 from the larger number.

12 + 3 = $\overline{15}$ Start at 12.   Count on 13, 14, 15.

`0 1 2 3 4 5 6 7 8 9 10 11 12 13 14 15 16 17 18 19 20`

Use the number lines.
Count on to find each sum.

`0 1 2 3 4 5 6 7 8 9 10 11 12 13 14 15 16 17 18 19 20`

1. 17 + 2 = $\underline{19}$

`0 1 2 3 4 5 6 7 8 9 10 11 12 13 14 15 16 17 18 19 20`

2. 14 + 3 = $\underline{17}$

`0 1 2 3 4 5 6 7 8 9 10 11 12 13 14 15 16 17 18 19 20`

3. 15 + 3 = $\underline{18}$

Count on to find each sum.

4. 14 + 2 = $\underline{16}$ 18 + 2 = $\underline{20}$ 13 + 3 = $\underline{16}$

5. 16 + 3 = $\underline{19}$ 13 + 1 = $\underline{14}$ 19 + 1 = $\underline{20}$

Use with Lesson 2-1. 13

© Pearson Education, Inc. 2

Practice

Name _____

Counting On   P 2-1

Count on to find each sum.

1. 11 + 3 = $\underline{14}$ 14 + 2 = $\underline{16}$ 18 + 3 = $\underline{21}$
2. 2 + 17 = $\underline{19}$ $\underline{17}$ = 16 + 1 $\underline{16}$ = 2 + 14
3. 19 + 2 = $\underline{21}$ $\underline{13}$ = 11 + 2   3 + 19 = $\underline{22}$
4. $\underline{15}$ = 13 + 2   18 + 1 = $\underline{19}$ 2 + 15 = $\underline{17}$
5. 13 + 3 = $\underline{16}$ 2 + 12 = $\underline{14}$ $\underline{14}$ = 3 + 11

6.
15	13	12	18	12	19
+3	+2	+2	+3	+1	+3
18	15	14	21	13	22

7.
14	17	13	19	16	12
+3	+1	+2	+2	+2	+3
17	18	15	21	18	15

Problem Solving *Number Sense*
Write a number sentence to solve each story. Solve.

8. Pam bought 13 flowers. Mark bought 3 flowers. How many flowers did they buy in all?

   $\underline{13} + \underline{3} = \underline{16}$ flowers

9. Lee collected 16 rocks. Meg collected 2 rocks. How many rocks did they collect in all?

   $\underline{16} + \underline{2} = \underline{18}$ rocks

Use with Lesson 2-1. 13

© Pearson Education, Inc. 2

Enrichment

Name _____

It's a Date   E 2-1
                                   VISUAL THINKING

Karen starts school on September 7th.

September

S	M	T	W	T	F	S
				1	2	3
4	5	6	⑦	8	9	10
11	12	13	14	15	16	17
18	19	20	21	22	23	24
25	26	27	28	29	30	

Use the calendar to answer the questions.

1. Three days after school starts, Karen goes to soccer practice.

   What date will that be? ____ September 10

2. Two days after soccer practice, Karen goes to her friend's house.

   What date will that be? ____ September 12

3. Three days after Karen visits her friend, she goes to music lessons.

   What date will that be? ____ September 15

4. One day after music lessons, Karen goes to the movies.

   What date will that be? ____ September 16

Use with Lesson 2-1. 13

© Pearson Education, Inc. 2

Problem Solving

Name _____

Counting On   PS 2-1

Use the number line to solve.
Write the number of jumps.
Count on to find the sum.

`0 1 2 3 4 5 6 7 8 9 10 11 12 13 14 15 16 17 18 19 20`

1. Mary starts at 13. She makes 2 jumps forward. What number does she land on?

   13 + $\underline{2}$ = $\underline{15}$

2. Jack starts at 11. He makes 3 jumps forward. What number does he land on?

   11 + $\underline{3}$ = $\underline{14}$

3. Paco starts at 9. He makes 3 jumps forward. What number does he land on?

   9 + $\underline{3}$ = $\underline{12}$

4. Keesha starts at 15. She makes 1 jump forward. What number does she land on?

   15 + $\underline{1}$ = $\underline{16}$

Write a number sentence to solve the problem.

5. Chen is 12 years old. How old will he be in 3 more years?

   $\underline{15}$ years old $\underline{12} + \underline{3} = \underline{15}$

Use with Lesson 2-1. 13

© Pearson Education, Inc. 2

Reteaching

Name _____

Doubles Facts to 18

R 2-2

Find 3 + 3.

Draw 3 more dots to show the double.
Then write the addition sentence.

> 3 + 3 = 6 is a **doubles fact.**
> Both addends are the same.

__3__ + __3__ = __6__

Draw dots on the domino to show the double.
Then write the addition sentence.

I.

4 + __4__ = __8__

2.

5 + __5__ = __10__

3.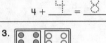

__6__ + __6__ = __12__

4.

__7__ + __7__ = __14__

5.

__8__ + __8__ = __16__

6.

__9__ + __9__ = __18__

Practice

Name _____

Doubles Facts to 18

P 2-2

Solve. Circle the doubles facts.

I. (12) = 6 + 6   16 + 2 = __18__   __17__ = 3 + 14

2. 15 + 1 = __16__   (2) = 1 + 1   2 + 18 = __20__

3. (7 + 7 = __14__)   __16__ = 13 + 3   (8 + 8 = __16__)

4.
15	(9)	11	19	(2)	16
+ 3	+ 9	+ 2	+ 1	+ 2	+ 3
18	18	13	20	4	19

5.
(6)	16	(1)	14	(5)	18
+ 6	+ 1	+ 1	+ 2	+ 5	+ 3
12	17	2	16	10	21

6.
(3)	17	15	(8)	13	0
+ 3	+ 1	+ 2	+ 8	+ 2	+ 0
6	18	17	16	15	0

Problem Solving *Visual Thinking*

Draw a picture to solve the problem.
Write the number sentence.

7. Carissa counted 5 black buttons.
Maurice counted the same number
of white buttons. How many buttons
did they count in all?

Drawings
should show
2 groups of
5 objects
each.

__5__ + __5__ = __10__

Enrichment

Name _____

Double Up

E 2-2
VISUAL THINKING

Solve the problem. Then write the addition fact.

I. Jacob wants to put the same number of
apples on each platter. He has 8 apples.
Draw the apples Jacob will put on each platter.

Children should
draw 4 apples
on each platter.

__4__ + __4__ = __8__

2. Luz wants to put the same number of
flowers in each flower box. She has 12 flowers.
Draw the flowers Luz will put in each box.

Children should
draw 6 flowers
in each box.

__6__ + __6__ = __12__

3. Elena wants to put the same number of
cups on each table. She has 10 cups.
Draw the cups Elena will put on each table.

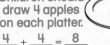

Children should
draw 5 cups
on each table.

__5__ + __5__ = __10__

Problem Solving

Name _____

Doubles Facts to 18

Objects in drawings
will vary.

PS 2-2

I. Draw a doubles fact
with 8 objects.
Write the doubles fact.

__4__ + __4__ = __8__

2. Draw a doubles fact
with 6 objects.
Write the doubles fact.

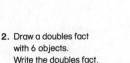

__3__ + __3__ = __6__

3. Draw a doubles fact
with 14 objects.
Write the doubles fact.

__7__ + __7__ = __14__

4. There are 12 oranges in all.
How many oranges are
in the bag?

There are __6__ oranges in the bag.

Name _____

Doubles Plus 1

R 2-3

You can use a doubles fact to find a doubles-plus-1 fact.

$6 + 6 = 12$ $6 + 7 = 13$

Doubles Fact   **Doubles-Plus-1 Fact**

$6 + 7 = 13$ is a **doubles-plus-1 fact** because it is equal to $6 + 6 = 12$ plus one more.

Add. Use doubles facts to help you.

1.

$4 + 4 = 8$ $4 + 5 = 9$

2.

$5 + 5 = 10$ $5 + 6 = 11$

3.

$8 + 8 = 16$ $8 + 9 = 17$

Use with Lesson 2-3. 15

Name _____

Doubles Plus 1

P 2-3

Add. Use doubles facts to help you.

1.
5	8	9	5	2	4
+5	+9	+9	+6	+2	+3
10	17	18	11	4	7

2.
10	7	8	0	4	8
+9	+7	+7	+0	+5	+8
19	14	15	0	9	16

3.
7	6	4	6	3	2
+8	+7	+4	+5	+3	+3
15	13	8	11	6	5

4. $7 + 6 = 13$ $5 + 4 = 9$ $7 = 3 + 4$

5. $9 + 10 = 19$ $4 + 4 = 8$ $9 + 8 = 17$

Problem Solving *Writing in Math*

6. Use pictures, numbers, or words to tell how $6 + 8$ and $6 + 6$ are related.

Answers may vary. Have children explain that since 8 is 2 more than 6, the sum of $6 + 8$, or 14, is 2 more than $6 + 6$, or 12.

Use with Lesson 2-3. 15

Name _____

Number Riddles

E 2-3
ALGEBRA

Write an addition sentence to solve the problem. Use doubles facts to help you.

1. 7 plus a number equals 13. What is the number?

$7 + 6 = 13$

The number is 6.

2. A number plus 9 equals 17. What is the number?

$8 + 9 = 17$

The number is 8.

3. 5 plus a number equals 11. What is the number?

$5 + 6 = 11$

The number is 6.

4. A number plus 8 equals 16. What is the number?

$8 + 8 = 16$

The number is 8.

5. A number plus 5 equals 9. What is the number?

$4 + 5 = 9$

The number is 4.

6. 8 plus a number equals 15. What is the number?

$8 + 7 = 15$

The number is 7.

7. A number plus 6 equals 12. What is the number?

$6 + 6 = 12$

The number is 6.

8. A number plus 9 equals 19. What is the number?

$10 + 9 = 19$

The number is 10.

Use with Lesson 2-3. 15

Name _____

Doubles Plus 1

PS 2-3

Find the number for each player's shirt.

1. Chenoa's number is between 4 and 7. Double the number. Then add 1 more to get 13. What is Chenoa's number?

_____

2. Jacob's number is between 7 and 10. Double the number. Then add 1 more to get 19. What is Jacob's number?

_____

3. Maria's number is between 3 and 6. Double the number. Then add 1 more to get 11. What is Maria's number?

_____

Writing in Math

4. Write a number riddle for the number 7. Use a doubles fact in your riddle.

Possible answer: The number is between 5 and 8. Double the number. Then add 1 to get 15.

Use with Lesson 2-3. 15

Name _____

Using Strategies to Add Three Numbers   R 2-4

You can use different strategies to add 3 numbers.

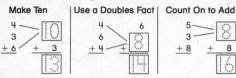

Make Ten	Use a Doubles Fact	Count On to Add
4 3 +6 →10 →13	4 6 +4 →8 →14	5 3 +8 →8 →16

Make ten to add.
Draw lines to the numbers that make 10.

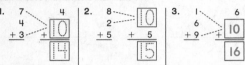

1. 7
   4
   +3 →10 →14

2. 8
   2
   +5 →10 →15

3. 1
   6
   +9 →10 →16

Use a doubles fact or count on to add.
Draw lines from the numbers added first.

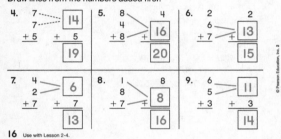

4. 7
   7
   +5 →14 →19

5. 8
   4
   +8 →16 →20

6. 2
   6
   +7 →13 →15

7. 4
   2
   +7 →6 →13

8. 1
   8
   +7 →8 →16

9. 6
   5
   +3 →11 →14

16 Use with Lesson 2-4.

Name _____

Using Strategies to Add Three Numbers   P 2-4

Add. Try different ways.

1. $3 + 7 + 3 = 13$

2. $15 = 3 + 6 + 6$

3. $6 + 4 + 5 = 15$

4. $16 = 8 + 0 + 8$

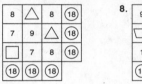

5.
10	9	6	4	4	8
3	2	5	1	6	3
+5	+2	+4	+9	+5	+8
18	13	15	14	15	19

6.
5	6	8	2	5	9
8	3	3	8	7	0
+4	+7	+6	+8	+3	+8
17	16	17	18	15	17

Problem Solving Algebra

Find the missing numbers. The same shapes
are the same numbers.

The numbers in ◯ are sums. Add across and down.

7.
8	△	8	(18)
7	9	△	(18)
▢	7	8	(18)
(18)	(18)	(18)	

8.
9	3	2	(14)
▽	6	▽	(14)
1	⬠	8	(14)
(14)	(14)	(14)	

△ = 2   ▢ = 3   ▽ = 4   ⬠ = 5

16 Use with Lesson 2-4.

Name _____

Which Strategy?   E 2-4
DECISION MAKING

Show 2 steps to solve each problem.
Circle the strategy you used in Step 1.

Strategies and
steps may vary.

	Step 1	Step 2

1. 7
   4
   +2 →13

   7
   +2 →9 (circled)

   (9)
   +4 →13

   Make a ten
   Look for doubles
   (Count on)

2. 3
   8
   +3 →14

   3
   +3 →6

   6
   +8 →14

   Make a ten
   (Look for doubles)
   Count on

3. 9
   7
   +1 →17

   9
   +1 →10

   10
   +7 →17

   (Make a ten)
   Look for doubles
   Count on

4. 2
   9
   +2 →13

   2
   +2 →4

   4
   +9 →13

   Make a ten
   (Look for doubles)
   Count on

16 Use with Lesson 2-4.

Name _____

Using Strategies to Add Three Numbers   PS 2-4

The map shows how many miles from
one place to another.

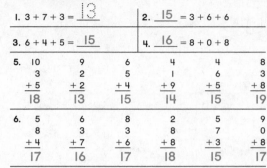

Make a 10
Count On
Doubles Plus 1

Find how many miles for each trip.
Tell what strategy you used to find the sum.

1. From the school, to the firehouse, to the post office, to the bank

   $\underline{8} + \underline{9} + \underline{2} = \underline{19}$ miles

   What strategy did you use? Possible answer:
   I made a ten and added 9.

2. From the school, to the library, to the post office, to the bank

   $\underline{7} + \underline{3} + \underline{2} = \underline{12}$ miles

   What strategy did you use? Possible answer:
   I made a ten and added 2.

3. From the firehouse, to the bank, to the park, to the library

   $\underline{6} + \underline{5} + \underline{4} = \underline{15}$ miles

   What strategy did you use? Possible answer:
   I counted on 5 + 4 = 9 and added 6.

16 Use with Lesson 2-4.

Reteaching

Name _____

Making 10 to Add 9

R 2-5

Find 9 + 6.

 Make 10 →   9 + 6 equals

10 + 5

9 + 6 = 15

Use counters and Workmat 2. Make 10 to find each sum.

1. Find 9 + 7.

Make 10 →   9 + 7 equals

10 + 6

9 + 7 = 16

2. Find 9 + 5.

Make 10 →   9 + 5 equals

10 + 4

9 + 5 = 14

© Pearson Education, Inc. 2

Use with Lesson 2-5. 17

Practice

Name _____

Making 10 to Add 9

P 2-5

Add. Use counters and Workmat 3 if you need to.

1.	9	6	0	9	2	5
	+ 3	+ 9	+ 9	+ 8	+ 9	+ 9
	12	15	9	17	11	14

2.	9	9	3	9	5	9
	+ 7	+ 1	+ 9	+ 8	+ 9	+ 6
	16	10	12	17	14	15

3.	9	4	7	9	9	8
	+ 5	+ 9	+ 9	+ 5	+ 2	+ 9
	14	13	16	14	11	17

4. 9 + 7 = 16   6 + 9 = 15   4 + 9 = 13

Problem Solving *Reasoning*

Solve by using pictures, numbers, or words.

5. Shana had 9 pins in her collection. She bought more pins. Now she has 17 pins. How many pins did Shana buy?

Answers will vary. Pictures should show 9 and 8 pins. Number sentences should show 8 + 9 = 17, 9 + 8 = 17, or 17 − 9 = 8. Words should reveal the missing addend of 8 or 8 + 9 = 17.

© Pearson Education, Inc. 2

Use with Lesson 2-5. 17

Enrichment

Name _____

Match a Sum

E 2-5
NUMBER SENSE

Add.
Circle the addition problem that has the same sum.

1. 9 + 6 = 15

10	10	10	(10	10
+ 4	+ 9	+ 8	+ 5)	+ 6
14	19	18	15	16

2. 9 + 8 = 17

10	(10	10	10	10
+ 5	+ 7)	+ 4	+ 9	+ 8
15	17	14	19	18

3. 9 + 5 = 14

10	10	10	(10	10
+ 3	+ 6	+ 5	+ 4)	+ 8
13	16	15	14	18

4. 9 + 7 = 16

(10	10	10	10	10
+ 6)	+ 5	+ 7	+ 9	+ 3
16	15	17	19	13

© Pearson Education, Inc. 2

Use with Lesson 2-5. 17

Problem Solving

Name _____

Making 10 to Add 9

PS 2-5

Help the children fill the sections in their boxes.

1. Tani has 9 shells in the box. She collects 7 more shells.

   How many shells will not fit in the box? 6

   How many shells does she have in all? 16

2. Ricky has 9 rocks in the box. He collects 5 more rocks.

   How many rocks will not fit in the box? 4

   How many rocks does he have in all? 14

3. Nelson has 9 quarters in the box. He collects 8 more quarters.

   How many quarters will not fit in the box? 7

   How many quarters does he have in all? 17

Solve by using pictures, numbers, or words.

4. Nora had 9 baseball cards. She collected some more. Now she has 15 cards. How many cards did she add to her collection?

   Answers may vary. Pictures, numbers, or words should reveal 6 as the missing addend of 9 + 6 = 15.

© Pearson Education, Inc. 2

Use with Lesson 2-5. 17

© Pearson Education, Inc. 2

Name _____

Making 10 to Add 7 or 8

R 2-6

Find 8 + 5.

 Make 10 →

8 + 5 equals

10 + _3_

_8_ + _5_   _10_ + _3_   8 + 5 = _13_

Make 10 to find each sum. Use counters and Workmat 2.

1. Find 7 + 6.

 Make 10 →

7 + 6 equals

10 + _3_

_7_ + _6_   _10_ + _3_   7 + 6 = _13_

2. Find 8 + 3.

Make 10 →

8 + 3 equals

10 + _1_

_8_ + _3_   _10_ + _1_   8 + 3 = _11_

18 Use with Lesson 2-6.

Name _____

Making 10 to Add 7 or 8

P 2-6

Add. Use counters and Workmat 3 if you need to.

1.	8	5	4	8	7	9
	+3	+9	+7	+8	+9	+5
	11	14	11	16	16	14

2.	8	4	6	8	5	7
	+7	+8	+7	+6	+7	+8
	15	12	13	14	12	15

3. 4 + 8 = _12_   10 + 7 = _17_   0 + 8 = _8_

4. 7 + 7 = _14_   9 + 3 = _12_   _19_ = 9 + 10

Problem Solving *Algebra*

Find the pattern. Write the missing numbers.

5. 7 + 9 = 10 + 6
7 + 8 = 10 + 5
7 + 7 = 10 + 4
7 + 6 = 10 + 3
7 + 5 = 10 + 2

18 Use with Lesson 2-6.

Name _____

Money Exchange

E 2-6
MENTAL MATH

Solve. Use dimes and pennies if you need to.

1. Mary has 8 pennies.
Jay has 6 pennies.
They exchange some pennies for 1 dime.
How many pennies do they still have?

1 dime and _4_ pennies

2. Nancy has 7 pennies.
Ahmed has 5 pennies.
They exchange some pennies for 1 dime.
How many pennies do they still have?

1 dime and _2_ pennies

3. Freddie has 4 pennies.
Margie has 8 pennies.
They exchange some pennies for 1 dime.
How many pennies do they still have?

1 dime and _2_ pennies

4. Suki has 9 pennies.
Marco has 7 pennies.
They exchange some pennies for 1 dime.
How many pennies do they still have?

1 dime and _6_ pennies

18 Use with Lesson 2-6.

Name _____

Making 10 to Add 7 or 8

PS 2-6

Put the objects from the boxes into a large box holding 10 objects and a small box holding the remaining objects.

Write how many objects are in the small box.

1. [7 cars] [5 cars] → [10 cars] [_2_]

7 + 5 = 10 + _2_

2. [8 dolls] [7 dolls] → [10 dolls] [_5_]

8 + 7 = 10 + _5_

3. [4 trains] [8 trains] → [10 trains] [_2_]

4 + 8 = 10 + _2_

4. [9 yo-yos] [7 yo-yos] → [10 yo-yos] [_6_]

9 + 7 = 10 + _6_

Write a number sentence to solve.

5. There are 7 balls in a box.
Pete puts more balls in the box.
Now there are 11 balls. How many
balls did Pete put in the box?

_7_ + _4_ = _11_

_4_ balls

18 Use with Lesson 2-6.

Name _____

PROBLEM-SOLVING STRATEGY   R 2-7

Write a Number Sentence

Read and Understand

Tim and Rosa played 3 games of tossing a bean bag. Here are their scores.

Players	Game 1	Game 2	Game 3
Tim	4	6	3
Rosa	7	2	5

How many points did Tim and Rosa score altogether in Game 1?

Plan and Solve

You need to find out how many points Tim and Rosa scored in Game 1.

Tim's score __4__   Rosa's score __7__

Write a number sentence to solve.

__4__ + __7__ = __11__ points

Look Back and Check

Check your work. Does your answer make sense?

Write a number sentence to solve the problem. Use the table to help you.

1. How many points did Tim and Rosa score altogether in Game 2?

   __6 + 2__ = __8__ points

2. How many points did Rosa score altogether in Games 2 and 3?

   __2 + 5__ = __7__ points

Use with Lesson 2-7. 19

Name _____

PROBLEM-SOLVING STRATEGY   P 2-7

Write a Number Sentence

Write a number sentence to solve the problem. Use the table to help you.

	Game Scores		
Teams	Game 1	Game 2	Game 3
Robins	7	4	6
Bluejays	5	8	5

1. How many points did the Bluejays score altogether in Games 1 and 2?

   __5 + 8__ = __13__ points

2. How many points did the Robins score altogether in Games 1 and 2?

   __7 + 4__ = __11__ points

3. Which team had scored more points after Game 2?   __Bluejays__

4. How many points did the Robins score altogether?

   __7 + 4 + 6__ = __17__ points

5. How many points did the Bluejays score altogether?

   __5 + 8 + 5__ = __18__ points

6. Which team, the Robins or the Bluejays, scored more points altogether?   __Bluejays__

Use with Lesson 2-7. 19

Name _____

Clean-Up Day

E 2-7
DATA

The chart shows how many cans each child collected.

Cans Collected

Billy	Shayla	Lucky	Mia	Sharon	Yoshi
8	5	3	7	6	4

Use the data from the chart to fill in the blanks. Write an addition sentence to find the number of cans the students collected.

1. Billy collected __8__ cans. Lucky collected __3__ cans.

   __Yoshi__ collected 4 cans.

   How many cans did they collect in all?

   __8__ + __3__ + __4__ = __15__ cans

2. Shayla collected __5__ cans. Lucky collected __3__ cans.

   __Mia__ collected 7 cans.

   How many cans did they collect in all?

   __5__ + __3__ + __7__ = __15__ cans

3. Mia collected __7__ cans. Shayla collected __5__ cans.

   __Lucky__ collected 3 cans.

   How many cans did they collect in all?

   __7__ + __5__ + __3__ = __15__ cans

Use with Lesson 2-7. 19

Name _____

PROBLEM-SOLVING STRATEGY   PS 2-7

Write a Number Sentence

The children at Smith Street School voted for their favorite pets. Use the information in the chart to write a number sentence.

Circle **add** or **subtract**.

Favorite Pets

	Dogs	Cats	Birds
Grade 1	卌	卌	川
Grade 2	卌	卌 卌卌	卌 卌卌
Grade 3	卌 川	卌	卌川

Plan

Find the bird tally marks.

川 = 3   卌 川 = 7   卌 = 4

(add) subtract

3 ⊕ 7 ⊕ 4 ⊜ 14

1. How many votes for birds in all?

   __14__ votes were for birds.

卌川 = 6   卌卌川 = 9   卌 = 5

(add) subtract

6 ⊕ 9 ⊕ 5 ⊜ 20

2. How many votes for cats in all?

   __20__ votes were for cats.

birds: 3 + 7 + 4 = 14
cats: 6 + 9 + 5 = 20

3. Which pet, birds or cats, got more votes?   __cats__

dogs: 6 + 5 + 6 = 17
cats: 6 + 9 + 5 = 20

4. Which pet, cats or dogs, got more votes?   __cats__

Using the page To help children *plan*, discuss which tally marks to use for each exercise. Then have them count the tallies and write a number sentence to *solve* the problem.

Use with Lesson 2-7. 19

© Pearson Education, Inc. 2

Name _____

Counting Back

R 2-8

You can count back to subtract.

$16 - 2 = \underline{14}$

1	2	3	4	5	6	7	8	9	10
11	12	13	14	15	16	17	18	19	20

Find 16 on the hundreds chart.
Then count back, first to 15, then to 14.

Subtract. Use the hundreds chart to count back.

1. $14 - 2 = \underline{12}$

1	2	3	4	5	6	7	8	9	10
11	12	13	14	15	16	17	18	19	20

2. $10 - 1 = \underline{9}$

1	2	3	4	5	6	7	8	9	10
11	12	13	14	15	16	17	18	19	20

Subtract. Use the hundreds chart to help you.

1	2	3	4	5	6	7	8	9	10
11	12	13	14	15	16	17	18	19	20

3. $16 - 1 = \underline{15}$ $13 - 1 = \underline{12}$ $14 - 1 = \underline{13}$

4. $10 - 2 = \underline{8}$ $17 - 2 = \underline{15}$ $19 - 2 = \underline{17}$

5. $18 - 2 = \underline{16}$ $15 - 2 = \underline{13}$ $11 - 2 = \underline{9}$

© Pearson Education, Inc. 2

20   Use with Lesson 2-8.

Name _____

Counting Back

P 2-8

Subtract. Use the number line if you need to.

0 1 2 3 4 5 6 7 8 9 10 11 12 13 14 15 16 17 18 19 20

1. $16 - 2 = \underline{14}$ $14 - 3 = \underline{11}$ $\underline{12} = 13 - 1$

2. $15 - 2 = \underline{13}$ $\underline{9} = 12 - 3$ $18 - 2 = \underline{16}$

3.
11	14	19	17	13	12
-3	-2	-1	-3	-2	-2
8	12	18	14	11	10

4.
11	17	13	15	18	16
-2	-2	-3	-3	-1	-3
9	15	10	12	17	13

5.
19	14	15	18	13	19
-3	-1	-2	-3	-2	-1
16	13	13	15	11	18

Problem Solving *Writing in Math*

Write a story or draw a picture to go with the problem.
Then solve.

6. $16 - 5 = \underline{11}$

Children's stories or drawings should show that 11 is the difference between 16 and 5.

© Pearson Education, Inc. 2

20   Use with Lesson 2-8.

Name _____

Sorry, Wrong Number

E 2-8
PATTERNS

Find the pattern in each row.
One number is incorrect.
Cross it out and write the number that continues the pattern.

1. 10 9 8 7 ~~5~~ 5 4 3 $\underline{6}$

2. 3 2 3 2 3 2 ~~X~~ 2 $\underline{3}$

3. 14 12 10 8 ~~X~~ 4 2 0 $\underline{6}$

4. 9 8 9 8 9 8 9 ~~X~~ $\underline{8}$

5. 18 17 16 15 ~~X~~ 13 12 11 $\underline{14}$

6. 21 19 17 15 ~~X~~ 11 9 7 $\underline{13}$

7. Make your own pattern with one number that does not fit. Ask a friend to solve it.

_____ _____ _____ _____ _____ _____

Answers may vary.

© Pearson Education, Inc. 2

20   Use with Lesson 2-8.

Name _____

Counting Back

PS 2-8

Use the picture of the building to help you solve.

1. Tracy starts on floor 7.
She goes down 1 floor.
What floor is Tracy on?

Tracy is on floor $\underline{6}$.

2. Bruce starts on floor 3.
He goes down 2 floors.
What floor is Bruce on?

Bruce is on floor $\underline{1}$.

3. Kareem starts on floor 9.
He goes down 2 floors.
What floor is Kareem on?

Kareem is on floor $\underline{7}$.

(Building floors labeled 12, 11, 10, 9, 8, 7, 6, 5, 4, 3, 2, 1)

Writing in Math

4. Write a math story about the sentence. Then solve.

$6 - 2 = \underline{4}$

Children's stories should show that 4 is the difference between 6 and 2.

© Pearson Education, Inc. 2

20   Use with Lesson 2-8.

---

20   Use with Chapter 2, Lesson 8.

Reteaching

Name

Thinking Doubles to Subtract
R 2-9

6 − 3 = ?

Think of a doubles fact.

3 + = 6   So, 6 − 3 = .

Use doubles facts to help you subtract.
Cross out the dots you take away.

1. 8 − 4 = ?

4 + **4** = 8   8 − 4 = **4**

2. 10 − 5 = ?

5 + **5** = 10   10 − 5 = **5**

3. 12 − 6 = ?

6 + **6** = 12   12 − 6 = **6**

4. 14 − 7 = ?

7 + **7** = 14   14 − 7 = **7**

5. 16 − 8 = ?

8 + **8** = 16   16 − 8 = **8**

6. 18 − 9 = ?

9 + **9** = 18   18 − 9 = **9**

Use with Lesson 2-9. 21

Practice

Name

Thinking Doubles to Subtract
P 2-9

Subtract. Write the doubles fact that helps you.

1. 10 − 5 = **5**   If 5 + 5 = 10
   5 + **5** = 10   then 10 − 5 = 5

2. 20 − 10 = **10**   3. **6** = 12 − 6
   10 + **10** = 20   **12** = **6** + **6**

4. 6 − 3 = **3**   5. **7** = 14 − 7
   3 + **3** = **6**   **14** = **7** + **7**

6. 8   7. 18
   − 4   − 9
   4   **4**   **9**   **9**
        + **4**   + **9**
          8   18

Problem Solving *Writing in Math*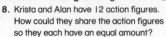

8. Krista and Alan have 12 action figures.
   How could they share the action figures
   so they each have an equal amount?

   Each child would get 6 action figures.
   6 + 6 = 12

Use with Lesson 2-9. 21

Enrichment

Name

Sharing
E 2-9
NUMBER SENSE

Separate the objects into 2 equal groups.
Write a subtraction sentence and the related doubles fact.

1. Becky has 10 apples.
   She shares 5 apples with Tom.
   How many apples do they
   each have?

   10 − **5** = **5**

   What doubles fact helps you?

   5 + **5** = **10**

2. Megan has 8 flowers.
   She shares 4 flowers with Nick.
   How many flowers do they
   each have?

   8 − **4** = **4**

   What doubles fact helps you?

   4 + **4** = **8**

3. Jake has 12 pears.
   He shares 6 pears with Sasha.
   How many pears do they
   each have?

   12 − **6** = **6**

   What doubles fact helps you?

   6 + **6** = **12**

4. Jamal has 14 cars.
   He shares 7 cars with Carla.
   How many cars do they
   each have?

   14 − **7** = **7**

   What doubles fact helps you?

   7 + **7** = **14**

Use with Lesson 2-9. 21

Problem Solving

Name

Thinking Doubles to Subtract
PS 2-9

Each basket should have the same amount of fruit.
Draw the fruit. Write how many are in each basket.
Then write a subtraction sentence using doubles.

1. There are 8 apples in all.

   4 apples are in one basket.

   4 apples are in the other basket.

   8 − **4** = **4**

2. There are 12 pears in all.

   6 pears are in one basket.

   6 pears are in the other basket.

   12 − **6** = **6**

Problem Solving *Writing in Math*

Write a subtraction story about
the cherries in the baskets.

Stories should use the subtraction

16 − 8 = 8.

Use with Lesson 2-9. 21

© Pearson Education, Inc. 2

Name _____

Thinking Addition to Subtract

R 2-10

Think addition to find the difference for $14 - 6$.

Addition Fact	Subtraction Fact
○○○○○	⊠⊠⊠⊠⊠
●●●●● ●●●●	⊠⊠⊠⊠ ●●●●●
Think $6 + \underline{8} = 14$.	So, $14 - 6 = \underline{8}$.

Use addition facts to help you subtract.

1. ○○○○○○○○○   ⊠⊠⊠⊠⊠⊠⊠⊠⊠
   ●●●● ●●●●

   Think $9 + \underline{4} = 13$.   So, $13 - 9 = \underline{4}$.

2. ○○○○○○○   ⊠⊠⊠⊠⊠⊠⊠
   ●●●●● ●●●●●

   Think $7 + \underline{5} = 12$.   So, $12 - 7 = \underline{5}$.

3. ○○○○○○○○   ⊠⊠⊠⊠⊠⊠⊠⊠
   ●●●●●●●●● ●●●●●●●●●

   Think $8 + \underline{9} = 17$.   So, $17 - 8 = \underline{9}$.

4. ○○○○○○○   ⊠⊠⊠⊠⊠⊠⊠
   ●●●●●● ●●●●●●

   Think $9 + \underline{6} = 15$.   So, $15 - 9 = \underline{6}$.

© Pearson Education, Inc. 2

Name _____

Thinking Addition to Subtract

P 2-10

Solve. Draw a line to match each subtraction fact with its related addition fact.

1. $14 - 8 = \underline{6}$ $5 + \underline{6} = 11$
   $16 - 7 = \underline{9}$ $2 + \underline{16} = 18$
   $11 - 5 = \underline{6}$ $8 + \underline{6} = 14$
   $18 - 2 = \underline{16}$ $7 + \underline{9} = 16$

2. $\underline{9} = 15 - 6$ $13 = 5 + \underline{8}$
   $\underline{5} = 12 - 7$ $15 = 6 + \underline{9}$
   $\underline{14} = 17 - 3$ $17 = 3 + \underline{14}$
   $\underline{8} = 13 - 5$ $12 = 7 + \underline{5}$

Problem Solving Mental Math

3. Randy has 20¢. He bought a used toy truck for 14¢. Circle the used toy that he has enough money left to buy.

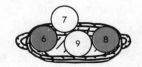

8¢   10¢   5¢

© Pearson Education, Inc. 2

Name _____

Which Fact?

E 2-10
REASONING

Circle the addition fact that will help you subtract.
Write a subtraction sentence to solve each problem.

1. Pam has 16 marbles. $16 + 9$ $8 + 8$ $(7 + 9)$
   She puts 9 marbles in a jar.
   How many marbles does
   she have out?

   $\underline{16} - \underline{9} = \underline{7}$ Pam has $\underline{7}$ marbles out.

2. Rhonda has 14 baseball cards. $4 + 8$ $(6 + 8)$ $8 + 14$
   Chet has 8 baseball cards.
   How many more cards does
   Rhonda have than Chet?

   $\underline{14} - \underline{8} = \underline{6}$ Rhonda has $\underline{6}$ more cards.

3. Marty has 15 stamps. $8 + 7$ $15 + 6$ $(9 + 6)$
   He puts 6 stamps in an album.
   How many stamps are not in
   the album?

   $\underline{15} - \underline{6} = \underline{9}$ Marty has $\underline{9}$ stamps out
   of the album.

4. Lucy has 12 books. $3 + 12$ $(9 + 3)$ $6 + 6$
   Michael has 3 books.
   How many more books does
   Lucy have than Michael?

   $\underline{12} - \underline{3} = \underline{9}$ Lucy has $\underline{9}$ more books.

© Pearson Education, Inc. 2

Name _____

Thinking Addition to Subtract

PS 2-10

Color some shapes red. Color some shapes blue. Write the parts and the whole. Write an addition and a subtraction sentence to go with each.

Check that number sentences match the shapes colored. Possible answers are given.

1.

   | Total 13 |
   | 5 | 8 |

   $\underline{5} + \underline{8} = 13$
   $13 - \underline{5} = \underline{8}$

2.

   | Total 11 |
   | 5 | 6 |

   $\underline{5} + \underline{6} = 11$
   $11 - \underline{5} = \underline{6}$

3.

   | Total 16 |
   | 9 | 7 |

   $\underline{9} + \underline{7} = 16$
   $16 - \underline{9} = \underline{7}$

4. Pam picked 2 balls
   out of the basket.
   Her score was 14.
   Color the balls
   she picked.

© Pearson Education, Inc. 2

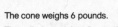

Name _____

PROBLEM-SOLVING SKILL   R 2-11

Use Data from a Picture

What does the cube weigh?

The cone weighs 6 pounds.
The cylinder weighs 15 pounds.

The cube weighs   If   6 + _9_ = 15,

_9_ pounds.   then   15 – 6 = _9_ .

Use the picture to find the missing number.
Write the number sentence.

1. What does the sphere weigh?

The cube weighs 7 pounds.
The cone weighs 12 pounds.

The sphere weighs   If   _5_ + 7 = 12,

_5_ pounds.   then   12 – _5_ = 7.

2. What does the cube weigh?

The cylinder weighs 4 pounds.
The sphere weighs 12 pounds.

The cube weighs   If   4 + _8_ = 12,

_8_ pounds.   then   12 – 4 = _8_ .

Use with Lesson 2-11. **23**

© Pearson Education, Inc. 2

Name _____

PROBLEM-SOLVING SKILL   P 2-11

Use Data from a Picture

Find the missing number.
Write the number sentence.

1. What does the cube weigh?

If _8_ + 5 = 13,

then 13 – 5 = _8_

The cube weighs _8_ pounds.

2. What does the cylinder weigh?

If 6 + _4_ = 10,

then 10 – 6 = _4_

The cylinder weighs _4_ pounds.

Reasoning
Write the missing number for each sentence.

3. _9_ + 8 = 17   4. 14 – _5_ = 9

7 + _6_ = 13   15 – _7_ = 8

Use with Lesson 2-11. **23**

© Pearson Education, Inc. 2

Name _____

What to Buy?   E 2-11
                                          DECISION MAKING

Use the price chart to solve the problems.
Write the number sentence you used.

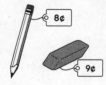 8¢   STICKERS 6¢   7¢

9¢

1. Joey has 16¢.
   If he buys the pencil, what
   other supply can he buy?

   16¢ ⊖ 8¢ = 8¢
   _____
   stickers or marker

2. Chen has 15¢.
   If he buys the marker, what
   other supply can he buy?

   15¢ ⊖ 7¢ = 8¢
   _____
   pencil or stickers

3. Sarah has 12¢.
   Does she have enough to
   buy 2 different supplies?

   6¢ ⊕ 7¢ = 13¢
   _____
   no

4. Vinnie has 13¢.
   He loses 4¢.
   Does he have enough
   left to buy something?

   13¢ ⊖ 4¢ = 9¢
   _____
   yes

Use with Lesson 2-11. **23**

© Pearson Education, Inc. 2

Name _____

PROBLEM-SOLVING SKILL   PS 2-11

Using Data from a Picture

Use the shapes to solve each problem.
Find and write the missing number.

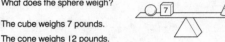 8   15   6   12   ?

1.

What does the cone weigh?

If 8 + ___ = 15,

then 15 – 8 = ___ .

The cone weighs ___ pounds.

2.

What does the rectangular prism weigh?

If 6 + _6_ = 12,

then 12 – 6 = _6_ .

The rectangular prism weighs _6_ pounds.

Using the page Ask children to *read* each question. To help them *understand* the problem, ask them what information is needed from the picture to solve each problem.

Use with Lesson 2-11. **23**

© Pearson Education, Inc. 2

Name _____

PROBLEM-SOLVING APPLICATIONS   R 2-12

Baby Birds

1. 2 birds were at the birdbath and 3 more joined them. Then, 4 more birds came. How many birds were at the birdbath in all?

   $\underline{2} + \underline{3} + \underline{4} = \underline{9}$ birds

2. The mother and father bird make many hunting trips each hour. How many hunting trips did the mother make during the second hour?

	Mom	Dad	Total
Hour 1	8 trips	12 trips	20 trips
Hour 2	$\underline{9}$ trips	10 trips	19 trips

   $\underline{9} + 10 = 19$ trips

   She made $\underline{9}$ trips during the second hour.

3. The father bird caught 5 worms the first hour and 9 worms the second hour. How many more worms did he catch the second hour?

   $\underline{9} \ominus \underline{5} = \underline{4}$ more worms

4. The mother bird caught 3 worms the first hour and 5 worms the second hour. How many worms did she catch in all?

   $\underline{3} \oplus \underline{5} = \underline{8}$ worms in all

Use with Lesson 2-12.

Name _____

PROBLEM-SOLVING APPLICATIONS   P 2-12

Baby Birds

Solve.

1. A nest has 13 eggs, and 5 of the eggs hatch. How many more eggs need to hatch?

   $\underline{13} - \underline{5} = \underline{8}$ eggs

2. A group of nestlings is 8 days old. In 9 more days, they will be ready to leave the nest. How old will they be then?

   $\underline{8} \oplus \underline{9} = \underline{17}$ days old

3. Look at the chart. How many nestlings are in the second family?

	Parents	Nestlings	Total
Family 1	2	4	6
Family 2	2	$\underline{6}$	8

   $2 + \underline{6} = 8$

   There are $\underline{6}$ nestlings in the second family.

Writing in Math

4. A group of 3 birds was at the bird feeder. Then 12 more birds came and chased them away. How many birds were left at the bird feeder?

   There were 12 birds left at the bird feeder.

Use with Lesson 2-12.

Name _____

At the Farm

E 2-12
REASONABLENESS

Circle the answer that best solves the problem.

1. A hen lays 8 eggs. Then she lays some more eggs. How many eggs could the hen have now?

   (15 eggs)   7 eggs   5 eggs

2. A cat has 7 kittens. Some kittens go off to play. How many kittens could still be with the cat?

   (5 kittens)   7 kittens   9 kittens

3. There are 9 horses in the field. Some more horses come into the field. How many horses could be in the field now?

   9 horses   8 horses   (12 horses)

4. A farmer collects 6 pails of milk. His wife collects some more pails of milk. How many pails of milk could they have collected in all?

   5 pails   6 pails   (9 pails)

5. There are 13 cows in the barn. Some cows leave the barn. How many cows could be left in the barn?

   13 cows   (8 cows)   15 cows

6. There are 12 pigs in the pigpen. Some pigs leave the pigpen. How many pigs could be in the pigpen now?

   15 pigs   (6 pigs)   12 pigs

Use with Lesson 2-12.

Name _____

PROBLEM-SOLVING APPLICATIONS   PS 2-12

Baby Birds

Use the chart.
Write a number sentence to solve each problem.
Tell what fact strategy you used.

Bird	Number of Nestlings
Sparrow	4
Robin	4
Woodpecker	3
Blue Jay	6

1. How many woodpecker and blue jay nestlings are there in all?

   Number of woodpecker nestlings $\underline{3}$

   Number of blue jay nestlings $\underline{6}$

   $3 \oplus 6 = 9$

   My strategy: Counting on

2. How many sparrow, robin, and blue jay nestlings are there in all?

   $\underline{4} \oplus \underline{4} \oplus \underline{6} = \underline{14}$

   My strategy: Possible answer: look for a double to add

3. How many more blue jay than woodpecker nestlings are there?

   $\underline{6} \ominus \underline{3} = \underline{3}$

   My strategy: Possible answer: count back to subtract

Using the page Have children look back and check that they used the right numbers from the table.

Use with Lesson 2-12.

Reteaching

Name _____

Counting with Tens and Ones

R 3-1

A class made a snack.
The children put 10 raisins on each piece of celery.
Some raisins were left over.

> The raisins on the celery show tens.

> The leftover raisins show the ones.

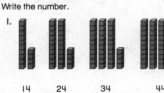

10   10   10   5

__3__ tens and __5__ ones is __35__ in all.

Count the tens and ones.
Write the numbers.

1.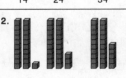

__2__ tens and __3__ ones is __23__ in all.

2.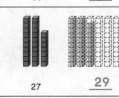

__4__ tens and __8__ ones is __48__ in all.

3.

__1__ ten and __4__ ones is __14__ in all.

© Pearson Education, Inc. 2

Use with Lesson 3-1. **25**

Practice

Name _____

Counting with Tens and Ones

P 3-1

Circle groups of ten. Count the tens and ones.
Write the numbers.

1.

__4__ tens and __5__ ones is __45__ in all.

2.

__5__ tens and __9__ ones is __59__ in all.

Problem Solving *Number Sense*

Solve.

3. Beth has 6 tens and 2 ones. Bobby gives her 1 more one. What is the number?

__6__ tens and __3__ ones

is __63__ in all.

4. Luis has 4 tens and 5 ones. Shayla gives him 1 more ten. What is the number?

__5__ tens and __5__ ones

is __55__ in all.

© Pearson Education, Inc. 2

Use with Lesson 3-1. **25**

Enrichment

Name _____

What Comes Next?

E 3-1
PATTERNS

Find the pattern.
Fill in the pattern that comes next.
Write the number.

1.

14   24   34   44   54

2.

21   23   25   27   __29__

3.

11   23   35   47   __59__

© Pearson Education, Inc. 2

Use with Lesson 3-1. **25**

Problem Solving

Name _____

Counting with Tens and Ones

PS 3-1

Crayons come in boxes of 10.
Solve each problem.
Draw your answer.

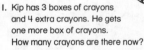

1. Kip has 3 boxes of crayons and 4 extra crayons. He gets one more box of crayons. How many crayons are there now?

__4__ boxes __4__ crayons

__44__ crayons in all

Drawings should show 4 boxes of crayons and 4 single crayons.

2. Tricia has 5 boxes of crayons and 8 extra crayons. She gets two more boxes of crayons. How many crayons are there now?

__7__ boxes __8__ crayons

__78__ crayons in all

Drawings should show 7 boxes of crayons and 8 single crayons.

3. Josh has 6 boxes of crayons and 2 extra crayons. He gets one box of crayons from his friend. How many crayons are there now?

__7__ boxes __2__ crayons

__72__ crayons in all

Drawings should show 7 boxes of crayons and 2 single crayons.

© Pearson Education, Inc. 2

Use with Lesson 3-1. **25**

Use with Chapter 3, Lesson 1. **25**

Name _____

Using Tens and Ones
R 3-2

Count the cubes. Then count the tens and ones.
Write how many there are.

Tens	Ones
2	5

__25__ ones = __2__ tens __5__ ones =

Count the cubes.
Write the number of tens and ones.

1.

Tens	Ones
4	3

__43__ ones = __4__ tens __3__ ones =

2.

Tens	Ones
3	7

__37__ ones = __3__ tens __7__ ones =

Problem Solving *Visual Thinking*

3. How many pairs of feet are needed to have at least 76 toes? Draw a picture to help you solve the problem.

__8__ pairs of feet

26 Use with Lesson 3-2.

© Pearson Education, Inc. 2

Name _____

Using Tens and Ones
P 3-2

Draw lines to match the numbers.
Use cubes and Workmat 4 if you need to.

1.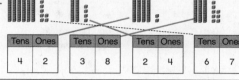

Tens	Ones
4	2

Tens	Ones
3	8

Tens	Ones
2	4

Tens	Ones
6	7

2.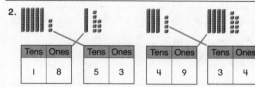

Tens	Ones
1	8

Tens	Ones
5	3

Tens	Ones
4	9

Tens	Ones
3	4

Problem Solving *Visual Thinking*

3. Crayons come in packs of ten. How many packs would you need to get at least 42 crayons? Draw a picture to solve the problem. Explain your answer.

__5__ packs

Drawings should show 5 packs of crayons.

26 Use with Lesson 3-2.

© Pearson Education, Inc. 2

Name _____

Egyptian Numerals
E 3-2
NUMBER SENSE

People in Ancient Egypt used these symbols for numbers.

They used ∩ to show 10.	The number 25 looked like this.
They used | to show 1.	∩∩ |||||

Write the number.

1. ∩∩\|\|\|\|\|
   __35__

2. ∩∩∩∩∩
   __50__

3. ∩\|\|\|\|\|\|
   __16__

4. ∩∩∩∩∩∩\|\|\|
   __63__

5. ∩∩∩∩\|\|\|\|\|\|\|
   __47__

6. ∩∩∩∩∩∩∩\|
   __71__

7. \|\|\|\|\|
   __5__

8. ∩∩\|\|\|\|\|\|\|\|
   __28__

Make up your own symbols for tens and ones. Use them to write these numbers.

Answers will vary.

10 is _____.   1 is _____.

9. 51 _____

10. 13 _____

26 Use with Lesson 3-2.

© Pearson Education, Inc. 2

Name _____

Using Tens and Ones
PS 3-2

Solve the number puzzles.

1. My tens digit is 3 more than 5. My tens digit is double the number of my ones digit. What number am I?
   __84__

2. My ones digit is 2 less than 8. My ones digit is 4 more than my tens digit. What number am I?
   __26__

3. My tens digit is 1 more than the sum of $3 + 3$. My ones digit is the difference of $3 - 2$. What number am I?
   __71__

4. My tens digit is 1 less than the sum of $4 + 3$. My ones digit is 2 more than my tens digit. What number am I?
   __68__

5. My ones digit is 1 less than 4. My tens digit is the greatest number of tens that can be in a number. What number am I?
   __93__

6. My tens digit is double my ones digit. Both of my digits add up to six. What number am I?
   __42__

7. If a softball team has 10 players, how many teams need to be formed for at least 68 players? Draw a picture to solve the problem.

   Pictures should show 7 teams.

26 Use with Lesson 3-2.

© Pearson Education, Inc. 2

Reteaching

Name _____

Number Words

Ones	Teens	Tens
1 one	11 eleven	10 ten
2 two	12 twelve	20 twenty
3 three	13 thirteen	30 thirty
4 four	14 fourteen	40 forty
5 five	15 fifteen	50 fifty
6 six	16 sixteen	60 sixty
7 seven	17 seventeen	70 seventy
8 eight	18 eighteen	80 eighty
9 nine	19 nineteen	90 ninety

Write the number.

7 tens and 8 ones is _78_

78 has two **digits**.

Write the number word.

seventy and **eight** is

seventy—eight

Write the number and the number word.

1. 2 tens and 9 ones is _29_.   twenty-nine

2. 6 tens and 3 ones is _63_.   sixty-three

3. 9 tens and 2 ones is _92_.   ninety-two

4. 8 tens and 6 ones is _86_.   eighty-six

Problem Solving *Number Sense*

What is the number?

5. It is greater than 43 and less than 52. If you add the digits, the sum is 8. Write the number word.

   forty-four

6. It is less than 60 and greater than 55. If you add the digits, the sum is 13. Write the number.

   58

Practice

Name _____

Number Words

Write the number.

1. eight _8_   twenty-five _25_   forty-nine _49_

2. sixty _60_   thirteen _13_   ninety-two _92_

3. fifty-seven _57_   eighty-four _84_   seventy-three _73_

Write the number word.

4. 18 _eighteen_   5. 77 _seventy-seven_

6. 5 tens _fifty_   7. 14 ones _fourteen_

8. 27 _twenty-seven_   9. 50 _fifty_

10. 1 ten 8 ones _eighteen_   11. 3 tens _thirty_

12. 4 tens 8 ones _forty-eight_

13. 9 tens 2 ones _ninety-two_

Problem Solving *Number Sense*

What is the number?

14. It is greater than 30 and less than 40. If you add the digits, the sum is 10. Write the number word.

   thirty-seven

15. It is greater than 7 tens and less than 8 tens. The number has 4 ones. Write the number word.

   seventy-four

Enrichment

Name _____

Number Match

Draw a line to connect the number to its word name.
Then connect the word name to the tens and ones.

1. 29	sixty-two	4 tens 7 ones
2. 47	twenty-nine	2 tens 9 ones
3. 62	fifty-nine	6 tens 2 ones
4. 19	forty-seven	7 tens 4 ones
5. 95	nineteen	1 ten 9 ones
6. 59	thirty	5 tens 9 ones
7. 30	ninety-five	9 tens 5 ones
8. 74	seventy-four	3 tens 0 ones

The letters in these words are all mixed up.
Find the number word.
Then write the number name and the number.

9. esvne   seven   7

10. lwtvee   twelve   12

11. ryitth   thirty   30

Problem Solving

Name _____

Number Words

Circle all the names and ways to show the number.

1. twenty-seven

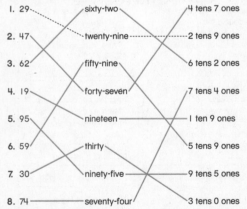

2. fifty-eight

3. 92

   (ninety-two)
   (9 tens 2 ones)

   nine plus two

4. 35

   thirteen-five
   (3 tens 5 ones)
   (thirty-five)

What is the number?

5. My tens digit is double my ones digit. My ones digit is the sum of 2 + 2. Write the number word.

   eighty-four

6. My ones digit is less than three. My tens digit is greater than seven. If you add the digits, the sum is 11. Write the number word.

   ninety-two

Name _____

PROBLEM-SOLVING STRATEGY R 3-4

Make an Organized List

Make 40 as many ways as you can by using groups of ten.

Read and Understand

You need to find groups of 10 that make 40.

Plan and Solve

Use tens models to help you find groups that make 40. Look at the tens shown in the first group. Draw the tens needed in the second group to make 40. Write the missing numbers in the list.

Look Back and Check

Check to see if each row makes 40.

	Tens	Tens	Total
1.	0 tens	4 tens	40
2.	1 ten	3 tens	40
3.	2 tens	2 tens	40
4.	3 tens	1 ten	40

Name _____

PROBLEM-SOLVING STRATEGY P 3-4

Make an Organized List

Use only tens to make the number in two parts.
Use cubes and Workmat 1 if you need to.

1. Make 40.

Tens	Tens	Total
0	4	40
1	3	40
2	2	40
3	1	40
4	0	40

2. Make 80.

Tens	Tens	Total
0	8	80
1	7	80
2	6	80
3	5	80
4	4	80
5	3	80
6	2	80
7	1	80
8	0	80

3. Make 70.

Tens	Tens	Total
0	7	70
1	6	70
2	5	70
3	4	70
4	3	70
5	2	70
6	1	70
7	0	70

Name _____

E 3-4
PATTERNS

Let's Go Riding!

A list can help you see patterns in numbers.
Complete the lists. Then answer the questions.

Bicycles	Wheels
1	2
2	4
3	6
4	8
5	10

Tricycles	Wheels
1	3
2	6
3	9
4	12
5	15

1. How many wheels are on 4 bicycles? __8__

2. What is the pattern of numbers of the bicycles?

   Counting by ones

3. What is the pattern of numbers of the wheels?

   Counting by twos

4. How many wheels are on 5 tricycles? __15__

5. What is the pattern of numbers of the tricycles?

   Counting by ones

6. What is the pattern of numbers of the wheels?

   Counting by threes

7. How could you use a list to show how many wheels are on 3 wagons? Possible answer:

   Make a list to show counting by fours.

   There are 12 wheels on 3 wagons.

Name _____

PROBLEM-SOLVING STRATEGY PS 3-4

Make an Organized List

A list helps you see all the ways you can organize information. Make a list to show all the ways you can add dimes to make 50¢.

When you have completed the list, look back to see if all the rows add up to 50¢.

1. Make 50¢.

Dimes	Dimes	Total
0	5	50¢
1	4	50¢
2	3	50¢
3	2	50¢
4	1	50¢
5	0	50¢

2. Make 90¢.

Dimes	Dimes	Total
0	9	90¢
1	8	90¢
2	7	90¢
3	6	90¢
4	5	90¢
5	4	90¢
6	3	90¢
7	2	90¢
8	1	90¢
9	0	90¢

Using the page To help students *look back* and *check* their answers, ask them whether each row has a total of 50¢ or 90¢.

Name _____

Comparing Numbers

R 3-5

You can compare numbers using words or the signs >, <, or =.

Step 1	Step 2	Step 3
Compare the tens.	If the tens are the same, compare the ones.	Tens and ones can be the same.
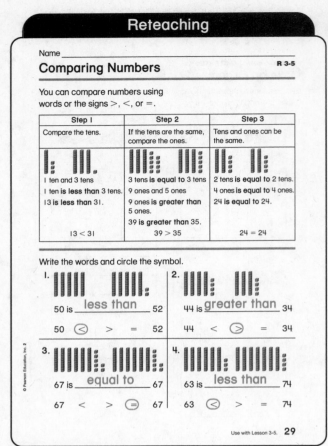		
1 ten and 3 tens	3 tens is equal to 3 tens.	2 tens is equal to 2 tens.
1 ten is less than 3 tens.	9 ones and 5 ones	4 ones is equal to 4 ones.
13 is less than 31.	9 ones is greater than 5 ones.	24 is equal to 24.
	39 is greater than 35.	
13 < 31	39 > 35	24 = 24

Write the words and circle the symbol.

1. 50 is __less than__ 52

50 (<) > = 52

2. 44 is __greater than__ 34

44 < (>) = 34

3. 67 is __equal to__ 67

67 < > (=) 67

4. 63 is __less than__ 74

63 (<) > = 74

Use with Lesson 3-5. **29**

© Pearson Education, Inc. 2

Name _____

Comparing Numbers

P 3-5

Write >, <, or =.

1. 32 (<) 51   15 (<) 51   43 (<) 48

2. 70 (>) 65   48 (<) 50   93 (>) 89

3. 27 (>) 21   67 (=) 67   70 (<) 77

4. 19 (<) 91   82 (>) 59   12 (=) 12

Write a number that makes each statement true.   **Answers will vary.**

5. __57 or greater__ > 56   39 = __39__   89 > __88 or less__

6. __72 or less__ < 73   __36 or greater__ > 35   __100__ = 100

Problem Solving Reasoning

What number am I?

7. My tens digit is double the ones digit. I am less than 50 and greater than 40.

__42__

8. My ones digit is 5 more than the tens digit. I am greater than 25 and less than 35.

__27__

Use with Lesson 3-5. **29**

© Pearson Education, Inc. 2

Name _____

Kitty Rescue

E 3-5
NUMBER SENSE

Choose the number or the symbol from the tree to complete each exercise. You may use a number only once.

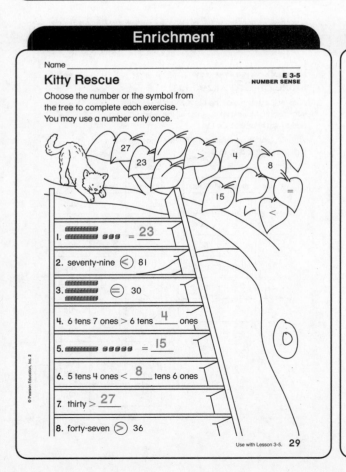

1. ▭▭▭ ▦▦▦ = __23__

2. seventy-nine (<) 81

3. ▭▭▭ (=) 30

4. 6 tens 7 ones > 6 tens __4__ ones

5. ▭▭ ▦▦▦▦▦ = __15__

6. 5 tens 4 ones < __8__ tens 6 ones

7. thirty > __27__

8. forty-seven (>) 36

Use with Lesson 3-5. **29**

© Pearson Education, Inc. 2

Name _____

Comparing Numbers

PS 3-5

Draw a circle around the correct answer.

1. Ryan picks more than 43 flowers but less than 67 flowers. How many flowers could Ryan have?

40   (60)   70

2. Rachel sells less than 30 tickets to a show. She sells more than 15 tickets. How many tickets could Rachel have sold?

14   (26)   32

3. The number of baseball cards in Jacy's collection is greater than 70. It is less than 90. How many baseball cards could Jacy have?

64   (78)   91

4. Sue picked less than 50 apples. The number of apples she picked was greater than 30. How many apples could Sue have picked?

27   (44)   52

What number am I?

5. I am a number less than 59. I am greater than 48. My ones digit is 2 more than my tens digit.

__57__

6. I am a number greater than 48. I am less than 60. My ones digit is 3 less than my tens digit.

__52__

Use with Lesson 3-5. **29**

© Pearson Education, Inc. 2

Reteaching

Name _____

Finding the Closest Ten

R 3-6

Are there **about** 40 or 50 pumpkins?

Use tens to tell **about** how many.
Find the closest ten.

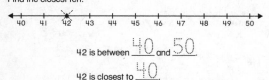

42 is between __40__ and __50__.

42 is closest to __40__.

Find the number on the basket on the number line.
Write the closest ten.

1.
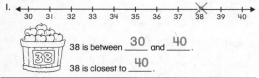

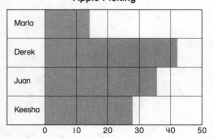
38 is between __30__ and __40__.

38 is closest to __40__.

2.
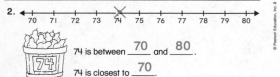

74 is between __70__ and __80__.

74 is closest to __70__.

30 Use with Lesson 3-6.

Practice

Name _____

Finding the Closest Ten

P 3-6

Find the number on the number line.
Write the closest ten.

1.
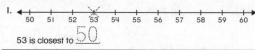

53 is closest to __50__.

2.
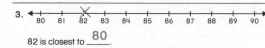

28 is closest to __30__.

3.

82 is closest to __80__.

Write the closest ten.

4. about __50__   5. about __20__

6. about __30__   7. about __60__

Problem Solving *Reasonableness*

8. Maria has a collection of about 20 toy cars.
Which could be the exact number of cars?

23   32   12   40   __23__ toy cars

30 Use with Lesson 3-6.

Enrichment

Name _____

Apple Picking Time

E 3-6
DATA

Use the graph to find about how many apples were picked.
Write the number of apples to the closest ten.

Apple Picking

Marla					
Derek					
Juan					
Keesha					

0   10   20   30   40   50

1. Marla picked about __10__ apples.

2. Juan picked about __40__ apples.

3. Together, Marla and Juan picked about __50__ apples.

4. Keesha picked about __30__ apples.

5. Derek picked about __40__ apples.

6. Together, Keesha and Derek picked about __70__ apples.

7. Together, Keesha , Marla, and Juan
picked about __80__ apples.

30 Use with Lesson 3-6.

Problem Solving

Name _____

Finding the Closest Ten

PS 3-6

Use the information in the chart.
Find the closest ten.

Animals at the Zoo	
Mammals	67
Birds	63
Reptiles	36
Amphibians	51

1. About how many reptiles
are at the zoo?

about __40__ reptiles

2. About how many birds are at the zoo?   about __60__ birds

3. An elephant belongs to the group that is
closest to 70. What group does an
elephant belong to?

mammals

4. A frog belongs to the group that is closest
to 50. What group does a frog belong to?

amphibians

5. Color the bar graph to
show about how many
animals are at the zoo.

6. Some reptiles
are snakes.
Which could be
the exact number
of snakes?

26   36   46

__26__ snakes

Animals at the Zoo

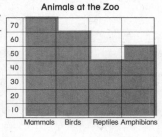

70			
60			
50			
40			
30			
20			
10			

Mammals   Birds   Reptiles   Amphibians

30 Use with Lesson 3-6.

Name _____

Before, After, and Between

R 3-7

1	2	3	4	5	6	7	8	9	10
11	12	13	14	15	16	17	18	19	20
21	22	23	24	25	26	27	28	29	30
31	32	33	34	35	36	37	38	39	40
41	42	43	44	45	46	47	48	49	50
51	52	53	54	55	56	57	58	59	60
61	62	63	64	65	66	67	68	69	70
71	72	73	74	75	76	77	78	79	80
81	82	83	84	85	86	87	88	89	90
91	92	93	94	95	96	97	98	99	100

Use the words **before, after,** and **between** to help you find the numbers.

One **before** 66 is _65_.

One **after** 66 is _67_.

_66_ is **between** 65 and 67.

Answer the questions.

1. One before 12 is _11_.
   One after 12 is _13_.
   The number between
   _11_ and _13_ is 12.

2. One before 70 is _69_.
   One after 70 is _71_.
   The number between
   _69_ and _71_ is 70.

3. One before 45 is _44_.
   One after 45 is _46_.
   The number between
   _44_ and _46_ is 45.

4. One before 91 is _90_.
   One after 91 is _92_.
   The number between
   _90_ and _92_ is 91.

© Pearson Education, Inc. 2

Use with Lesson 3-7. **31**

Name _____

Before, After, and Between

P 3-7

Write the missing numbers.
Use the hundreds chart if you need to.

1	2	3	4	5	6	7	8	9	10
11	12	13	14	15	16	17	18	19	20
21	22	23	24	25	26	27	28	29	30
31	32	33	34	35	36	37	38	39	40
41	42	43	44	45	46	47	48	49	50
51	52	53	54	55	56	57	58	59	60
61	62	63	64	65	66	67	68	69	70
71	72	73	74	75	76	77	78	79	80
81	82	83	84	85	86	87	88	89	90
91	92	93	94	95	96	97	98	99	100

1.
   61 62 63 **64**
   71 **72** 73
   83 **84** 85

2.
   71 **72** 73
   82 83 **84**
   90 91 **92**

3. _37_, 38, _39_, _40_, 41

4. 49, _50_, _51_, 52, _53_

Write the number.

5. What number is one after 28? _29_

6. What number is between 69 and 71? _70_

7. What number is one before 45? _44_

Problem Solving *Writing in Math*

8. Pick a number from 1 to 100. Describe the number using the words before, after, and between.

   Answers will vary.
   Possible answer: 57.
   It is one after 56. It is
   between 56 and 58.
   It is one before 58.

© Pearson Education, Inc. 2

Use with Lesson 3-7. **31**

Name _____

Hat Tricks

E 3-7
NUMBER SENSE

Look at the numbers in the hat.
Use two of the numbers.
Write a two-digit number that will make the sentence true.

Answers will vary.
Possible answers are given.

1.
   (2, 5, 4)
   _24_ comes before 27.

2.
   (7, 1, 3)
   _71_ comes after 48.

3.
   (9, 6, 1)
   _69_ comes between 60 and 70.

4.
   (8, 2, 3)
   _82_ comes after 35.

5.
   (2, 9, 4)
   _29_ comes before 81.

6.
   (5, 3, 7)
   _35_ comes between 30 and 40.

© Pearson Education, Inc. 2

Use with Lesson 3-7. **31**

Name _____

Before, After, and Between

PS 3-7

Match the numbers to the mailboxes.
Use the clues.

50	24	30	55	33	76
Smith	Lopez	Jackson	Ling	Cohen	Russo

1. The number on the Smith mailbox is between 49 and 51. What number belongs on the Smith mailbox?
   _50_

2. The number on the Lopez mailbox is one after 23. What number belongs on the Lopez mailbox?
   _24_

3. The number on the Jackson mailbox is one before 31. What number belongs on the Jackson mailbox?
   _30_

4. The number on the Ling mailbox is between 54 and 56. What number belongs on the Ling mailbox?
   _55_

5. The number on the Cohen mailbox is one before 34. What number belongs on the Cohen mailbox?
   _33_

6. **Writing in Math** The number on the Russo mailbox is 76. Write a number story to go with 76. Use "one after," "one before," or "between" in your story.
   Stories will vary.

© Pearson Education, Inc. 2

Use with Lesson 3-7. **31**

© Pearson Education, Inc. **2**

Use with Chapter 3, Lesson 7. **31**

Reteaching

Name ____________________

Skip Counting on the Hundred Chart

R 3-8

1	2	3	4	5	6	7	8	9	10
11	12	13	14	15	16	17	18	19	20
21	22	23	24	25	26	27	28	29	30
31	32	33	34	35	36	37	38	39	40
41	42	43	44	45	46	47	48	49	50
51	52	53	54	55	56	57	58	59	60
61	62	63	64	65	66	67	68	69	70
71	72	73	74	75	76	77	78	79	80
81	82	83	84	85	86	87	88	89	90
91	92	93	94	95	96	97	98	99	100

A pattern is something that repeats. A **hundred chart** makes number patterns easy to see.

Start at 10.
Skip count by 10s.
What is the ones digit in each number? 0

Use the hundred chart to answer the questions.

1. Start at 5. Skip count by 5s. Shade the numbers. What numbers do you find in the ones digit? 5 and 0

2. Start at 3. Skip count by 3s. Circle the numbers. What numbers do you find in the ones digit?
0, 1, 2, 3, 4, 5, 6, 7, 8, 9

Problem Solving *Number Sense*

3. Count by 4s. 4, 8, 12, 16, 20, 24, 28, 32

4. Count backward by 8s. 80, 72, 64, 56, 48, 40, 32, 24

Practice

Name ____________________

Skip Counting on the Hundred Chart

P 3-8

1. Finish coloring skip counts by 10s.
2. Circle skip counts by 3s.
3. What patterns do you see with skip counts by 10s and 3s?
Tens are up and down in a column. Threes are diagonal.

1	2	3	4	5	6	7	8	9	10
11	12	13	14	15	16	17	18	19	20
21	22	23	24	25	26	27	28	29	30
31	32	33	34	35	36	37	38	39	40
41	42	43	44	45	46	47	48	49	50
51	52	53	54	55	56	57	58	59	60
61	62	63	64	65	66	67	68	69	70
71	72	73	74	75	76	77	78	79	80
81	82	83	84	85	86	87	88	89	90
91	92	93	94	95	96	97	98	99	100

Problem Solving *Number Sense*

4. Count by 2s. 12, 14, 16, 18, 20, 22, 24, 26
5. Count by 3s. 30, 33, 36, 39, 42, 45, 48, 51
6. Count by 5s. 50, 55, 60, 65, 70, 75, 80, 85
7. Count by 10s. 30, 40, 50, 60, 70, 80, 90, 100
8. Count backward by 2s. 40, 38, 36, 34, 32, 30, 28
9. Count backward by 3s. 30, 27, 24, 21, 18, 15, 12
10. Count backward by 5s. 100, 95, 90, 85, 80, 75, 70
11. Count backward by 10s. 80, 70, 60, 50, 40, 30, 20

Enrichment

Name ____________________

Stepping Stones

E 3-8
PATTERNS

1. Use a calculator. Press 4 + to help the jaguar find each stone on the way across the river. Color each stone the jaguar steps on.

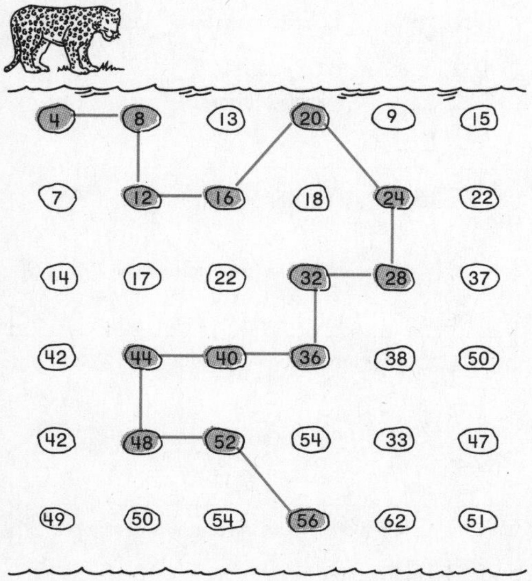

2. Look at the jaguar's path. What is the pattern? add 4

Problem Solving

Name ____________________

Skip Counting on the Hundred Chart

PS 3-8

Solve. Use a hundred chart.

1. There are 5 chairs. Each chair has 4 legs. How many legs in all? 20 legs

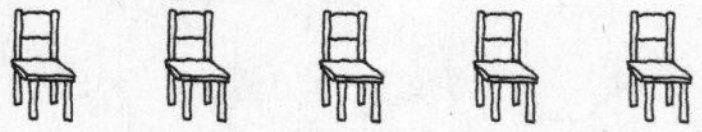

2. There are 6 chimps. Each chimp has 2 legs. How many legs in all? 12 legs

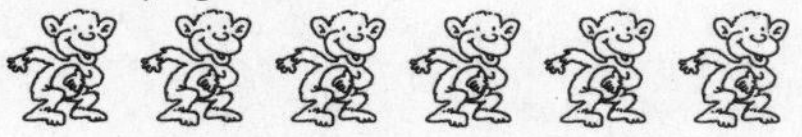

3. There are 7 tricycles. Each tricycle has 3 wheels. How many wheels in all? 21 wheels

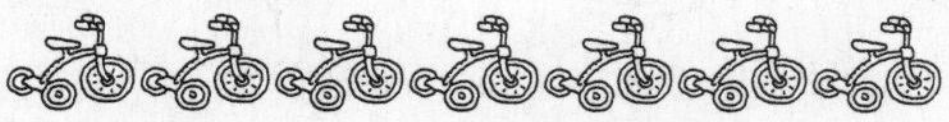

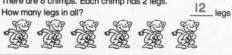

4. There are 5 starfish. Each starfish has 5 arms. How many arms in all? 25 arms

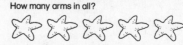

5. There are 80 petals. Each flower has 10 petals. How many flowers in all? 8 flowers

Name _____

Even and Odd Numbers

R 3-9

An **even** number of things can be matched.	An **odd** number of things cannot be matched.

Draw lines. 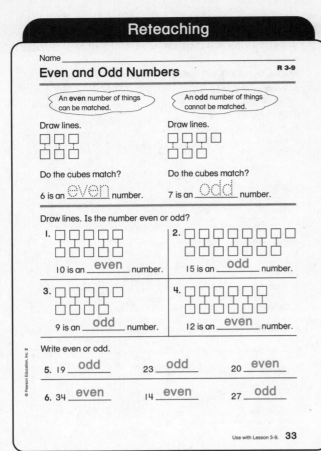 Draw lines.

Do the cubes match?   Do the cubes match?

6 is an _even_ number.   7 is an _odd_ number.

Draw lines. Is the number even or odd?

1. 10 is an _even_ number.

2. 15 is an _odd_ number.

3. 9 is an _odd_ number.

4. 12 is an _even_ number.

Write even or odd.

5. 19 _odd_   23 _odd_   20 _even_

6. 34 _even_   14 _even_   27 _odd_

© Pearson Education, Inc. 2

Use with Lesson 3-9. **33**

Name _____

Even and Odd Numbers

P 3-9

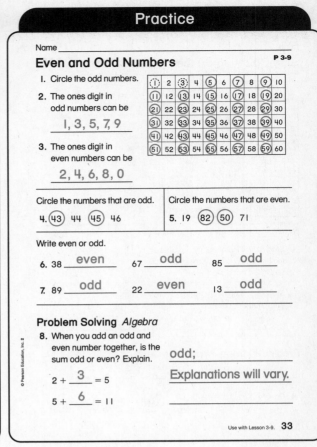

1. Circle the odd numbers.

2. The ones digit in odd numbers can be
   _1, 3, 5, 7, 9_

3. The ones digit in even numbers can be
   _2, 4, 6, 8, 0_

Circle the numbers that are odd.	Circle the numbers that are even.
4. (43) 44 (45) 46	5. 19 (82) (50) 71

Write even or odd.

6. 38 _even_   67 _odd_   85 _odd_

7. 89 _odd_   22 _even_   13 _odd_

Problem Solving *Algebra*

8. When you add an odd and even number together, is the sum odd or even? Explain.

   2 + _3_ = 5

   5 + _6_ = 11

   odd;

   Explanations will vary.

© Pearson Education, Inc. 2

Use with Lesson 3-9. **33**

Name _____

Adding Up Odd or Even

E 3-9
NUMBER SENSE

Choose the number that will make the sentence true. Complete the number sentence.

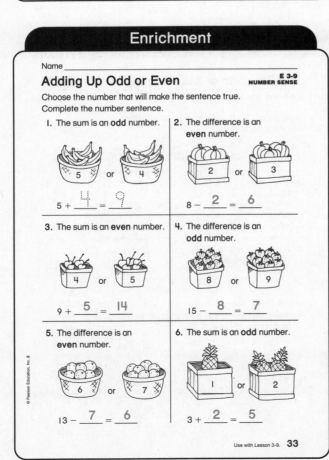

1. The sum is an **odd** number.
   5 or 4
   5 + _4_ = _9_

2. The difference is an **even** number.
   2 or 3
   8 − _2_ = _6_

3. The sum is an **even** number.
   4 or 5
   9 + _5_ = _14_

4. The difference is an **odd** number.
   8 or 9
   15 − _8_ = _7_

5. The difference is an **even** number.
   6 or 7
   13 − _7_ = _6_

6. The sum is an **odd** number.
   1 or 2
   3 + _2_ = _5_

© Pearson Education, Inc. 2

Use with Lesson 3-9. **33**

Name _____

Even and Odd Numbers

PS 3-9

Count the number of odd and even numbers in each jar. Then decide whether you are more likely to pick an odd or even number. Circle **odd** or **even** to show your choice.

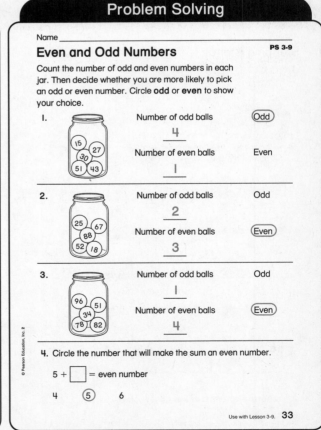

1. Number of odd balls _4_   (Odd)
   Number of even balls _1_   Even

2. Number of odd balls _2_   Odd
   Number of even balls _3_   (Even)

3. Number of odd balls _1_   Odd
   Number of even balls _4_   (Even)

4. Circle the number that will make the sum an even number.
   5 + ☐ = even number
   4   (5)   6

© Pearson Education, Inc. 2

Use with Lesson 3-9. **33**

Use with Chapter 3, Lesson 9. **33**

Name _____

Ordinal Numbers Through Twentieth

R 3-10

Sometimes we need to tell the **order** of things.
We use **ordinal numbers** to tell the order.

1st	2nd	3rd	4th	5th	6th	7th	8th	9th	10th
first	second	third	fourth	fifth	sixth	seventh	eighth	ninth	tenth

Match the ordinal number with the ordinal word.

1.

sixth	fourth	ninth	first
9th	6th	4th	1st

2.

seventh	third	tenth	second
3rd	7th	2nd	10th

Write the ordinal number.

3. eleven __11th__   sixteenth __16th__   twentieth __20th__

34 Use with Lesson 3-10.

Name _____

Ordinal Numbers Through Twentieth

P 3-10

Use the crayons to solve.
Write the letter or number.

A B C D E F G H I J K L M N O P Q R S T
1st   10th   20th

1. The eighth crayon is __H__.

2. The 4th crayon is __D__.

3. The fifth crayon is __E__.

4. The twelfth crayon is __L__.

5. How many crayons are before the 16th crayon? __15__

6. How many crayons are after the 18th crayon? __2__

Mark your answers on the stars.

7. Write an X on the 12th star.

8. Circle the fifteenth star.

9. Write a ✓ on the 20th star.

10. Put a box around the seventh star.

Problem Solving *Reasonableness*

Solve the riddle.

11. This letter comes after the second letter. It comes before the fifth letter. The letter is not a vowel.

R	E	C	E	S	S

What is the secret letter? __C__

34 Use with Lesson 3-10.

Name _____

Animal Lineup

E 3-10
VISUAL THINKING

1. Color the second kitten red.
   Make an X on the 9th kitten.

2. Draw a square around the eighth puppy.
   Color the 3rd puppy orange.

3. Color the fourth bird yellow.
   Draw a circle around the 10th bird.

4. The circle is around the __6th__ rabbit.

   The square is around the __7th__ rabbit.

34 Use with Lesson 3-10.

Name _____

Ordinal Numbers Through Twentieth

PS 3-10

1. There are 20 children in a line. Pam is 5th in line. How many children are behind her in line?

   __15__ children

2. There are 20 children in a line. Robert is 15th. How many children are ahead of him in line?

   __14__ children

3. Max is 14th in line. Sydney is 11th in line. Rolf is at an odd numbered place between them. What place in line is Rolf?

   __thirteenth__ place

4. Jenny is 9th in line to ride the roller coaster. The fourth child leaves the line. What place in line is Jenny now?

   __eighth__ place

5. Sixteen children are in a line. Pablo is 6th in line. The ninth and tenth place children leave the line. What place in line is Pablo now?

   __sixth__ place

6. Mia is 5th in line. Jill is 8 places after Mia. Frank is 1 place ahead of Jill. What place in line is Frank?

   __twelfth__ place

34 Use with Lesson 3-10.

© Pearson Education, Inc. 2

Name_____

PROBLEM-SOLVING SKILL　　　　　　　　　R 3-11

Use Data From a Chart

Use clues to find the secret number on the chart.
Cross out numbers on the chart that do not fit each clue.

Clues:

It is greater than 25. → Cross out the numbers 25 and *less*.

It is less than 30. → Cross out the numbers 30 and *greater*.

It has a 7 in the ones place. → Cross out the numbers that don't have a 7 in the ones place. 26, 28, 29

The secret number is **27**.

Use the clues to find the secret number.

It is greater than 40. → Cross out the numbers **40** and less.

It is less than 46. → Cross out the numbers **46** and greater.

It has a 5 in the ones place. → Cross out the numbers **41, 42, 43, 44**.

The secret number is **45**.

© Pearson Education, Inc. 2

Use with Lesson 3-11. **35**

Name_____

PROBLEM-SOLVING SKILL　　　　　　　　　P 3-11

Use Data From a Chart

Use clues to find the secret number.
Cross out the numbers on the chart that do not fit the clue.

1. It is greater than 47.
   It has a 4 in the tens place.
   It is an even number.

   The secret number is **48**.

2. It is less than 64.
   It has 5 ones.

   The secret number is **55**.

3. It has 8 tens.
   It is greater than 87.
   It is an odd number.

   The secret number is **89**.

Problem Solving *Writing in Math*

4. Choose an odd number between 31 and 59. Write 3 clues. Ask a friend to find your secret number.

   Clues:

   Clues will vary.

© Pearson Education, Inc. 2

Use with Lesson 3-11. **35**

Name_____

Secret Shapes　　　　　　　　　E 3-11 DATA

Use the clues to find the secret shape.
Cross out the shapes on the chart that do not fit the clue.

What is the secret shape?

1. It is not a square.
   It is not a circle.
   It is not in row 3.
   It is in row 4.
   Circle the secret shape.

   Row 1
   Row 2
   Row 3
   Row 4

   The secret shape is a __Children__ should draw a triangle.

What is the secret shape?

2. It is not a square.
   It is not a star.
   It is not in row 4.
   It is in row 2.
   Circle the secret shape.

   Row 1
   Row 2
   Row 3
   Row 4

   The secret shape is a __Children__ should draw a circle.

© Pearson Education, Inc. 2

Use with Lesson 3-11. **35**

Name_____

PROBLEM-SOLVING SKILL　　　　　　　　　PS 3-11

Use Data from a Chart

This dinosaur measured less than 50 feet.
It measured more than 25 feet.
Its length has more than 3 in the tens place. Name the dinosaur.

Think: Which dinosaurs in the chart were less than 50 feet?

Tyrannosaurus, Stegosaurus, Triceratops, and Allosaurus

Think: Of these dinosaurs, which were more than 25 feet?

Tyrannosaurus, Triceratops, and Allosaurus

Which of these dinosaurs has more than 3 in its tens place?

Tyrannosaurus

Lengths of Dinosaurs	
Tyrannosaurus	42 feet
Stegosaurus	15 feet
Diplodocus	90 feet
Triceratops	30 feet
Brachiosaurus	75 feet
Allosaurus	38 feet

Use the clues to solve the number riddles.

1. This dinosaur had a length of more than 50 feet. It measured less than 80 feet. Its length has a 5 in the ones place. Name the dinosaur.

   Brachiosaurus

2. This dinosaur measured more than 30 feet. Its length is an even number. Its length has more than 7 tens. Name the dinosaur.

   Diplodocus

3. **Writing in Math** Choose a dinosaur from the chart. Write a number riddle about its length. Give your riddle to a friend to solve.

Using the page Students should *plan* their approach to each riddle by analyzing the data in the chart, and then proceed to *solve* each riddle.

© Pearson Education, Inc. 2

Use with Lesson 3-11. **35**

Name _____

Dime, Nickel, and Penny

R 3-12

 dime
10 cents
10¢

 nickel
5 cents
5¢

 penny
1 cent
1¢

Count dimes by tens. | Count nickels by fives. | Count pennies by ones.

10¢ 20¢ | 5¢ 10¢ | 1¢ 2¢

Count on to find the total amount. Use coins if you need to.

1. Start with 5¢. Count on by ones.

5¢ 6¢ 7¢ 8¢ 9¢ | Total Amount 9¢

2. Start with 10¢. Count on by fives.

10¢ 15¢ 20¢ 25¢ 30¢ | Total Amount 30¢

Problem Solving *Writing in Math*

3. You have 5 coins that total 23¢. Label the coins D, N, or P for dimes, nickels, or pennies.

(D) (D) (P) (P) (P)

36 Use with Lesson 3-12.

© Pearson Education, Inc. 2

Name _____

Dime, Nickel, and Penny

P 3-12

Count on to find the total amount.

1.
10¢ 20¢ 30¢ 35¢ 40¢ | Total Amount 40¢

2.
10¢ 20¢ 25¢ 26¢ 27¢ | Total Amount 27¢

3.
10¢ 15¢ 20¢ 25¢ 30¢ | Total Amount 30¢

4.
5¢ 10¢ 15¢ 20¢ 21¢ | Total Amount 21¢

Problem Solving *Writing in Math*
5. Which stack of money would you like to spend? Explain.

Answers will vary, but students should choose the stack of 2 nickels.

36 Use with Lesson 3-12.

© Pearson Education, Inc. 2

Name _____

Which Coins?

E 3-12
REASONING

Count on to find the total amount in each purse.
Write the total amount.
Then find the missing amount.

1.  Total Amount 27¢

2. 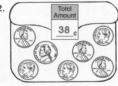 Total Amount 38¢

Circle the coin that you need to make 37¢.

Circle the coins that you need to make 44¢.

3. 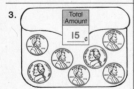 Total Amount 15¢

4.  Total Amount 45¢

Circle the coins that you need to make 26¢.

Circle the coins that you need to make 60¢.

36 Use with Lesson 3-12.

© Pearson Education, Inc. 2

Name _____

Dime, Nickel, and Penny

PS 3-12

Draw how many pennies, nickels, and dimes each child has.

	Dime	Nickel	Penny
1. Bonnie has 5 coins. This is how she counts the coins: 10¢, 20¢, 30¢, 31¢, 32¢ How many of each coin does Bonnie have?	3 dimes		2 pennies
2. Leo has 4 coins. This is how he counts the coins: 10¢, 15¢, 20¢, 21¢ How many of each coin does Leo have?	1 dime	2 nickels	1 penny
3. Nick has 6 coins. This is how he counts the coins: 10¢, 20¢, 25¢, 30¢, 35¢, 40¢ How many of each coin does Nick have?	2 dimes	4 nickels	

4. **Writing in Math** Diana has 5 coins that total 17¢. Draw and label the coins.

Children should draw 3 nickels and 2 pennies.

36 Use with Lesson 3-12.

© Pearson Education, Inc. 2

Name _____

Quarter and Half-Dollar

R 3-13

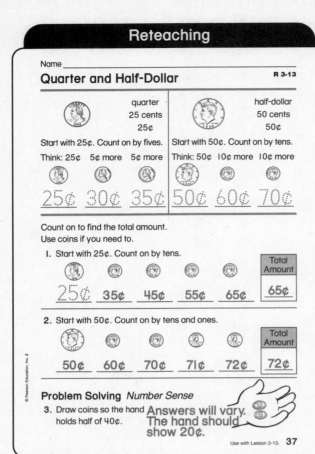

	quarter 25 cents 25¢		half-dollar 50 cents 50¢

Start with 25¢. Count on by fives. | Start with 50¢. Count on by tens.

Think: 25¢ 5¢ more 5¢ more | Think: 50¢ 10¢ more 10¢ more

25¢ 30¢ 35¢ 50¢ 60¢ 70¢

Count on to find the total amount.
Use coins if you need to.

1. Start with 25¢. Count on by tens.

25¢ 35¢ 45¢ 55¢ 65¢ Total Amount **65¢**

2. Start with 50¢. Count on by tens and ones.

50¢ 60¢ 70¢ 71¢ 72¢ Total Amount **72¢**

Problem Solving *Number Sense*

3. Draw coins so the hand holds half of 40¢.

Answers will vary. The hand should show 20¢.

Use with Lesson 3-13. 37

Name _____

Quarter and Half-Dollar

P 3-13

Count on to find the total amount.
You may use Workmat 6 if you need to.

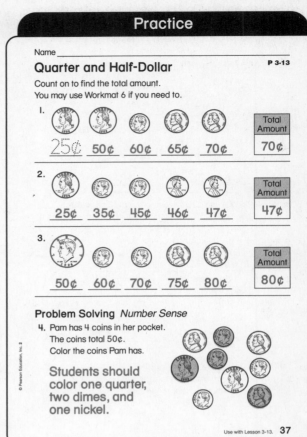

1. 25¢ 50¢ 60¢ 65¢ 70¢ Total Amount **70¢**

2. 25¢ 35¢ 45¢ 46¢ 47¢ Total Amount **47¢**

3. 50¢ 60¢ 70¢ 75¢ 80¢ Total Amount **80¢**

Problem Solving *Number Sense*

4. Pam has 4 coins in her pocket.
The coins total 50¢.
Color the coins Pam has.

Students should color one quarter, two dimes, and one nickel.

Use with Lesson 3-13. 37

Name _____

Coin Sense

E 3-13
REASONING

Find the coins needed to buy the toy.
Write how many coins to use. **Answers will vary.**

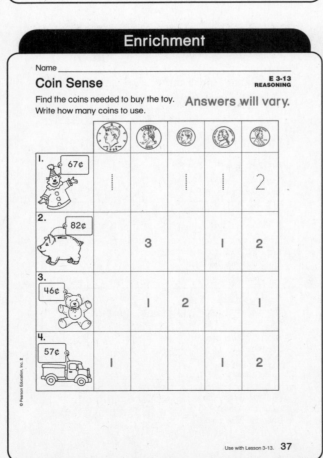

1. 67¢	1		1	1	2
2. 82¢		3		1	2
3. 46¢		1	2		1
4. 57¢	1			1	2

Use with Lesson 3-13. 37

Name _____

Quarter and Half-Dollar

PS 3-13

Count the coins.
Do you have enough money to buy the object?
Circle **yes** or **no**.

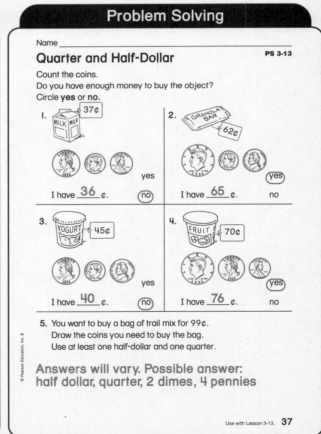

1. 37¢
I have **36** ¢. (no)

2. 62¢
I have **65** ¢. (yes)

3. 45¢
I have **40** ¢. (no)

4. 70¢
I have **76** ¢. (yes)

5. You want to buy a bag of trail mix for 99¢.
Draw the coins you need to buy the bag.
Use at least one half-dollar and one quarter.

Answers will vary. Possible answer: half dollar, quarter, 2 dimes, 4 pennies

Use with Lesson 3-13. 37

Name _____

Counting Sets of Coins
R 3-14

To count coins, start with the coin that has the greatest value.
Count on coins from the greatest to the least value.

Find the total amount.
Draw an X on the coin with the greatest value.

 Think: 50¢   60¢   70¢   75¢

Start with 50¢. 50¢ 60¢ 70¢ 75¢

Draw an X on the coin with the greatest value.
Count on to find the total amount.

1.

Start with 25¢. 25¢ 35¢ 40¢ 45¢

2.

Start with 50¢. 50¢ 75¢ 80¢ 81¢

38 Use with Lesson 3-14.

Name _____

Counting Sets of Coins
P 3-14

Draw coins from the greatest to the least value.
Count on to find the total amount.

1.
25¢ 50¢ 60¢ 65¢ 70¢
The total amount is 70¢.

2.
50¢ 75¢ 85¢ 95¢
The total amount is 95¢.

3.
25¢ 35¢ 45¢ 55¢ 60¢
The total amount is 60¢.

Problem Solving *Estimation* Answers will vary.
4. Kobe has about 50¢. Circle the coins he might have.

38 Use with Lesson 3-14.

Name _____

Let's Go Shopping
E 3-14
DECISION MAKING

You have these coins in your piggy bank.
Choose two toys.
Cross out the coins you use to buy each toy.

47¢   55¢   62¢   36¢

How much do you have left in your piggy bank? _____ Answers will vary.

38 Use with Lesson 3-14.

Name _____

Counting Sets of Coins
PS 3-14

1. Mike has 27¢. Anica has 35¢.
Circle the coins Mike might have.
Put an X on the coins Anica might have.

Answers will vary but should total 27¢ and 35¢.

2. Juan has 32¢. Patty has 56¢.
Circle the coins Juan might have.
Put an X on the coins Patty might have.

Answers will vary but should total 32¢ and 56¢.

3. About how much money do Juan and Patty have together? Circle the answer.

70¢   80¢   (90¢)

38 Use with Lesson 3-14.

© Pearson Education, Inc. 2

38 Use with Chapter 3, Lesson 14.

Name _____

Comparing Sets of Coins
R 3-15

Which pocket has more money?
Write the total amounts in each pocket and compare them.

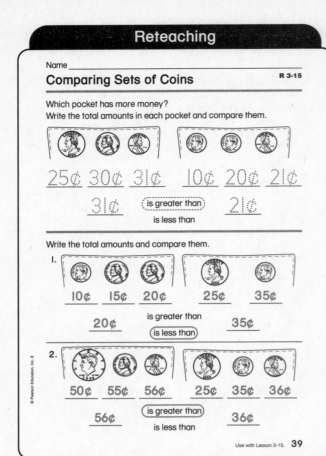

25¢ 30¢ 31¢   10¢ 20¢ 21¢

31¢   (is greater than)   21¢
      is less than

Write the total amounts and compare them.

1.

10¢ 15¢ 20¢   25¢ 35¢

20¢   is greater than   35¢
      (is less than)

2.

50¢ 55¢ 56¢   25¢ 35¢ 36¢

56¢   (is greater than)   36¢
      is less than

© Pearson Education, Inc. 2

Use with Lesson 3-15. **39**

Name _____

Comparing Sets of Coins
P 3-15

Write the total amounts and compare them.
Write >, <, or =.

1.

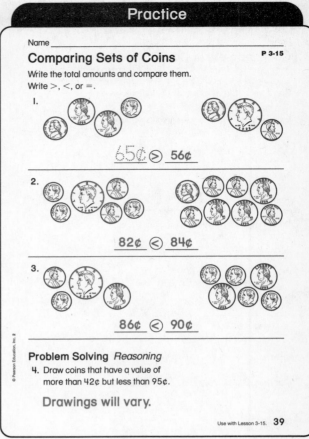

65¢ (>) 56¢

2.

82¢ (<) 84¢

3.

86¢ (<) 90¢

Problem Solving *Reasoning*

4. Draw coins that have a value of more than 42¢ but less than 95¢.

Drawings will vary.

© Pearson Education, Inc. 2

Use with Lesson 3-15. **39**

Name _____

Mystery Coins
E 3-15
REASONABLENESS

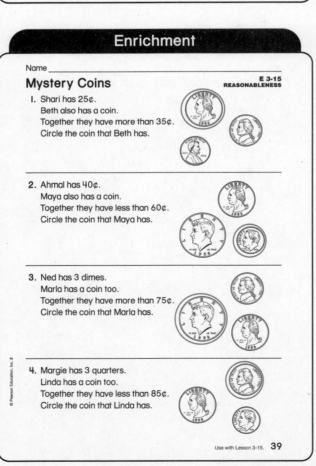

1. Shari has 25¢.
   Beth also has a coin.
   Together they have more than 35¢.
   Circle the coin that Beth has.

2. Ahmal has 40¢.
   Maya also has a coin.
   Together they have less than 60¢.
   Circle the coin that Maya has.

3. Ned has 3 dimes.
   Marla has a coin too.
   Together they have more than 75¢.
   Circle the coin that Marla has.

4. Margie has 3 quarters.
   Linda has a coin too.
   Together they have less than 85¢.
   Circle the coin that Linda has.

© Pearson Education, Inc. 2

Use with Lesson 3-15. **39**

Name _____

Comparing Sets of Coins
PS 3-15

Write how much money each child has.
Compare the coins.
Draw a circle around the child who has more money.

1. Ricardo has 2 quarters, 1 dime, and 1 nickel.

   Millie has 3 dimes and 3 nickels.

   Who has more money?

   _65_ ¢   _45_ ¢   (Ricardo)
                            Millie

2. Eve has 1 half dollar, 2 dimes, and 1 nickel.

   Leon has 3 quarters and 1 nickel.

   Who has more money?

   _75_ ¢   _80_ ¢   Eve
                            (Leon)

3. Ramona has 2 quarters and 2 dimes.

   Emil has 5 dimes, 2 nickels, and 2 pennies.

   Who has more money?

   _70_ ¢   _62_ ¢   (Ramona)
                            Emil

Read the clues. Circle the answer.

4. Alex has more than 40¢.
   Alex has less than 60¢.
   Which toy can Alex buy?

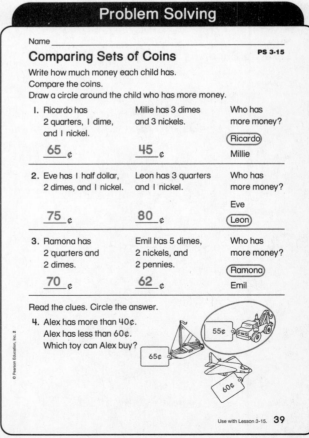

55¢
65¢
60¢

© Pearson Education, Inc. 2

Use with Lesson 3-15. **39**

Name _____

Ways to Show the Same Amount   R 3-16

You can show the same amount in different ways.

31¢   31¢
(penny)(penny)(penny)(penny)   (nickel)(nickel)(penny)
10, 20, 30, 31   25, 30, 31

Count on to find the total amounts.
Draw a line to the matching amount.

1. 21¢

(penny)(penny)(penny)   (penny)(penny)(nickel)(nickel)
10, 20, 21   10, 20, 30, 35, 36

2. 36¢

(nickel)(penny)(penny)   (penny)(penny)(penny)(penny)(nickel)(nickel)(penny)
25, 35, 36   10, 20, 30, 35, 36, 37

3. 37¢

(nickel)(penny)(penny)(penny)   (nickel)(nickel)(nickel)(nickel)(penny)
25, 35, 36, 37   5, 10, 15, 20, 21

Name _____

Ways to Show the Same Amount   P 3-16

Use coins to show the same amount in different ways. **Answers will vary.**
Record with tally marks. **Sample answers are given.**

Ways to Show 80¢

	Half Dollar	Dime	Nickel	Total Amount
1.	l	lll		80¢
2.		||||| l	||||	80¢
3.		lll	||||| |||||	80¢
4.	l	ll	ll	80¢
5.	l		||||	80¢

Which row shows
the fewest number
of coins used?

1

Ways to Show 66¢

	Quarter	Dime	Penny	Total Amount
6.	l	||||	l	66¢
7.	ll	l	||||| l	66¢
8.		||||| l	||||| l	66¢
9.	l	lll	||||| ||||| l	66¢

Which row shows
the fewest number
of coins used?

6

Problem Solving *Reasoning*

10. Jamal has coins in a piggy bank.
    Circle the coin Jamal needs to
    put in the bank to make 75¢.

Name _____

Coin Count   E 3-16
                                 REASONING

Circle the correct number of coins to show the amount.

1. Megan has 45¢.
   Circle the 5 coins she has.

2. Yoshi has 45¢.
   Circle the 3 coins he has.

3. Kayla has 56¢.
   Circle the 3 coins she has.

4. Peter has 56¢.
   Circle the 6 coins he has.

Name _____

Ways to Show the Same Amount   PS 3-16

Draw coins to show two ways that you could pay for the toy.
Use half-dollars, quarters, dimes, nickels, and pennies.

1.	86¢	86¢	86¢
		Possible answer: half-dollar, quarter, dime, penny	Possible answer: 3 quarters, dime, penny
2.	90¢	90¢	90¢
		Possible answer: half-dollar, 4 dimes	Possible answer: half-dollar, 1 quarter, 3 nickels
3.	62¢	Draw 62¢ with 5 coins.	Draw 62¢ with 4 coins.
		Possible answer: 2 quarters, 1 dime, 2 pennies	Possible answer: half-dollar, 1 dime, 2 pennies

Name _____

Making Change

R 3-17

A yo-yo costs 34¢.
You pay 50¢.

Start with 34¢
Count on to 50¢

To **make change,** start counting on from the price until you reach what you paid.

Now count these coins to find the change.

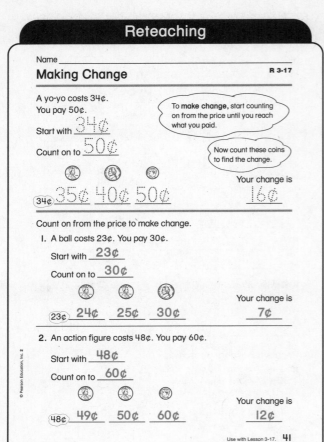

Your change is
16¢

34¢ 35¢ 40¢ 50¢

Count on from the price to make change.

1. A ball costs 23¢. You pay 30¢.

Start with 23¢

Count on to 30¢

Your change is
7¢

23¢ 24¢ 25¢ 30¢

2. An action figure costs 48¢. You pay 60¢.

Start with 48¢

Count on to 60¢

Your change is
12¢

48¢ 49¢ 50¢ 60¢

© Pearson Education, Inc. 2

Use with Lesson 3-17. **41**

Name _____

Making Change

P 3-17

Count on from the price.
Draw the coins you would get for change.
Write the amount of change.

Price	You Give	You Get	Change
1. 12¢	15¢	13¢ 14¢ 15¢	3¢
2. 23¢	30¢	24¢ 25¢ 30¢	or 7 pennies 7¢
3. 74¢	90¢	75¢ 80¢ 90¢	or 1 dime and 6 pennies 16¢
4. 89¢	$1.00	90¢ 95¢ $1.00	or 1 dime and 1 penny 11¢

Problem Solving *Algebra*

5. Michael has 34¢.
He needs 45¢ to buy a toy.
Circle the coins Michael needs.
Write the number.

34¢ + 11¢ = 45¢

© Pearson Education, Inc. 2

Use with Lesson 3-17. **41**

Name _____

What Is My Change?

E 3-17
ESTIMATION

Use the chart to answer the questions below.

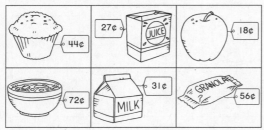

muffin 44¢ · juice 27¢ · apple 18¢
soup 72¢ · milk 31¢ · granola 56¢

Circle the coin that is about how much change each person gets.

1. Amy buys 1 muffin.
She pays with 50¢.
About how much is Amy's change?

2. Michael buys 1 carton of milk.
He pays with 40¢.
About how much is Michael's change?

3. Jamal buys 1 bowl of soup.
He pays with 80¢.
About how much is Jamal's change?

4. Erica buys 1 carton of juice.
She pays with 50¢.
About how much is Erica's change?

© Pearson Education, Inc. 2

Use with Lesson 3-17. **41**

Name _____

Making Change

PS 3-17

Solve. Use the workspace to draw or figure out your answer.

Workspace

1. Carly buys a notebook for 74¢. She pays for it with 8 dimes. What is her change?

6 ¢

2. Gene buys an eraser for 27¢. He pays for it with 6 nickels. What is his change?

3 ¢

3. Maria buys a roll of tape for 81¢. She pays for it with 9 dimes. What is her change?

9 ¢

4. Melvin buys a pen for 63¢. He gets 12¢ in change. How much money did Melvin pay?

75 ¢ − 63¢ = 12¢

© Pearson Education, Inc. 2

Use with Lesson 3-17. **41**

© Pearson Education, Inc. **2**

Use with Chapter 3, Lesson 17. **41**

Name _____

Dollar Bill and Dollar Coin

R 3-18

> A **dollar bill** is equal to 100¢.
> Remember to use a **dollar sign** and **decimal point** when you write $1.00.

100 pennies = 1 dollar

$100¢ = \$1.00$

Circle coins to show $1.00.
Write the number of coins.

1.  _____**10**_____ dimes = 1 dollar

2.  _____**4**_____ quarters = 1 dollar

3.   _____**2**_____ half-dollars = 1 dollar

Problem Solving *Algebra*

4. What 2 coins will make the statement true?

   (**D**) (**N**) = $1.00

42 Use with Lesson 3-18.

Name _____

Dollar Bill and Dollar Coin

Write each total amount.
Circle sets of coins that equal one dollar.

P 3-18

1.   Total Amount **80¢**

2.   Total Amount **90¢**

3.  Total Amount **$1.00**

4.    Total Amount **$1.00**

Problem Solving *Algebra*

5. Draw the coin that makes each set the same amount.

42 Use with Lesson 3-18.

Name _____

It's All in the Clues

E 3-18
REASONING

Use the clue cards to complete the chart.
Write how many of each coin.
Write the total amount.

Derek has two coins that equal $1.00.	Roxanne has 10¢ more than Nina. She has 3 coins.	Jamie has one half-dollar.
Nina has 25¢ less than Derek. She has 3 coins.	Elena has 50¢ more than Derek. She has 2 coins.	Todd has 5¢ less than Nina. He has 3 coins.

Child	(dollar)	(quarter)	(half-dollar)	(dime)	(nickel)	Total Amount
1. Derek	2					$1.00
2. Jamie			1			50¢
3. Nina		3				75¢
4. Elena	1	1				$1.50
5. Todd		1			2	70¢
6. Roxanne		1	1	1		85¢

42 Use with Lesson 3-18.

Name _____

Dollar Bill and Dollar Coin

PS 3-18

Circle the coin or coins on the right to make the row total $1.00.

1. |

2.  |

3.  |

4.  |

42 Use with Lesson 3-18.

© Pearson Education, Inc. 2

Reteaching

Name _____

PROBLEM-SOLVING APPLICATIONS   R 3-19

Money, Money, Money

Long ago, coins looked very different in the United States.
Here are some old United States coins.
Count old coins the same way you count coins of today.

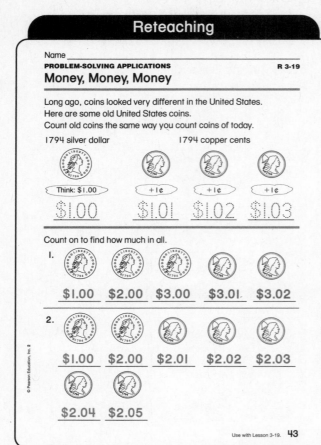

1794 silver dollar   1794 copper cents

Think: $1.00   +1¢   +1¢   +1¢

$1.00 $1.01 $1.02 $1.03

Count on to find how much in all.

1. $1.00 $2.00 $3.00 $3.01 $3.02

2. $1.00 $2.00 $2.01 $2.02 $2.03

     $2.04 $2.05

Use with Lesson 3-19.   43

Practice

Name _____

PROBLEM-SOLVING APPLICATIONS   P 3-19

Money, Money, Money

Solve.

1. Count on to find how much in all.

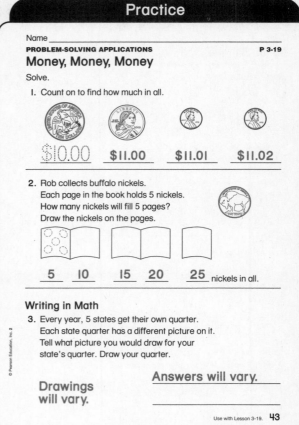

$10.00 $11.00 $11.01 $11.02

2. Rob collects buffalo nickels.
   Each page in the book holds 5 nickels.
   How many nickels will fill 5 pages?
   Draw the nickels on the pages.

   _5_ _10_ _15_ _20_ _25_ nickels in all.

Writing in Math

3. Every year, 5 states get their own quarter.
   Each state quarter has a different picture on it.
   Tell what picture you would draw for your
   state's quarter. Draw your quarter.

   Drawings will vary.   _Answers will vary._

Use with Lesson 3-19.   43

Enrichment

Name _____

E 3-19
NUMBER SENSE

Mexican Pesos

Many countries have their own kinds of coins and
bills. In Mexico, people use a coin called the peso.
Sometimes people exchange one kind of money
for another. One peso can be exchanged for about
10¢ in United States coins.

Count the pesos. Then answer the questions.

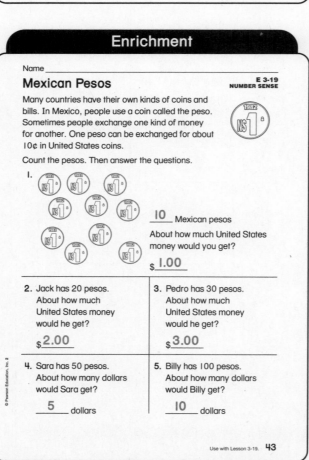

1.   _10_ Mexican pesos
     About how much United States
     money would you get?

     $_1.00_

2. Jack has 20 pesos.   3. Pedro has 30 pesos.
   About how much   About how much
   United States money   United States money
   would he get?   would he get?

   $_2.00_ $_3.00_

4. Sara has 50 pesos.   5. Billy has 100 pesos.
   About how many dollars   About how many dollars
   would Sara get?   would Billy get?

   _5_ dollars   _10_ dollars

Use with Lesson 3-19.   43

Problem Solving

Name _____

PROBLEM-SOLVING APPLICATIONS   PS 3-19

Money, Money, Money

You must find a pattern to solve the problem.
Skip count by 5s.

1. Each envelope has 5 nickels in it.
   Count by 5s to find out how many coins there are in all.

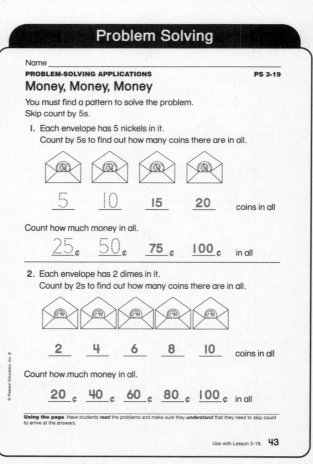

   _5_   _10_   _15_   _20_   coins in all

   Count how much money in all.

   _25_¢ _50_¢ _75_¢ _100_¢ in all

2. Each envelope has 2 dimes in it.
   Count by 2s to find out how many coins there are in all.

   _2_ _4_ _6_ _8_ _10_ coins in all

   Count how much money in all.

   _20_¢ _40_¢ _60_¢ _80_¢ _100_¢ in all

Using the page Have students *read* the problems and make sure they *understand* that they need to skip count
to arrive at the answers.

Use with Lesson 3-19.   43

© Pearson Education, Inc. 2

Use with Chapter 3, Lesson 19.   **43**

Name _____

Adding Tens

R 4-1

To add tens, count on by tens.

Add: 35 and 20

When you add tens, only the digit in the tens place changes.

Think: Count on 2 tens.

35, <u>45</u>, <u>55</u>

So, 35 + 20 = <u>55</u>.

Add tens. Use mental math or cubes.

1.

46 and 30 = <u>76</u>

Count on 3 tens:

46, <u>56</u>, <u>66</u>, <u>76</u>

46 + 30 = <u>76</u>

2. (bars) (bars)

34 and 50 <u>84</u>

Count on 5 tens:

34, <u>44</u>, <u>54</u>, <u>64</u>, <u>74</u>, <u>84</u>

34 + 50 = <u>84</u>

3. (bars)

13 and 40 = <u>53</u>

Count on 4 tens:

13, <u>23</u>, <u>33</u>, <u>43</u>, <u>53</u>

13 + 40 = <u>53</u>

Name _____

Adding Tens

P 4-1

Add tens. Use mental math or cubes.

1. (bars) <u>35</u> + 20 = <u>55</u>

2. (bars) <u>28</u> + 40 = <u>68</u>

3. (bars) <u>16</u> + 40 = <u>56</u>

4. (bars) <u>42</u> + 10 = <u>52</u>

5. (bars) <u>57</u> + 30 = <u>87</u>

6. (bars) <u>18</u> + 20 = <u>38</u>

7. (bars) <u>61</u> + 10 = <u>71</u>

8. (bars) <u>34</u> + 30 = <u>64</u>

Problem Solving *Number Sense*

9. Allie had 38¢. On Thursday she found 10¢, and on Friday she found 10¢ more. How much money does she have now? <u>58</u>¢

Name _____

What's Missing?

E 4-1
ALGEBRA

Circle the tens that make each addition sentence true. Then write the number.

1. 35 + <u>20</u> = 55

2. 28 + <u>40</u> = 68

3. 42 + <u>30</u> = 72

4. 53 + <u>10</u> = 63

5. 31 + <u>50</u> = 81

6. 36 + <u>40</u> = 76

7. 73 + <u>20</u> = 93

8. 18 + <u>30</u> = 48

Name _____

Adding Tens

PS 4-1

Add tens.

1. David has: David finds: How much money does David have now?

<u>35</u>¢ + <u>20</u>¢ = <u>55</u>¢

2. Karen has: Karen finds: How much money does Karen have now?

<u>28</u>¢ + <u>30</u>¢ = <u>58</u>¢

3. Brian has: Brian finds: How much money does Brian have now?

<u>52</u>¢ + <u>10</u>¢ = <u>62</u>¢

4. Elena has 42¢. She gets one more dime. How much money does Elena have now?

<u>52</u>¢

5. Leon has 16¢. He gets 30¢ more. How much money does Leon have now?

<u>46</u>¢

© Pearson Education, Inc. **2**

---

44 Use with Chapter 4, Lesson 1.

Name _____

Adding Ones

R 4-2

Add the ones to make a ten.

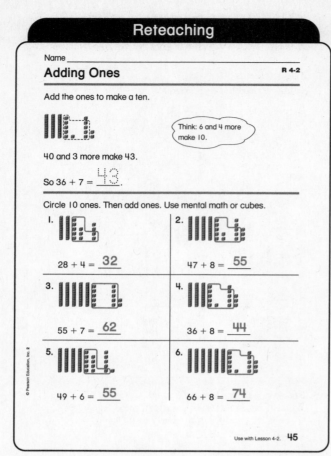

Think: 6 and 4 more make 10.

40 and 3 more make 43.

So 36 + 7 = 43.

Circle 10 ones. Then add ones. Use mental math or cubes.

1. 28 + 4 = 32

2. 47 + 8 = 55

3. 55 + 7 = 62

4. 36 + 8 = 44

5. 49 + 6 = 55

6. 66 + 8 = 74

Name _____

Adding Ones

P 4-2

Add ones. Use mental math or cubes.

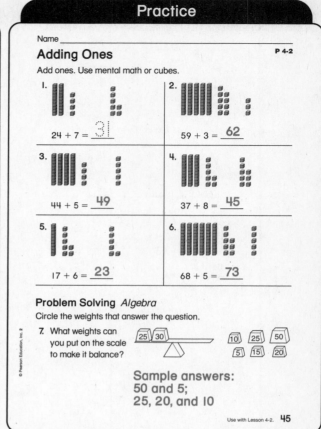

1. 24 + 7 = 31

2. 59 + 3 = 62

3. 44 + 5 = 49

4. 37 + 8 = 45

5. 17 + 6 = 23

6. 68 + 5 = 73

Problem Solving *Algebra*

Circle the weights that answer the question.

7. What weights can you put on the scale to make it balance?

Sample answers:
50 and 5;
25, 20, and 10

Name _____

Make a Ten

E 4-2
VISUAL THINKING

Each triangle can hold ten balls.
Circle the number of balls that will fill the last triangle to make 10.
Then add all the balls and write the sum.

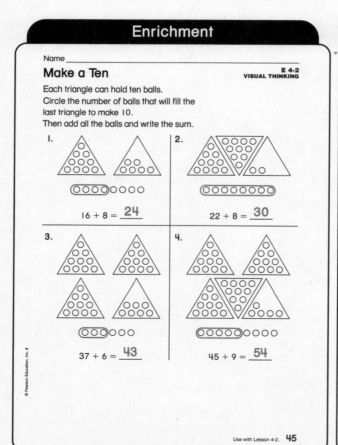

1. 16 + 8 = 24

2. 22 + 8 = 30

3. 37 + 6 = 43

4. 45 + 9 = 54

Name _____

Adding Ones

PS 4-2

Circle the coin(s) that answer each question.

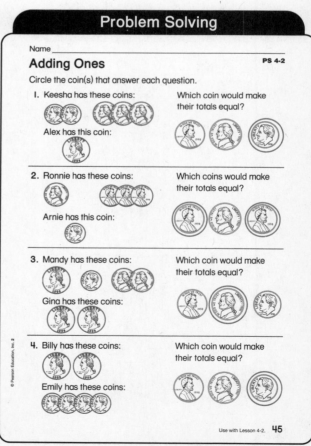

1. Keesha has these coins:

Alex has this coin:

Which coin would make their totals equal?

2. Ronnie has these coins:

Arnie has this coin:

Which coins would make their totals equal?

3. Mandy has these coins:

Gina has these coins:

Which coin would make their totals equal?

4. Billy has these coins:

Emily has these coins:

Which coin would make their totals equal?

Name _____

Adding Tens and Ones

R 4-3

How many cubes are there in all?

25 and

First, count on by tens to add the tens:

Think: 25 and 3 tens

Then add the ones.

25, 35, 45, 55

55 and 4 ones is 59.

So, 25 + 34 = 59.

Add. Use mental math or cubes.

1.
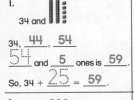
34 and

34, 44, 54

54 and 5 ones is 59.

So, 34 + 25 = 59.

2.
52 and

52, 62, 72, 82

82 and 3 ones is 85.

So, 52 + 33 = 85.

3.
36 and

36, 46, 56, 66

66 and 2 ones is 68.

So, 36 + 32 = 68.

4.
11 and

11, 21, 31, 41, 51

51 and 4 ones is 55.

So, 11 + 44 = 55.

46 Use with Lesson 4-3.

Name _____

Adding Tens and Ones

P 4-3

Add. Use mental math or cubes.

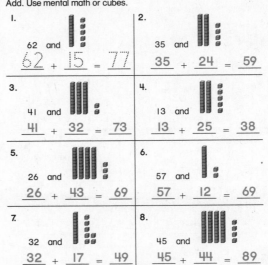

1.
62 and

62 + 15 = 77

2.
35 and

35 + 24 = 59

3.
41 and

41 + 32 = 73

4.
13 and

13 + 25 = 38

5.
26 and

26 + 43 = 69

6.
57 and

57 + 12 = 69

7.
32 and

32 + 17 = 49

8.
45 and

45 + 44 = 89

Problem Solving *Number Sense*

Circle the ones digit to make the number sentence true.

9. 35 + 2▨ = 59

    3 (4) 5

10. 4▨ + 36 = 78

   (2) 4 6

46 Use with Lesson 4-3.

Name _____

What Comes Next?

E 4-3
PATTERNS

Look at each number pattern.
Write the numbers for the addition sentences that come next.

1.
32 + 12 = 44
42 + 12 = 54
52 + 12 = 64
62 + 12 = 74
72 + 12 = 84

2.
17 + 22 = 39
27 + 22 = 49
37 + 22 = 59
47 + 22 = 69
57 + 22 = 79

3.
30 + 27 = 57
40 + 27 = 67
50 + 27 = 77
60 + 27 = 87
70 + 27 = 97

4.
15 + 11 = 26
25 + 11 = 36
35 + 11 = 46
45 + 11 = 56
55 + 11 = 66

5.
34 + 14 = 48
44 + 14 = 58
54 + 14 = 68
64 + 14 = 78
74 + 14 = 88

6.
21 + 13 = 34
31 + 13 = 44
41 + 13 = 54
51 + 13 = 64
61 + 13 = 74

46 Use with Lesson 4-3.

Name _____

Adding Tens and Ones

PS 4-3

Count the tens and ones.
Write the number in the addition sentence.
Then add.

1. 25 + 33 = 58

2. 34 + 54 = 88

3. 13 + 27 = 40

4. 46 + 11 = 57

Problem Solving *Number Sense*

Circle the digit to make the number sentence true.

5. 21 + 4▨ = 67

  (6) 7 5

6. ▨3 + 23 = 76

  3 6 (5)

46 Use with Lesson 4-3.

© Pearson Education, Inc. 2

---

46 Use with Chapter 4, Lesson 3.

Name _____

Estimating Sums

R 4-4

Use mental math to **estimate**.

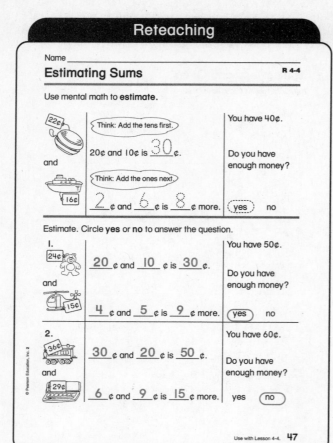

22¢	Think: Add the tens first.	You have 40¢.
and	20¢ and 10¢ is _30_ ¢.	Do you have enough money?
16¢	Think: Add the ones next.	
	_2_ ¢ and _6_ ¢ is _8_ ¢ more.	(yes) no

Estimate. Circle **yes** or **no** to answer the question.

1.

24¢	_20_ ¢ and _10_ ¢ is _30_ ¢.	You have 50¢.
and		Do you have enough money?
15¢	_4_ ¢ and _5_ ¢ is _9_ ¢ more.	(yes) no

2.

36¢	_30_ ¢ and _20_ ¢ is _50_ ¢.	You have 60¢.
and		Do you have enough money?
29¢	_6_ ¢ and _9_ ¢ is _15_ ¢ more.	yes (no)

© Pearson Education, Inc. 2

Use with Lesson 4-4. **47**

Name _____

Estimating Sums

P 4-4

Estimate. Circle **yes** or **no** to answer the question for each exercise.

You have	Can you buy these items?	Answer
1. 50¢	and	(yes) no
2. 70¢	and	yes (no)
3. 60¢	and	(yes) no
4. 80¢	and	yes (no)

Problem Solving *Reasoning*

5. Sam has 45¢. He has exactly enough money to buy both toys. How much does the car cost? _19¢_

© Pearson Education, Inc. 2

Use with Lesson 4-4. **47**

Name _____

Target Practice

E 4-4
ESTIMATION

Each child threw two bean bags at the target.
Write the number the second bean bag landed on.

1. Allison scores about 50 points. If one bean bag landed on 32, what number did the other bean bag land on?

_19_

2. Kenji scores about 90 points. If one bean bag landed on 68, what number did the other bean bag land on?

_18_

3. Berto scores about 40 points. If one bean bag landed on 12, what number did the other bean bag land on?

_26_

4. Melissa scores about 50 points. If one bean bag landed on 28, what number did the other bean bag land on?

_21_

© Pearson Education, Inc. 2

Use with Lesson 4-4. **47**

Name _____

Estimating Sums

PS 4-4

Each child took two handfuls of beans from the jar below. Estimate the sum of the two handfuls each child took.   **Sample answers given.**

1. Jason:

   21 and 48 is about _70_

2. Sally:

   37 and 12 is about _50_

3. Abdul:

   32 and 57 is about _90_

4. Jessica:

   28 and 16 is about _50_

5. Dawn:

   13 and 39 is about _50_

6. Mickey:

   13 and 17 is about _30_

7. Pete:

   8 and 13 is about _20_

8. Ruben:

   28 and 27 is about _60_

9. Chen:

   43 and 37 is about _80_

10. Judy:

    14 and 11 is about _20_

Problem Solving *Reasoning*

11. Maria has 80¢. She has exactly enough money to buy both toys. How much does the boat cost?

    _48_ ¢

© Pearson Education, Inc. 2

Use with Lesson 4-4. **47**

Use with Chapter 4, Lesson 4.   **47**

Name _____

Subtracting Tens

R 4-5

Use tens and ones blocks to subtract tens.

Think: Count back 3 tens.

When you subtract tens, only the digit in the tens place changes.

Subtract: 57, _47, 37, 27_

57 take away 30

So, $57 - 30 = 27$.

Count back to subtract tens. Use mental math or cubes.

1.   64 take away 30
Count back 3 tens.

64, _54_, _44_, _34_

$64 - 30 = 34$

2.   49 take away 20
Count back 2 tens.

49, _39_, _29_

$49 - 20 = 29$

3.   72 take away 50
Count back 5 tens.

72, _62_, _52_, _42_, _32_, _22_

$72 - 50 = 22$

48   Use with Lesson 4-5.

Name _____

Subtracting Tens

P 4-5

Subtract tens. Use mental math or cubes.

1.
_46_ – 10 = _36_

2.
_82_ – 30 = _52_

3.
_75_ – 40 = _35_

4.
_38_ – 20 = _18_

5.
_69_ – 40 = _29_

6.
_41_ – 10 = _31_

7.
_55_ – 30 = _25_

8.
_32_ – 20 = _12_

Problem Solving *Mental Math*

9. Nick has 90¢. He used his money to buy a bat and a ball. How much money does he have left?   _20_ ¢

48   Use with Lesson 4-5.

Name _____

Up the Ladder

E 4-5
NUMBER SENSE

Play this game with a partner.
You will need a pencil and a paper clip.

Start at 93. Take turns spinning.
Use the number you spin to subtract.
Then move your piece. The first player to reach the top of the ladder wins.

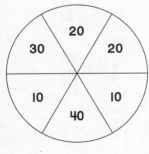

3
13
23
33
43
53
63
73
83
93 ←Start

48   Use with Lesson 4-5.

Name _____

Subtracting Tens

PS 4-5

Each crayon box has 10 crayons. Cross out the crayon boxes given away. Subtract. Write the number.

1. Lea has 38 crayons. She gives one box to her sister. How many crayons does Lea have left?

$38 - \underline{10} = \underline{28}$

2. Greg has 42 crayons. He gives two boxes to his friend. How many crayons does Greg have left?

$42 - \underline{20} = \underline{22}$

3. Liz has 26 crayons. She gives one box to her grandmother. How many crayons does Liz have left?

$26 - \underline{10} = \underline{16}$

4. Zack has 54 crayons. He gives one box to his brother. He gives two boxes to his sister. How many crayons does Zack have left?

$54 - \underline{30} = \underline{24}$

48   Use with Lesson 4-5.

Name _____

Subtracting Tens and Ones

R 4-6

How many are left?

IIIIII :: take away 31

First, count back by tens to subtract the tens.

Think: 57 take away 3 tens. 57, 47, 37, 27

Then take away the ones. 27 take away 1 one is 26.

So, 57 – 31 = 26.

1. IIIIII :: take away 26   58, 48, 38
   38 take away 6 ones is 32.
   58 – 26 = 32

2. IIIIII :: take away 43   67, 57, 47, 37, 27
   27 take away 3 ones is 24.
   67 – 43 = 24

Solve.

3. Pam has 59 marbles.
   She gives
   35 marbles away.
   How many marbles
   does Pam have left?

   59, 49, 39, 29
   29 take away 5 ones is 24.
   59 – 35 = 24

Use with Lesson 4-6. **49**

© Pearson Education, Inc. 2

Name _____

Subtracting Tens and Ones

P 4-6

Subtract. Use mental math or cubes.

1.
   57 – 14 = 43

2. 78 – 25 = 53

3. 64 – 22 = 42

4. 45 – 32 = 13

5. 86 – 21 = 65

6. 39 – 13 = 26

7. 97 – 46 = 51

8. 73 – 41 = 32

Problem Solving *Writing in Math*

9. Draw cubes to show 56 – 23.
   Describe how you found the difference.

   Answers will vary.

Use with Lesson 4-6. **49**

© Pearson Education, Inc. 2

Name _____

Treasure Chests of Numbers

E 4-6
NUMBER SENSE

Look at the numbers in each treasure chest.
Find the missing number to write the subtraction sentence.

1.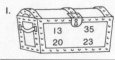
   13 35
   20 23
   55 – [13] = 42

2.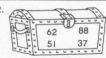
   62 88
   51 37
   [88] – 51 = 37

3.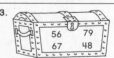
   56 79
   67 48
   [48] – 36 = 12

4.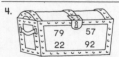
   79 57
   22 92
   79 – [22] = 57

5.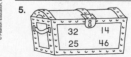
   32 14
   25 46
   46 – 14 = [32]

Use with Lesson 4-6. **49**

© Pearson Education, Inc. 2

Name _____

Subtracting Tens and Ones

PS 4-6

Cross out some tens. Cross out some ones.
Write the number sentence. Subtract.

Answers will vary.
A sample answer is given.

1. 56 – 21 = 35

2. 68 – ___ = ___

3. 92 – ___ = ___

4. 75 – ___ = ___

Problem Solving *Writing in Math*

5. Write a subtraction sentence
   to match the picture.

   47 – 23 = 24

Use with Lesson 4-6. **49**

© Pearson Education, Inc. 2

Name _____

Estimating Differences

R 4-7

Use mental math to estimate.

You have 40¢.
You buy:

Will you have more or
less than 20¢ left?

Think: Subtract the tens first.

40¢ − 20¢ is 20¢.

Think about the ones.

40¢ − 24¢ is _____ than 20¢.
(more) / (less)

Estimate. Circle **more** or **less** to complete each sentence.

1. You have 60¢.
You buy:

{37¢}

60¢ − __30__ ¢ is __30__ ¢.

Will you have more or
less than 30¢ left?

__60__ ¢ − 37¢ is ____ than 30¢.
more / (less)

2. You have 70¢.
You buy:

{42¢}

70¢ − __40__ ¢ is __30__ ¢.

Will you have more or
less than 20¢ left?

__70__ ¢ − 42¢ is ____ than 20¢.
(more) / less

50 Use with Lesson 4-7.

Name _____

Estimating Differences

P 4-7

Estimate. Circle **more** or **less** to complete each sentence.

1. 70 − 33 is ____ than 40.
more / (less)

2. 90 − 42 is ____ than 50.
more / (less)

3. 50 − 24 is ____ than 30.
more / (less)

4. 80 − 17 is ____ than 60.
(more) / less

5. 30 − 15 is ____ than 10.
(more) / less

6. 40 − 21 is ____ than 20.
more / (less)

7. 60 − 13 is ____ than 50.
more / (less)

8. 70 − 49 is ____ than 20.
(more) / less

Problem Solving *Reasonableness*

Circle the more reasonable estimate.

9. There is room for 60 people on the bus.
27 people are already on the bus.
About how many people can still fit on the bus?

20 people
(30 people)
40 people

10. There were 40 people at the movie.
18 people left. About how many
people are still at the movie?

10 people
(20 people)
30 people

50 Use with Lesson 4-7.

Name _____

What Should I Buy?

E 4-7
DECISION MAKING

Circle two toys you will buy. **Answers may vary.**
Estimate to find about how much money you will have left.

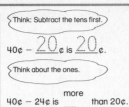

43¢   37¢   28¢   19¢   52¢   23¢

Sample answers are given.

You have	Which toys will you buy?	Estimate how much you have left.
1. 70¢		__20__ ¢
2. 90¢		__30__ ¢
3. 80¢		__10__ ¢

50 Use with Lesson 4-7.

Name _____

Estimating Differences

PS 4-7

The children at the Elm Street School voted for their
favorite pets. Use the chart to answer the questions.
Write a number sentence.
Estimate. Circle **more** or **less**
to complete each sentence.

Pet	Votes
Cat	90
Dog	70
Fish	35
Bird	50
Rabbit	31

1. About how many
more children liked
cats than fish?

__90__ − __35__ is ____ than 50.
(more) / less

2. About how many
more children liked
dogs than rabbits?

__70__ − __31__ is ____ than 30.
(more) / less

Circle the most reasonable estimate.

3. Another class voted for
favorite pets. There were
12 more votes for birds.
About how many votes
are there for birds now?

30   50   (60)

4. 11 children changed their
votes from cats to dogs.
About how many votes
are there for dogs now?

60   70   (80)

50 Use with Lesson 4-7.

© Pearson Education, Inc. 2

50 Use with Chapter 4, Lesson 7.

Name _____

PROBLEM-SOLVING STRATEGY   R 4-8

Try, Check, and Revise

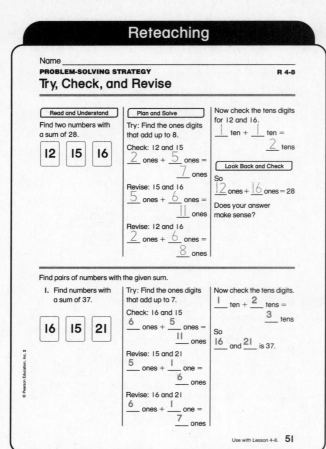

Read and Understand

Find two numbers with a sum of 28.

| 12 | 15 | 16 |

Plan and Solve

Try: Find the ones digits that add up to 8.

Check: 12 and 15

$\underline{2}$ ones + $\underline{5}$ ones =
$\underline{7}$ ones

Revise: 15 and 16

$\underline{5}$ ones + $\underline{6}$ ones =
$\underline{11}$ ones

Revise: 12 and 16

$\underline{2}$ ones + $\underline{6}$ ones =
$\underline{8}$ ones

Now check the tens digits for 12 and 16.

$\underline{1}$ ten + $\underline{1}$ ten =
$\underline{2}$ tens

Look Back and Check

So
$\underline{12}$ ones + $\underline{16}$ ones = 28

Does your answer make sense?

Find pairs of numbers with the given sum.

1. Find numbers with a sum of 37.

| 16 | 15 | 21 |

Try: Find the ones digits that add up to 7.

Check: 16 and 15

$\underline{6}$ ones + $\underline{5}$ ones =
$\underline{11}$ ones

Revise: 15 and 21

$\underline{5}$ ones + $\underline{1}$ one =
$\underline{6}$ ones

Revise: 16 and 21

$\underline{6}$ ones + $\underline{1}$ one =
$\underline{7}$ ones

Now check the tens digits.

$\underline{1}$ ten + $\underline{2}$ tens =
$\underline{3}$ tens

So
$\underline{16}$ and $\underline{21}$ is 37.

Name _____

PROBLEM-SOLVING STRATEGY   P 4-8

Try, Check, and Revise

Find pairs of numbers with the given sum.
The sum of the ones digits must be 10.

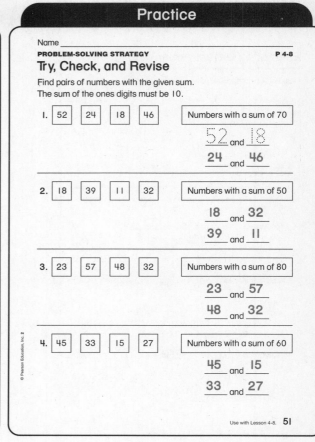

1. | 52 | 24 | 18 | 46 | Numbers with a sum of 70

$\underline{52}$ and $\underline{18}$
$\underline{24}$ and $\underline{46}$

2. | 18 | 39 | 11 | 32 | Numbers with a sum of 50

$\underline{18}$ and $\underline{32}$
$\underline{39}$ and $\underline{11}$

3. | 23 | 57 | 48 | 32 | Numbers with a sum of 80

$\underline{23}$ and $\underline{57}$
$\underline{48}$ and $\underline{32}$

4. | 45 | 33 | 15 | 27 | Numbers with a sum of 60

$\underline{45}$ and $\underline{15}$
$\underline{33}$ and $\underline{27}$

Name _____

At the Fruit Stand

E 4-8
NUMBER SENSE

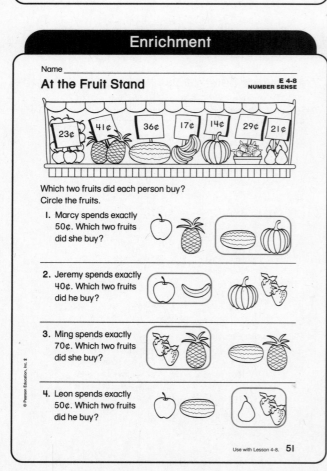

Which two fruits did each person buy?
Circle the fruits.

1. Marcy spends exactly 50¢. Which two fruits did she buy?

2. Jeremy spends exactly 40¢. Which two fruits did he buy?

3. Ming spends exactly 70¢. Which two fruits did she buy?

4. Leon spends exactly 50¢. Which two fruits did he buy?

Name _____

PROBLEM-SOLVING STRATEGY   PS 4-8

Try, Check, and Revise

Use the target to solve each problem.

Vito throws two darts for a score of 40.
On which two numbers did his darts land?

Try two numbers: 24 and 11.

Check: $\underline{24}$ and $\underline{11}$ = $\underline{35}$

35 does not equal 40.

Revise: try 24 and 16.

$\underline{24}$ and $\underline{16}$ = $\underline{40}$

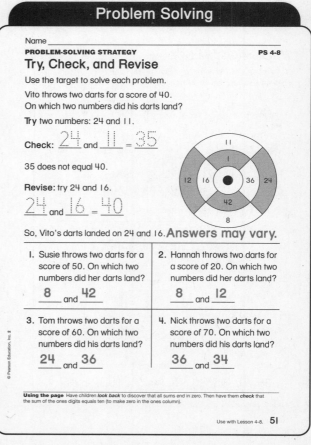

So, Vito's darts landed on 24 and 16. **Answers may vary.**

1. Susie throws two darts for a score of 50. On which two numbers did her darts land?

$\underline{8}$ and $\underline{42}$

2. Hannah throws two darts for a score of 20. On which two numbers did her darts land?

$\underline{8}$ and $\underline{12}$

3. Tom throws two darts for a score of 60. On which two numbers did his darts land?

$\underline{24}$ and $\underline{36}$

4. Nick throws two darts for a score of 70. On which two numbers did his darts land?

$\underline{36}$ and $\underline{34}$

Using the page Have children *look back* to discover that all sums end in zero. Then have them *check* that the sum of the ones digits equals ten (to make zero in the ones column).

Name _____

Addition and Subtraction Patterns

R 4-9

Find the numbers in the pattern:

7, 17, 27, 37, 47, 57, 67, 77

1	2	3	4	5	6	7	8	9	10
11	12	13	14	15	16	17	18	19	20
21	22	23	24	25	26	27	28	29	30
31	32	33	34	35	36	37	38	39	40
41	42	43	44	45	46	47	48	49	50
51	52	53	54	55	56	57	58	59	60
61	62	63	64	65	66	67	68	69	70
71	72	73	74	75	76	77	78	79	80
81	82	83	84	85	86	87	88	89	90
91	92	93	94	95	96	97	98	99	100

Look at the ones digit.
It is 7 each time.

Look at the tens digit.
It goes up 1 each time.

The pattern is ___add 10___.

Find the pattern.

1. Color these numbers on the hundred chart:
4, 9, 14, 19, 24, 29, 34, 39.

Look at the ones. The ones pattern is 4, 9, 4, 9, 4, 9, 4, 9, and so on.

Look at the tens. The tens pattern is 0, 0, 1, 1, 2, 2, 3, 3, and so on.

The pattern is ___add 5___.

2. Color these numbers on the hundred chart:
71, 73, 75, 77, 79, 81, 83, 85, 87, 89.

Look at the ones. The ones pattern is 1, 3, 5, 7, 9, 1, 3, 5, 7, 9, and so on.

Look at the tens. The tens pattern is 7, 7, 7, 7, 7, 8, 8, 8, 8, 8, and so on.

The pattern is ___add 2___.

Name _____

Addition and Subtraction Patterns

P 4-9

What is the pattern? Write the numbers.

1. 20, 25, 30, 35, 40, _45_, _50_, _55_, _60_,
_65_, _70_, _75_, _80_, _85_, _90_, _95_

What is the pattern? ___add five___

2. 69, 66, 63, 60, _57_, _54_, _51_, _48_, _45_, _42_,
_39_, _36_, _33_, _30_, _27_, _24_, _21_, _18_

What is the pattern? ___subtract 3___

Problem Solving *Algebra*
Find the pattern. Write the missing numbers.

3. 30 and 4 is 34.

40 and 4 is _44_.

50 and _4_ is _54_.

_60_ and _4_ is _64_.

_70_ and _4_ is _74_.

4. 58 take away 5 is 53.

48 take away 5 is _43_.

38 take away _5_ is _33_.

_28_ take away _5_ is _23_.

_18_ take away _5_ is _13_.

Name _____

Find the Secret Number

E 4-9
PATTERNS

A treasure is hidden under one of the rocks.
Follow the clues to find the treasure.
Color the rocks you land on.

(1) (2) (3) (4) (5) (6) (7) (8) (9) (10)
(11) (12) (13) (14) (15) (16) (17) (18) (19) (20)
(21) (22) (23) (24) (25) (26) (27) (28) (29) (30)
(31) (32) (33) (34) (35) (36) (37) (38) (39) (40)
(41) (42) (43) (44) (45) (46) (47) (48) (49) (50)
(51) (52) (53) (54) (55) (56) (57) (58) (59) (60)
(61) (62) (63) (64) (65) (66) (67) (68) (69) (70)
(71) (72) (73) (74) (75) (76) (77) (78) (79) (80)

1. Start at 55.
2. Subtract 20.
3. Add 5.
4. Add 20.
5. Add 10.
6. Subtract 5.
7. Subtract 20.
8. Add 5.
9. Subtract 20.
10. Subtract 5.

11. Under which rock is the treasure hidden? _25_

12. Write the pattern you see in the numbers you colored.

___25, 30, 35, 40, 45, 50, 55, 60, 65, 70___

Name _____

Addition and Subtraction Patterns

PS 4-9

Each pattern below has a rule. Find the rule for the pattern. Then write the next number in the pattern.

| 1. | 7 | 11 | 15 | 19 | 23 | The rule is ___add 4___ The next number is _27_ |

| 2. | 30 | 25 | 20 | 15 | 10 | The rule is ___subtract 5___ The next number is _5_ |

| 3. | 8 | 11 | 14 | 17 | 20 | The rule is ___add 3___ The next number is _23_ |

| 4. | 6 | 12 | 18 | 24 | 30 | The rule is ___add 6___ The next number is _36_ |

| 5. | 32 | 30 | 28 | 26 | 24 | The rule is ___subtract 2___ The next number is _22_ |

6. Find the pattern. Write the missing numbers.

64, 54, _44_, 34, _24_, _14_, 4

20, 24, 28, _32_, _36_, _40_, 44

Name

Finding Parts of 100

R 4-10

Find parts for 100.
Draw more tens to make 100.

 Think: Count up to make 100

60 and **40** is 100.

60 and 10 is 70.
70 and 10 is 80.
80 and 10 is 90.
90 and 10 is 100.

Now draw tens and ones to make 100.

75 and **25** is 100.

75 and 10 is 85.
85 and 10 is 95.
95 and 5 is 100.

Draw tens to find the other part of 100.

1. ▌▌▌▌▌▌   Children should draw 5 tens.

50 and **50** is 100.

Draw tens and ones to make 100. Count up.

2. ▌▌▌▌▌   Children should draw 5 tens
and 5 ones.

45 and **55** is 100.

3. ▌▌▌▌   Children should draw 6 tens
and 5 ones.

35 and **65** is 100.

Use with Lesson 4-10. **53**

Name

Finding Parts of 100

P 4-10

Add on to find the other part of 100.
Use mental math or cubes.

1. 40 and **60** is 100.	2. 65 and **35** is 100.
3. 20 and **80** is 100.	4. 95 and **5** is 100.
5. 45 and **55** is 100.	6. 70 and **30** is 100.
7. 50 and **50** is 100.	8. 90 and **10** is 100.
9. 15 and **85** is 100.	10. 75 and **25** is 100.
11. 5 and **95** is 100.	12. 10 and **90** is 100.
13. 30 and **70** is 100.	14. 35 and **65** is 100.

Problem Solving *Algebra*

15. If 60 and **40** is 100,

then 100 take away 60 is **40**

16. If 45 and **55** is 100,

then 100 take away 45 is **55** .

Use with Lesson 4-10. **53**

Name

Missing Parts

E 4-10
MENTAL MATH

Circle the basket that makes the other part of 100.
Write the number.

1. 25 and 25 and **50** is 100.   (50)   30

   25 and **25** and **50**

2. 30 and 30 and **40** is 100.   30   (40)

   30 and **30** and **40**

3. 10 and 45 and **45** is 100.   50   (45)

   10 and **45** and **45**

4. 15 and 60 and **25** is 100.   20   (25)

   15 and **60** and **25**

5. 40 and 25 and **35** is 100.   (35)   25

   40 and **25** and **35**

Use with Lesson 4-10. **53**

Name

Finding Parts of 100

PS 4-10

Circle the coin or coins that will make 100¢.
Write the number sentence.

1. Jerry has these coins.   Which coin will make 100¢?

   75 ¢ and **25** ¢ is 100¢.

2. Maria has these coins.   Which coins will make 100¢?

   80 ¢ and **20** ¢ is 100¢.

3. Hakeem has these coins.   Which coins will make 100¢?

   70 ¢ and **30** ¢ is 100¢.

4. If 30¢ and **70** ¢ is 100¢,

then 100¢ take away 30¢ is **70** ¢.

Use with Lesson 4-10. **53**

Name _____

PROBLEM-SOLVING SKILL   R 4-11
Look Back and Check

	Check
Pat has 42 stamps. He gets 20 more stamps. Now Pat has (62) / 22 stamps.	Think: Which number makes sense? Pat gets 20 more stamps. 62 is _more_ than 42. 22 is _less_ than 42. So, Pat has (62) / 22 stamps.

Circle the number that makes sense.
Check if your answer should be more or less.

	Check
1. Eric has 67 marbles. He gives 20 marbles away. Now Eric has 87 / (47) marbles.	Eric gives 20 marbles _away_. 87 is _more_ than 67. 47 is _less_ than 67.
2. Mary has 25 flowers. She picks 10 more flowers. Now Mary has (35) / 15 flowers.	Mary _picks_ 10 more flowers. 35 is _more_ than 25. 15 is _less_ than 25.

Name _____

PROBLEM-SOLVING SKILL   P 4-11
Look Back and Check

Circle the number that makes sense.

1. Vinnie has 30 baseball cards.
   His friend gave him 15 more cards.

   Now Vinnie has (45) / 15 baseball cards.

2. Mary painted 11 pictures.
   Simon painted 8 pictures.

   Together, Mary and Simon painted 3 / (19) pictures.

3. Scott collected 42 coins.
   He put 12 coins in an album.

   There are (30) / 54 coins out of the album.

4. Debbie made 52 puppets for the craft fair.
   She sold 22 of the puppets.

   Now Debbie has (30) / 54 puppets left.

Problem Solving *Visual Thinking*

5. How many cubes are there in all? Circle your answer.

 + = or

Name _____

PROBLEM-SOLVING STRATEGY   E 4-11
Look Back and Check   REASONABLENESS

Circle the most reasonable answer.

1. There are 12 children at a party. More children   12 children
   come to the party. How many children could be   6 children
   at the party now?   (15 children)
   Tell why you chose your answer.

   There would have to be more than 12,

   so 15 is the most reasonable answer.

2. There are 15 people at a picnic. Some people   (11 people)
   leave to go home. How many people could be   15 people
   at the picnic now?   18 people
   Tell why you chose your answer.

   There would have to be less than 15,

   so 11 is the most reasonable answer.

3. Bridget has 26 stickers. She gives some stickers   26 stickers
   to her little brother. How many stickers could   (8 stickers)
   Bridget's little brother have?   30 stickers
   Tell why you chose your answer.

   There would have to be less than 26,

   so 8 is the most reasonable answer.

Name _____

PROBLEM-SOLVING SKILL   PS 4-11
Look Back and Check

Meg has 46 pennies. She gives her sister 22 pennies. Now Meg has (24) / 68 pennies.	**Think:** If Meg gives away 22 pennies, does she add or subtract? _subtract_

Circle the number that makes the sentence correct.

1. Marvin has 29 apples.   Write whether to add or
   He eats 4 apples.   subtract.

   Now Marvin has 33 / (25) apples.   _subtract_

2. Michelle has $14.   Write whether to add or
   She saves $21.   subtract.

   Now Michelle has 7 / (35) dollars. _add_

3. Harvey has 37 balloons.   Write whether to add or
   Janis breaks 8 of them.   subtract.

   Now Harvey has (29) / 45 balloons. _subtract_

Using the page Have children *read* each exercise. To help them *understand*, have children answer whether
the objects are being added or subtracted.

© Pearson Education, Inc. 2

Name _____

R 4-12

Take Me Out to the Ball Game!

Use the chart to answer the questions.

Innings	1	2	3	4	5	6	7	8	9	Final Score
Green Team	3	2	4	5	3	1	2	4	2	26
Blue Team	1	2	2	4	3	1	1	2	1	17

How many more runs were scored by the Green Team than the Blue Team in the first inning?

Write a subtraction sentence to compare.

$\underline{3} - \underline{1} = \underline{2}$ more runs

How many runs in all were scored in the 3rd inning?

Write an addition sentence to find out how many in all.

$\underline{4} + \underline{2} = \underline{6}$ runs

Add or subtract.

1. How many more runs were scored by the Green Team than the Blue Team?

$\underline{26} \ominus \underline{17} = \underline{9}$ more runs

2. How many runs were scored by the Blue Team in the 3rd and 4th innings?

$\underline{2} \oplus \underline{4} = \underline{6}$ runs

© Pearson Education, Inc. 2

Use with Lesson 4-12. **55**

Name _____

P 4-12

Take Me Out to the Ball Game!

Fun Fact!
In 1998, Mark McGwire hit 70 home runs.
In 2001, Barry Bonds hit 73 home runs.

1. How many more home runs did Barry Bonds hit than Mark McGwire?

$\underline{73} - \underline{70} = \underline{3}$

2. In 1999, McGwire hit 65 home runs. Write the missing numbers.

65, $\underline{66}$, $\underline{67}$, 68, $\underline{69}$, 70

3. In his last two seasons, McGwire hit 32 and 29 home runs. How many home runs did he hit in all? Is this more or less than the number of home runs he hit in 1998?

$\underline{32} + \underline{29} = \underline{61}$ less

Writing in Math

4. There are 9 positions on a baseball field where players stand. Choose a position that you would like to play. Tell why you chose that position.

Answers will vary.

© Pearson Education, Inc. 2

Use with Lesson 4-12. **55**

Name _____

Batter Up   E 4-12
NUMBER SENSE

Use the chart to solve the problems below.

Home Runs Hit by the Bluebirds Baseball Team

Mickey	Shawna	Jose	Benji	Chrissy	Billy
28	14	31	9	18	36

1. How many home runs did Mickey and Benji hit altogether?

$\underline{37}$ home runs

2. How many more home runs did Billy hit than Chrissy?

$\underline{18}$ home runs

3. Suppose Jose hits 5 more home runs. How many home runs would he have now?

$\underline{36}$ home runs

4. How many home runs did Mickey and Jose hit altogether?

$\underline{59}$ home runs

5. Who hit the most home runs? How many more home runs did that person hit than Shawna?

$\underline{\text{Billy}}$ hit the most home runs.

$\underline{22}$ more home runs than Shawna

6. Who hit the least home runs? How many fewer home runs did that person hit than Mickey?

$\underline{\text{Benji}}$ hit the least home runs.

$\underline{19}$ less home runs than Mickey

© Pearson Education, Inc. 2

Use with Lesson 4-12. **55**

Name _____

PS 4-12

Take Me Out to the Ball Game!

Baseball Tickets		Gift Stand		Snack Bar	
Adults	$23	T-shirt	$16	Hot Dog	$4
Children	$15	Cap	$8	Soda	$2
Seniors	$21	Bat	$4	Pretzel	$3

Write a number sentence to solve.

1. Dean buys a T-shirt and a cap. How much money does he spend?

$\underline{\$16} \oplus \underline{\$8} = \underline{\$24}$

2. A 65-year-old grandfather takes his 7-year-old grandson to the game. How much do the two tickets cost?

$\underline{\$21} \oplus \underline{\$15} = \underline{\$36}$

3. How much more would you spend for a T-shirt than a bat?

$\underline{\$16} \ominus \underline{\$4} = \underline{\$12}$

4. How much would it cost to buy two hot dogs and a soda?

$\underline{\$4} \oplus \underline{\$4} \oplus \underline{\$2} = \underline{\$10}$

5. How much more does an adult ticket cost than a child's ticket?

$\underline{\$23} \ominus \underline{\$15} = \underline{\$8}$

6. Maria buys two T-shirts. How much money does she spend?

$\underline{\$16} \oplus \underline{\$16} = \underline{\$32}$

© Pearson Education, Inc. 2

Use with Lesson 4-12. **55**

Name _____

Adding With and Without Regrouping   R 5-1

Add 37 + 6.

Show 37.	Add the ones.		Regroup. Add.

7 + 6 = 13
There are more than 10 ones.
Do you need to regroup?

(Yes) No   37 + 6 = __43__

Use cubes and Workmat 4. Add. Regroup if you need to.

1. Show 28.   Add 4.   Regroup. Add.

8 + 4 = __12__

Do you need to regroup?

(Yes) No   28 + 4 = __32__

2. Show 26.   Add 9.   Regroup. Add.

6 + 9 = __15__

Do you need to regroup?

(Yes) No   26 + 9 = __35__

56 Use with Lesson 5-1.

© Pearson Education, Inc. 2

Name _____

Adding With and Without Regrouping   P 5-1

Use cubes and Workmat 4.
Add. Regroup if you need to.

	Show	Add	Do you need to regroup?	Find the sum
1.	24	7	yes	24 + 7 = 31
2.	56	9	yes	56 + 9 = 65
3.	92	6	no	92 + 6 = 98
4.	35	8	yes	35 + 8 = 43
5.	69	3	yes	69 + 3 = 72
6.	48	5	yes	48 + 5 = 53
7.	70	4	no	70 + 4 = 74

Problem Solving *Writing in Math*

8. Write 3 different ones numbers you could add to 15 without needing to regroup.

Possible answers: 1, 2, 3, 4

9. Write 3 different ones numbers you could add to 15 where you need to regroup to find the sum.

Possible answers: 5, 6, 7, 8, 9

56 Use with Lesson 5-1.

© Pearson Education, Inc. 2

Name _____

Which Team?   E 5-1
NUMBER SENSE

Decide if you need to regroup. Color the shirts red if you do. Color the shirts blue if you don't. Find each sum and write the number on the shirt.

1. 34 + 9 = __43__   2. 42 + 7 = __49__   3. 57 + 4 = __61__

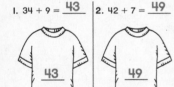

43 — red   49 — blue   61 — red

4. 71 + 6 = __77__   5. 64 + 4 = __68__   6. 89 + 7 = __96__

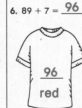

77 — blue   68 — blue   96 — red

7. Write the numbers of each shirt under the correct team.

Red Team	Blue Team
43, 61, 96	49, 77, 68

56 Use with Lesson 5-1.

© Pearson Education, Inc. 2

Name _____

Adding With and Without Regrouping   PS 5-1

1. Help the rabbit find the carrots.
Trace the path that follows the addition problems for which you need to regroup.

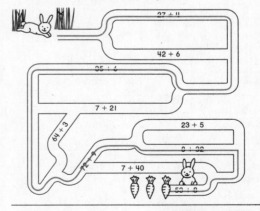

27 + 11
42 + 6
35 + 6
7 + 21
64 + 3
23 + 5
8 + 32
7 + 40
53 + 6

Writing in Math

2. Explain how both pictures show 42.

3 tens and 12 ones can be regrouped to show 4 tens and 2 ones, so both show the same number.

56 Use with Lesson 5-1.

© Pearson Education, Inc. 2

Reteaching

Name _____

Recording Addition

R 5-2

Add 35 + 7.

Step 1:
How many ones?

5 + 7 = 12

Step 2:
Regroup 12 as
1 ten and 2 ones.
Write 2 ones.

Step 3:
How many tens?

3 + 1 = 4 tens

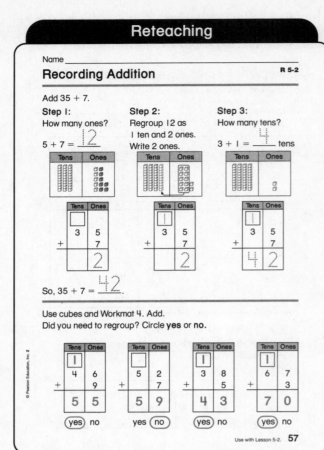

So, 35 + 7 = 42.

Use cubes and Workmat 4. Add.
Did you need to regroup? Circle **yes** or **no**.

Tens	Ones		Tens	Ones		Tens	Ones		Tens	Ones
1	4 6			5 2		1	3 8		1	6 7
+	9		+	7		+	5		+	3
	5 5			5 9			4 3			7 0

(yes) no   yes (no)   (yes) no   (yes) no

Practice

Name _____

Recording Addition

P 5-2

Use cubes and Workmat 4 if needed.
Add. Regroup if you need to.

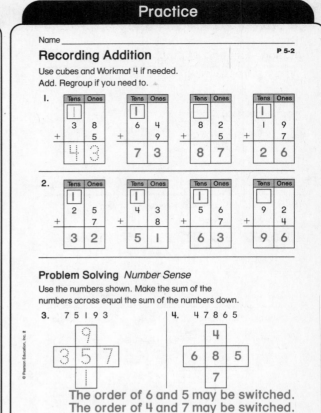

1.

Tens	Ones		Tens	Ones		Tens	Ones		Tens	Ones
1	3 8		1	6 4		1	8 2		1	1 9
+	5		+	9		+	5		+	7
	4 3			7 3			8 7			2 6

2.

Tens	Ones		Tens	Ones		Tens	Ones		Tens	Ones
1	2 5		1	4 3		1	5 6			9 2
+	7		+	8		+	7		+	4
	3 2			5 1			6 3			9 6

Problem Solving *Number Sense*

Use the numbers shown. Make the sum of the
numbers across equal the sum of the numbers down.

3. 7 5 1 9 3

4. 4 7 8 6 5

The order of 6 and 5 may be switched.
The order of 4 and 7 may be switched.

Enrichment

Name _____

Which Number Will You Add?

E 5-2
PATTERNS

Look for a pattern in each row. Circle the number
that will make each addition problem true.

1. 46 + ☐ = 52   56 + ☐ = 62   66 + ☐ = 72   76 + ☐ = 82   (6) 7

2. 21 + ☐ = 26   31 + ☐ = 36   41 + ☐ = 46   51 + ☐ = 56   4 (5)

3. 35 + ☐ = 44   45 + ☐ = 54   55 + ☐ = 64   65 + ☐ = 74   8 (9)

4. 58 + ☐ = 65   68 + ☐ = 75   78 + ☐ = 85   88 + ☐ = 95   (7) 8

5. 49 + ☐ = 53   59 + ☐ = 63   69 + ☐ = 73   79 + ☐ = 83   3 (4)

Problem Solving

Name _____

Recording Addition

PS 5-2

Read each exercise.
Circle the correct numbers.

1. Brenda and Juan went fishing.
   They caught 31 fish in all.
   How many fish did Brenda catch and
   how many fish did Juan catch?

   (5)   21   3   (26)

2. Sam and Elise collect shells. They have
   collected 47 shells in all. How many
   has Sam collected and how many
   has Elise collected?

   33   (42)   3   (5)

Use the numbers shown. Use each number
only once. Make the sum of the numbers
across equal the sum of the numbers down.

**Sample
groupings
shown.**

3. 4 7 9 2 6

4. 2 6 3 13 9

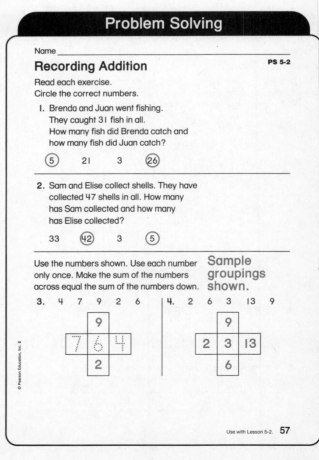

Name _____

Adding Two-Digit Numbers With and Without Regrouping

R 5-3

Add 46 + 18.

Step 1:
How many ones?

$6 + 8 = \underline{14}$

Step 2:
Do I need to regroup?

(yes)   no

Step 3:
How many tens?

$5 + 1 = \underline{6}$ tens

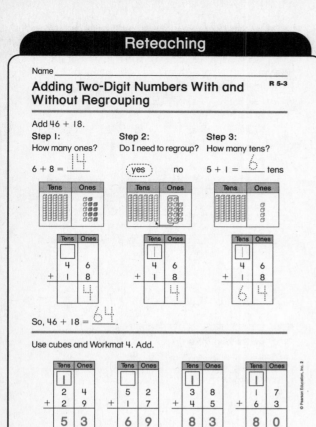

So, $46 + 18 = \underline{64}$

Use cubes and Workmat 4. Add.

Tens	Ones
2	4
+ 2	9
5	3

Tens	Ones
5	2
+ 1	7
6	9

Tens	Ones
3	8
+ 4	5
8	3

Tens	Ones
1	7
+ 6	3
8	0

Name _____

Adding Two-Digit Numbers With and Without Regrouping

P 5-3

Add. Regroup if you need to.
Use cubes and Workmat 4 if needed.

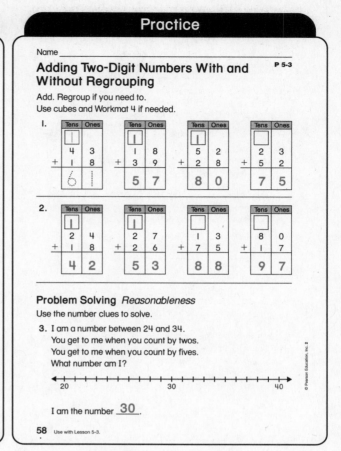

1.

Tens	Ones
4	3
+ 1	8
6	1

Tens	Ones
1	8
+ 3	9
5	7

Tens	Ones
5	2
+ 2	8
8	0

Tens	Ones
2	3
+ 5	2
7	5

2.

Tens	Ones
2	4
+ 1	8
4	2

Tens	Ones
2	7
+ 2	6
5	3

Tens	Ones
1	3
+ 7	5
8	8

Tens	Ones
8	0
+ 1	7
9	7

Problem Solving *Reasonableness*

Use the number clues to solve.

3. I am a number between 24 and 34.
   You get to me when you count by twos.
   You get to me when you count by fives.
   What number am I?

   20 .... 30 40

   I am the number __30__.

Name _____

Empty Circles

E 5-3
ALGEBRA

Write the number in the circle to complete each addition problem.

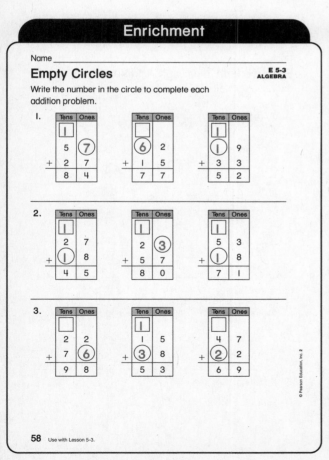

1.

Tens	Ones
5	(7)
+ 2	7
8	4

Tens	Ones
(6)	2
+ 1	5
7	7

Tens	Ones
(1)	9
+ 3	3
5	2

2.

Tens	Ones
2	7
+ (1)	8
4	5

Tens	Ones
2	(3)
+ 5	7
8	0

Tens	Ones
5	3
+ (1)	8
7	1

3.

Tens	Ones
2	2
+ 7	(6)
9	8

Tens	Ones
1	5
+ (3)	8
5	3

Tens	Ones
4	7
+ (2)	2
6	9

Name _____

Adding Two-Digit Numbers With and Without Regrouping

PS 5-3

Use the digits in the circles to complete two addition problems. Have one regroup to add and the other add without regrouping. **Order of numbers may vary.**

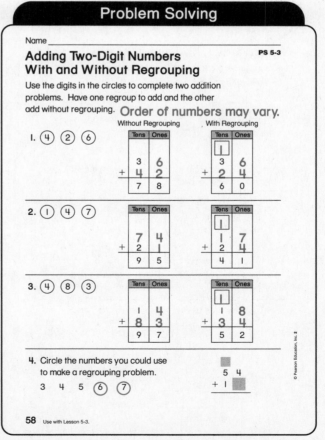

1. (4) (2) (6)

Without Regrouping

Tens	Ones
3	6
+ 4	2
7	8

With Regrouping

Tens	Ones
3	6
+ 2	4
6	0

2. (1) (4) (7)

Tens	Ones
7	4
+ 2	1
9	5

Tens	Ones
1	7
+ 2	4
4	1

3. (4) (8) (3)

Tens	Ones
1	4
+ 8	3
9	7

Tens	Ones
1	8
+ 3	4
5	2

4. Circle the numbers you could use to make a regrouping problem.

   3 4 5 (6) (7)

Tens	Ones
5	4
+ 1	

Name _____

Practice With Two-Digit Addition
R 5-4

Remember the steps for adding:

Step 1: Add the ones. **Step 2:** Regroup if you need to. **Step 3:** Add the tens.

$34 + 27 = ?$
Regroup 11 ones as 1 ten and 1 one.

Tens	Ones
1	
3	4
+ 2	7
6	1

$12 + 36 = ?$
You do not need to regroup 8 ones.

Tens	Ones
1	2
+ 3	6
4	8

Write the addition problem. Find the sum.

1.

15 + 26	32 + 24	28 + 15	49 + 13

Tens	Ones	Tens	Ones	Tens	Ones	Tens	Ones
1				1		1	
1	5	3	2	2	8	4	9
+ 2	6	+ 2	4	+ 1	5	+ 1	3
4	1	5	6	4	3	6	2

Problem Solving *Algebra*

2. Begin with 39. Find the number that gives you a sum of 56. Use cubes to help.

The number is __17__.

Tens	Ones
1	
3	9
+ 1	7
5	6

Name _____

Practice with Two-Digit Addition
P 5-4

Write the addition problem. Find the sum.

1.

34 + 29	15 + 34	25 + 48	36 + 30

Tens	Ones	Tens	Ones	Tens	Ones	Tens	Ones
1				1			
3	4	1	5	2	5	3	6
+ 2	9	+ 3	4	+ 4	8	+ 3	0
6	3	4	9	7	3	6	6

2.

56 + 29	45 + 25	36 + 17	34 + 57

Tens	Ones	Tens	Ones	Tens	Ones	Tens	Ones
1		1		1		1	
5	6	4	5	3	6	3	4
+ 2	9	+ 2	5	+ 1	7	+ 5	7
8	5	7	0	5	3	9	1

Problem Solving *Algebra*

3. Write the missing number in each box. You will need to regroup when you add.

	4	5
+	2	7
	7	2

	3	2
+	1	9
	5	1

Name _____

Pathways Through the Farm
E 5-4
VISUAL THINKING

Use the map to write each problem. Add.
Use tens and ones models if you like.

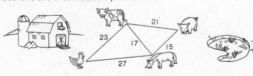

1. How long is the path from the pig to the horse to the cow?

	Tens	Ones
	1	
pig to horse →	1	5
horse to cow →+	1	7
	3	2

2. How long is the path from the horse to the chicken to the cow?

	Tens	Ones
	1	
horse to chicken →	2	7
chicken to cow →+	2	3
	5	0

3. How long is the path from the chicken to the cow to the pig?

	Tens	Ones
chicken to cow →	2	3
cow to pig →+	2	1
	4	4

4. Use the map to write your own problem. Add.

Answers will vary.

	Tens	Ones
___ to ___ →		
___ to ___ →+		

Name _____

Practice with Two-Digit Addition
PS 5-4

Write the addition problem. Find the sum.

1. There are 29 girls and 36 boys at camp. How many children in all are at camp?

__65__ children

Tens	Ones
1	
2	9
+ 3	6
6	5

2. Bobby collects 35 logs for firewood. Lisa collects 42 logs. How many logs do they collect in all?

__77__ logs

Tens	Ones
3	5
+ 4	2
7	7

3. There are 26 cans of stew and 18 cans of beans. How many cans are there in all?

__44__ cans

Tens	Ones
1	
2	6
+ 1	8
4	4

4. Write the number for the .

$75 + $ $= 95$ $= $ __20__

Name _____

Adding Money
R 5-5

Adding money is the same as adding two-digit numbers.

Add two-digit numbers.

Tens	Ones
	3	5
+	2	8
	6	3

Add money.

Tens	Ones
	3	5¢
+	2	8¢
	6	3¢

Remember to write the ¢ sign in your answer.

Add to find the total amount.

1.

Tens	Ones
1	
	1	8
+	4	7
	6	5

Tens	Ones
1	
	1	8¢
+	4	7¢
	6	5¢

2.

Tens	Ones
	3	3
+	2	5
	5	8

Tens	Ones
	3	3¢
+	2	5¢
	5	8¢

Problem Solving *Visual Thinking*

3. Sarah spends 25¢ on an apple.
Sarah has 60¢. Does she have
enough ¢ to buy juice for
39¢ too? Circle **yes** or **no**.

yes   (no)

25¢

39¢

+

64 ¢

Name _____

Adding Money
P 5-5

Add to find the total amount.

1.
```
  1 7¢        2 4¢        6 8¢        4 4¢
+ 4 5¢      + 1 9¢      + 2 2¢      + 1 5¢
  6 2¢        4 3¢        9 0¢        5 9¢
```

2.
```
  5 2¢        1 4¢        2 8¢        6 2¢
+ 2 7¢      + 6 9¢      + 1 9¢      + 2 6¢
  7 9¢        8 3¢        4 7¢        8 8¢
```

3.
```
  4 5¢        2 5¢        1 7¢        6 1¢
+ 2 6¢      + 3 1¢      + 4 4¢      + 2 9¢
  7 1¢        5 6¢        6 1¢        9 0¢
```

Problem Solving *Visual Thinking*

4. Jessie has 35¢. He wants to spend all of his money.
Which 2 pieces of fruit can he buy? Circle them.

23¢ 11¢ 12¢ 9¢ 16¢

Name _____

Lunch Time!
E 5-5
DECISION MAKING

Write your name and a classmate's name.
Write 2 things each of you would like for lunch.
Add. Then answer the questions.

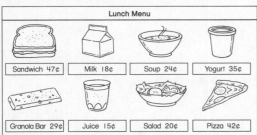

Lunch Menu

Sandwich 47¢   Milk 18¢   Soup 24¢   Yogurt 35¢

Granola Bar 29¢   Juice 15¢   Salad 20¢   Pizza 42¢

Answers will vary.

Your name _____	Classmate _____
_____ ¢	_____ ¢
+ _____ ¢	+ _____ ¢
TOTAL _____ ¢	TOTAL _____ ¢

Who spent more money? Explain how you know.

Name _____

Adding Money
PS 5-5

Solve each problem.
Write the highest priced item that the children can buy.

62¢ 48¢ 95¢ 85¢ 76¢ 53¢ 37¢

1. Ian has 17¢.
Liz has 45¢.
Together, what can
they buy?

____dog____

2. Sonny has 56¢.
Tara has 39¢.
Together, what can
they buy?

____horse____

3. Amy has 31¢.
Her sister gives her 22¢.
What can Amy buy?

____rabbit____

4. Your brother has 19¢.
You give him 29¢.
What can your brother buy?

____duck____

5. Frank has 60¢.
He gets these coins.
What can Frank buy now?

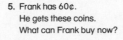

____cat____

Name _____

Adding Three Numbers
R 5-6

> Remember you can add in any order. Try different ways to add.

Look for doubles facts.
Add the doubles first.

$$
\begin{array}{r}
1\,4 \\
3\,5 \\
+\,2\,4 \\
\hline
7\,3
\end{array}
\qquad
\begin{array}{l}
4 + 4 = 8 \\
8 + 5 = 13
\end{array}
$$

Count on 1, 2, or 3.

$$
\begin{array}{r}
5\,3 \\
1\,9 \\
+\,2\,2 \\
\hline
9\,4
\end{array}
\qquad
\begin{array}{l}
9 + 3 = 12 \\
12 + 2 = 14
\end{array}
$$

Make a ten fact.
Look for a ten first.

$$
\begin{array}{r}
1\,3 \\
2\,6 \\
+\,2\,4 \\
\hline
6\,3
\end{array}
\qquad
\begin{array}{l}
6 + 4 = 10 \\
10 + 3 = 13
\end{array}
$$

1. Add.
Look for doubles.

$$
\begin{array}{r}
1\,1 \\
3\,5 \\
+\,2\,5 \\
\hline
7\,1
\end{array}
\qquad
\begin{array}{r}
2\,6 \\
2\,2 \\
+\,1\,6 \\
\hline
6\,4
\end{array}
$$

2. Add.
Count on.

$$
\begin{array}{r}
3\,2 \\
1\,7 \\
+\,2\,4 \\
\hline
7\,3
\end{array}
\qquad
\begin{array}{r}
4\,0 \\
2\,9 \\
+\,1\,2 \\
\hline
8\,1
\end{array}
$$

3. Add.
Make a ten.

$$
\begin{array}{r}
1\,5 \\
2\,8 \\
+\,2\,2 \\
\hline
6\,5
\end{array}
\qquad
\begin{array}{r}
1\,7 \\
2\,3 \\
+\,1\,2 \\
\hline
5\,2
\end{array}
$$

Use with Lesson 5-6. 61

© Pearson Education, Inc. 2

Name _____

Adding Three Numbers
P 5-6

Add in any order.

1.
$$
\begin{array}{r}
4\,5 \\
1\,5 \\
+\,2\,6 \\
\hline
8\,6
\end{array}
\quad
\begin{array}{r}
1\,6 \\
2\,5 \\
+\,\ \,6 \\
\hline
4\,7
\end{array}
\quad
\begin{array}{r}
2\,3 \\
3\,7 \\
+\,1\,2 \\
\hline
7\,2
\end{array}
\quad
\begin{array}{r}
3\,6 \\
1\,4 \\
+\,2\,6 \\
\hline
7\,6
\end{array}
$$

2.
$$
\begin{array}{r}
3\,1 \\
8 \\
+\,4\,4 \\
\hline
8\,3
\end{array}
\quad
\begin{array}{r}
2\,8 \\
2\,5 \\
+\,4\,1 \\
\hline
9\,4
\end{array}
\quad
\begin{array}{r}
3\,7 \\
1\,2 \\
+\,1\,8 \\
\hline
6\,7
\end{array}
\quad
\begin{array}{r}
2\,8 \\
4\,7 \\
+\,1\,3 \\
\hline
8\,8
\end{array}
$$

3.
$$
\begin{array}{r}
2\,9 \\
1\,1 \\
+\,2\,2 \\
\hline
6\,2
\end{array}
\quad
\begin{array}{r}
3\,4 \\
7 \\
+\,1\,6 \\
\hline
5\,7
\end{array}
\quad
\begin{array}{r}
5\,2 \\
1\,5 \\
+\,2\,6 \\
\hline
9\,3
\end{array}
\quad
\begin{array}{r}
4\,3 \\
2\,1 \\
+\,1\,3 \\
\hline
7\,7
\end{array}
$$

Problem Solving *Reasoning*

| 1 | 2 | 3 | 4 | 5 | 6 |

4. Use the numbers on the cards to write 2 two-digit numbers that have the sum of 78.
Possible answer:
36 + 42

5. Use the numbers on the cards to write 2 two-digit numbers that have the sum of 83.
Possible answer:
51 + 32

Use with Lesson 5-6. 61

© Pearson Education, Inc. 2

Name _____

It's in the Clues
E 5-6
REASONING

Three of the numbers added make the sum.
Read the clues to help you.
Circle the three numbers.
Check by adding to find the sum.

1. Sum 83   5 (44) 12 (19) 10 (20)

$$
\begin{array}{r}
4\,4 \\
1\,9 \\
+\,2\,0 \\
\hline
8\,3
\end{array}
$$

One number is the sum of 22 + 22.
One number is one less than 20.
One number is greater than 19 and less than 44.

2. Sum 72   36 12 (25) 7 (33) (14)

$$
\begin{array}{r}
3\,3 \\
1\,4 \\
+\,2\,5 \\
\hline
7\,2
\end{array}
$$

One number has the same number in both digits.
One number is more than 12 and less than 25.
One number is 20 more than 5.

3. Sum 80   29 (19) (49) (12) 20 11

$$
\begin{array}{r}
1\,2 \\
4\,9 \\
+\,1\,9 \\
\hline
8\,0
\end{array}
$$

One number is 8 less than 20.
One number is the sum of 24 + 25.
One number is more than 12 and less than 20.

4. Sum 88   24 31 (17) (43) (28) 35

$$
\begin{array}{r}
2\,8 \\
4\,3 \\
+\,1\,7 \\
\hline
8\,8
\end{array}
$$

One number is the sum of 14 + 14.
One number has the greatest value.
One number is 9 more than 8.

Use with Lesson 5-6. 61

© Pearson Education, Inc. 2

Name _____

Adding Three Numbers
PS 5-6

Look at the sum in the train engine.
Which car is missing from the train? Circle the car.

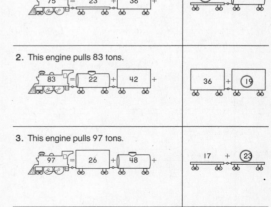

1. This engine pulls 75 tons.

75 = 23 + 36 +   (16) + 22

2. This engine pulls 83 tons.

83 = 22 + 42 +   36 + (19)

3. This engine pulls 97 tons.

97 = 26 + 48 +   17 + (23)

4. Lisa makes a necklace with 90 beads. She has 40 red beads and 30 blue beads. Beads come in bags of 10. Circle the bags of green beads she will need to finish the necklace.

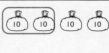

Use with Lesson 5-6. 61

© Pearson Education, Inc. 2

Use with Chapter 5, Lesson 6. **61**

Name _____

PROBLEM-SOLVING SKILL   R 5-7

Use Data from a Table

This table shows data about how many animal books are in the library.

Animal Books in the Library	
Kinds of Books	Number of Books
Mammals	42
Birds	28
Insects	14
Reptiles	33

Use data from the table to solve problems.

How many books about birds and reptiles are there in all?

Do I add or subtract?

What numbers do I use in the chart?

Birds: 28 books
Insects: 14 books
Add to find how many in all.

$$\begin{array}{r} 28 \\ +14 \\ \hline 42 \end{array}$$ books in all

Use data from the table to solve the problems.

1. How many books about mammals and reptiles are there in all?

What numbers do I use?

$$\begin{array}{r} 42 \text{ mammals} \\ +33 \text{ reptiles} \\ \hline 75 \text{ books in all} \end{array}$$

2. How many books about birds and reptiles are there in all?

What numbers do I use?

$$\begin{array}{r} 28 \text{ birds} \\ +33 \text{ reptiles} \\ \hline 61 \text{ books in all} \end{array}$$

3. How many books about birds, insects, and reptiles are there in all?   75 books in all

---

Name _____

PROBLEM-SOLVING SKILL   P 5-7

Use Data from a Table

Use the data from the table to solve the problems.

Sports Books in the Library					
Kind	Baseball	Football	Soccer	Hockey	Tennis
Number	47	36	25	33	8

1. How many books about football and soccer are there in all?

61 books

$$\begin{array}{r} 36 \\ +25 \\ \hline 61 \end{array}$$

2. How many books about baseball and hockey are there in all?

80 books

3. How many books about football, soccer, and tennis are there in all?

69 books

4. If the library got 18 more books about baseball, how many baseball books would there be?

65 books

Name _____

Favorite Animals in the Wild

E 5-7
DATA

Use the data from the table to solve each problem.
Use paper and pencil to show your work.

Favorite Wild Animals					
	Lion	Elephant	Monkey	Zebra	Giraffe
Grade 1	R 24	B 16	13	8	11
Grade 2	16	9	26	19	21

1. Write the total number of votes for each wild animal.

Lion	Elephant	Monkey	Zebra	Giraffe
40	25	39	27	32

2. Draw a red circle around the name of the animal that has the most votes.

3. Draw a blue circle around the name of the animal that has the least votes.

4. How many children voted for lions and zebras in Grade 2?

35

5. How many children voted for elephants, monkeys, and giraffes in Grade 1?

40

Name _____

PROBLEM-SOLVING SKILL   PS 5-7

Use Data from a Table

The second grade classes ordered gym clothes. How many orders are there in all for T-shirts and shorts?

Gym Clothes Orders	
Kind	Number
T-shirt	48
Sweatshirt	27
Shorts	36
Jogging Pants	15

Step 1:

Find the number of T-shirt orders 48

Find the number of shorts orders 36

Step 2:

Add.

$$\begin{array}{r} 48 \\ +36 \\ \hline 84 \end{array}$$

84 orders in all

Use the table to solve.

1. How many orders are there in all for sweatshirts and jogging pants?

42 orders in all

$$\begin{array}{r} 27 \\ +15 \\ \hline 42 \end{array}$$

2. How many orders are there in all for T-shirts and sweatshirts?

75 orders in all

$$\begin{array}{r} 48 \\ +27 \\ \hline 75 \end{array}$$

Using the page To help children *plan* have them look for the correct item. Then have them write down the corresponding numbers to *solve* the problem.

© Pearson Education, Inc. 2

Name _____

Estimating Sums

R 5-8

Remember when you estimate, you find the closest ten.
Estimate 22 + 37.

20 21 22 23 24 25 26 27 28 29 30 31 32 33 34 35 36 37 38 39 40

Step 1:
Find the closest ten.

Step 2:
Estimate.

Step 3:
Add.

22
+ 37

22 is about   20.
37 is about + 40.

22
+ 37
59

22 is closest to **20**
37 is closest to **40**

22 + 37
is about **60**

22 + 37 = **59**

Estimate the sum. Then solve and compare.

Find the closest ten.

Estimate.

Solve.

1.   18
   + 34

18 is about **20**
34 is about **30**

18
+ 34
52

18 is closest to **20**
34 is closest to **30**

18 + 34
is about **50**

18 + 34 = **52**

2.   42
   + 13

42 is about **40**
13 is about **10**

42
+ 13
55

42 is closest to **40**
13 is closest to **10**

42 + 13
is about **50**

42 + 13 = **55**

Use with Lesson 5-8. **63**

Name _____

Estimating Sums

P 5-8

Estimate the sum. Then solve and compare.

Find the closest 10	Estimate	Solve
1. 53 + 28 53 is closest to **50** 28 is closest to **30**.	50 + 30 80 53 + 28 is about **80**	53 + 28 81 53 + 28 = **81**
2. 36 + 23 36 is closest to **40** 23 is closest to **20**	40 + 20 60 36 + 23 is about **60**	36 + 23 59 36 + 23 = **59**
3. 67 + 18 67 is closest to **70** 18 is closest to **20**	70 + 20 90 67 + 18 is about **90**	67 + 18 85 67 + 18 = **85**

Problem Solving *Estimation*
Circle the best estimate.

4. Brittany has 27 animal stickers.
Her brother has 33 animal stickers.
About how many stickers do they
have in all?

about 50 stickers

(about 60 stickers)

about 70 stickers

Use with Lesson 5-8. **63**

Name _____

Card Collections

E 5-8
ESTIMATION

The chart shows how many sports cards each child
collects. Use the chart to estimate your answers.
Circle the closest ten.

	Jason	Linda	Cora	Roberto
Baseball	28	19	43	34
Football	34	22	17	57

About how many baseball and football cards does
each child have?

1. Cora	(60)	70	80
2. Jason	50	(60)	70
3. Roberto	80	(90)	100
4. Linda	30	(40)	50

5. About how many football cards do Jason and Cora have in all?	40	(50)	60
6. About how many baseball cards do Linda and Roberto have in all?	40	(50)	60

Use with Lesson 5-8. **63**

Name _____

Estimating Sums

PS 5-8

Use the table to solve each problem.

Gifts at the Museum Shop

Posters		Models	
Animals	42	Cars	24
Insects	31	Planes	57
Books		Postcards	
Dinosaurs	28	Cities	17
Flowers	19	Paintings	63

Estimate your answer.

1. About how many posters
are there in all?

about **70** posters

2. About how many models
are there in all?

about **80** models

3. About how many books
are there in all?

about **50** books

4. About how many postcards
are there in all?

about **80** postcards

5. The museum gets 12 new books
on flowers. About how many flower
books are there now?

about **30** books

6. The museum gets 14 new car models.
About how many car models are
there now?

about **40** models

Use with Lesson 5-8. **63**

Name _____

Ways to Add

R 5-9

Use **mental math** to add.
43 + 20
I can count up by tens to add. → 43, 53, 63 → 43 + 20 = _63_

Use **cubes** to add.
27 + 18
Regroup 10 ones for one ten. → 27 + 18 = _45_

Use **paper and pencil** to add.
45 + 15

```
    1
   4 5
 + 1 5
```

Write 1 ten over the tens column. → 0   45 + 15 = _60_

Use a **calculator** to add.
56 + 29   [5] [6] [+] [2] [9]   56 + 29 = _85_

Circle the best way to solve the problem. Then add.

1.
```
  1
  7 3
+ 1 8
  9 1
```
mental math
calculator

2.
```
  4 6
+ 3 0
  7 6
```
mental math
paper and pencil

Methods may vary.

3.
```
  1
  5 4
+ 1 7
  7 1
```
mental math
cubes

4.
```
  3 4
+ 2 3
  5 7
```
mental math
paper and pencil

© Pearson Education, Inc. 2

Name _____

Ways to Add

P 5-9

Write the way you will solve the problem.
Then add and write the sum.

Methods may vary.
Possible methods shown.

- mental math
- paper and pencil
- cubes
- calculator

1. 28 + 22 = _50_
mental math,
paper and pencil

2. 48 + 29 = _77_
paper and pencil,
cubes, calculator

3. 53 + 7 = _60_
mental math,
paper and pencil

4. 36 + 19 = _55_
paper and pencil,
cubes, calculator

5. 60 + 28 = _88_
mental math
_____

6. 45 + 25 = _70_
mental math,
paper and pencil

Problem Solving *Mental Math*

7. Lisa bought some fruit.
She spent 87¢. Which
two pieces of fruit did
she buy? Circle them.

© Pearson Education, Inc. 2

Name _____

Sum Boxes

E 5-9
REASONING

Circle all the number pairs in each box that
equal the sum above it. Then write the way
you solved the problem.

Methods may vary.

- mental math
- paper and pencil
- cubes
- calculator

1. Sum 22

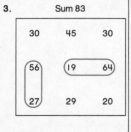

```
(10)  (4    18)
(12)   15   14
 22    21   13
```

2. Sum 55

```
(25    30)   14
 18    14   (45)
 15    21   (10)
```

3. Sum 83

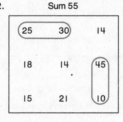

```
 30    45    30
(56)  (19    64)
(27)   29    20
```

4. Sum 40

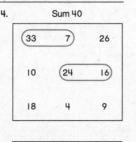

```
(33     7)   26
 10    (24    16)
 18     4     9
```

© Pearson Education, Inc. 2

Name _____

Ways to Add

PS 5-9

Solve. Tell how you solved the problem.

Methods used
may vary.

Mental math	Cubes	Paper and pencil	Calculator

1. Mrs. Jones's class goes on a nature hike.
They see 10 bluebirds and 15 robins.
How many birds do they see in all?

_25_ birds   I used _____.

2. One group collects 57 leaves.
Another group collects 38 leaves.
How many leaves do they collect in all?

_95_ leaves   I used _____.

3. There are 18 boys in Mrs. Jones' class.
There are 12 girls. How many children are there in all?

_30_ children   I used _____.

4. The class counts 32 squirrels and 15 chipmunks.
How many animals do they count in all?

_47_ animals   I used _____.

5. Two groups of children collected more than
70 rocks. How many rocks did each group collect?
Circle two numbers.

21   (35)   (40)

© Pearson Education, Inc. 2

Reteaching

PROBLEM-SOLVING STRATEGY   R 5-10

Try, Check, and Revise

Read and Understand

Ken collects animal stickers.
He paid 43¢ for two stickers.
Which stickers did he choose?

Find two stickers that add up to 43¢.

Animal Stickers	
Animal	Cost
Elephant	33¢
Lion	18¢
Tiger	25¢
Zebra	21¢

Plan and Solve

First, pick two numbers: → 25¢ and 21¢
Next, add the numbers: → 25¢ + 21¢ = 46¢
Compare the numbers: → 46¢ does not equal 43¢.

Try again. Pick 18¢ and 25¢. → 18¢ + 25¢ = 43

So, Ken chose the ___lion___ and ___tiger___ stickers.

Look Back and Check

Are there other pairs of stickers you should check?

Try and check to solve each problem.

1. Nina paid 51¢ for two stickers.
   Which stickers did she choose?
   ___elephant___ and ___lion___ stickers

2. Keesha paid 46¢ for two stickers.
   Which stickers did she choose?
   ___tiger___ and ___zebra___ stickers

Practice

PROBLEM-SOLVING STRATEGY   P 5-10

Try, Check, and Revise

Children bought flowers for school.
What did they buy? Try and check
to solve each problem.

Flower Prices	
Flower	Price
Rose	52¢
Daisy	25¢
Tulip	37¢
Pansy	23¢
Violet	48¢

1. Tammy paid 71¢ for 2 flowers. What did she buy?
   ___pansy___ and ___violet___

2. Rico paid 89¢ for 2 flowers. What did he buy?
   ___rose___ and ___tulip___

3. Katie paid 48¢ for 2 flowers. What did she buy?
   ___daisy___ and ___pansy___

4. Glen paid 85¢ for 3 flowers. What did he buy?
   ___daisy___, ___tulip___, and ___pansy___

Problem Solving *Algebra*

5. Zack spent 55¢ for two flowers.
   One flower cost 30¢. Circle the
   coin that shows how much Zack
   spent on the other flower.

Enrichment

Bean Bag Champs
                                   E 5-10
                            REASONABLENESS

Each child gets two tosses. Shade the squares on
each game board that could show what each child
might have tossed.

1. Benji scores about
   50 points.

12	32
46	19

2. Terry scores about
   80 points.

18	27
52	43

3. Zack scores about
   70 points.

43	28
21	17

4. Mindy scores about
   40 points.

12	38
22	26

5. Leroy scores about
   60 points.

38	46
21	32

6. Yuki scores about
   90 points.

18	14
13	67

Problem Solving

PROBLEM-SOLVING STRATEGY   PS 5-10

Try, Check, and Revise

You can use try, check, and revise
to solve problems.

Red 18   Blue 25
Green 37   Yellow 42

Marty has 79 marbles.
Which two bags of marbles did he buy?

Try: Choose two bags.   ___red___ ___blue___

        Add the numbers.   18 + 25 = 43

Check: Is the sum 79?

Revise: If the sum is not 79,   37 + 42 = 79
        try green and yellow.

So Marty has green and yellow marbles.

1. Carol has 62 marbles.
   Which two bags of marbles
   did she buy?
   Try: ___green and blue___
   Check: ___37___ + ___25___ = ___62___
   Revise: ___ + ___ = ___

2. Seth has 55 marbles.
   Which two bags of marbles
   did he buy?
   Try: ___red and green___
   Check: ___18___ + ___37___ = ___55___
   Revise: ___ + ___ = ___

Using the page To help students *read and understand* the problem, ask them to explain why Marty can only
buy two kinds of marbles with his money. (Only two numbers will add up to 79.)

Reteaching

Name _____

The Wonderful World of Plants

There are 26 plants in one patch.
There are 17 plants in another patch.
How many plants are there in all?

Add to find how many in all.

Step 1: Add the ones. Regroup.

$$\begin{array}{r} \square \\ 26 \\ + 17 \\ \hline 3 \end{array}$$

Remember to regroup 10 ones as 1 ten if needed.

Step 2: Add the tens.

$$\begin{array}{r} \square \\ 26 \\ + 17 \\ \hline 43 \end{array}$$

Solve.

1. One Venus's-flytrap plant has 15 traps.
   Another Venus's-flytrap plant has 19 traps.
   How many traps do the plants have in all?

   $15 \oplus 19 = 34$ plants in all

2. One group of plants catches 23 insects.
   Another group of plants catches 16 insects.
   How many insects are caught in all?

   $23 \oplus 16 = 39$ insects in all

3. If 17 insects got stuck on one plant,
   and 9 insects got stuck on another plant,
   and 5 insects got stuck on a third plant,
   how many insects in all would be stuck?

   $17 \oplus 9 \oplus 5 = 31$ insects in all

Practice

Name _____

The Wonderful World of Plants

Fun Fact!
Some meat-eating plants trap animals such
as worms, or even tiny frogs.

Solve.

1. One group of plants traps 17 insects.
   Another group of plants traps 28 insects.
   How many insects in all have been trapped?

   $17 \oplus 28 = 45$ insects

2. A plant has 12 traps. Another plant has 13 traps.
   How many traps do the two plants have in all?

   $12 \oplus 13 = 25$ traps

3. If one plant can capture one insect in one second,
   how many insects could 25 plants trap in 2 seconds?

   $25 \oplus 25 = 50$ insects

Writing in Math

4. Write an addition number story about meat-eating plants.
   Try to use two-digit numbers in your problem.

   Stories will vary.

Enrichment

Name _____

How Tall?

Mr. Reynolds's second grade class grew some
plants. Every week, they measured the plants to see
how much they grew. Here is a chart showing the
plant growth. Use the chart to answer the questions.

Plant Growth in Centimeters

Week	1	2	3	4
Plant A	2	1	3	1
Plant B	2	4	3	2
Plant C	3	5	2	6

1. How many centimeters
   did plant A grow during
   weeks 2 and 3?

   __4__ centimeters

2. How many centimeters
   did plant C grow during
   weeks 1 and 2?

   __8__ centimeters

3. If plant B continues to grow
   2 centimeters every week,
   how tall will it be during
   week 6?

   __15__ centimeters tall

4. What was the total number
   for plant growth for all
   three plants during
   week 4?

   __9__ centimeters

5. Which plant is the tallest, plant A or plant B?
   Explain how you know.

   Plant B is taller;

   11 centimeters > 7 centimeters

Problem Solving

Name _____

The Wonderful World of Plants

Mr. Benz planted a garden.
He planted 27 tomato plants and 35 corn plants.
How many plants does he have in all?

$27 \oplus 35 = 62$ plants

Does your answer make sense? Does it answer the question?

Solve.

1. Yola planted 42 bean plants and 27 herb plants.
   How many plants are in Yola's garden?

   $42 \oplus 27 = 69$ plants

2. On Monday, Yola picked 48 beans. On Tuesday she
   picked 39 beans. How many beans did she pick in all?

   $48 \oplus 39 = 87$ beans

3. Sue picked 27 red tomatoes from her garden.
   There are still 25 green tomatoes on the plants.
   How many tomatoes is that in all?

   $27 \oplus 25 = 52$ tomatoes

Writing in Math

Stories will vary.

4. Write an addition story about Sue's tomato garden.
   Use two-digit numbers.

Using the page Have children *look back* to make sure they have correctly written each number sentence. Then
have them *check* to see if they have answered the question.

Reteaching

Name _____   R 6-1

Subtracting With and Without Regrouping

Subtract 7 from 42.

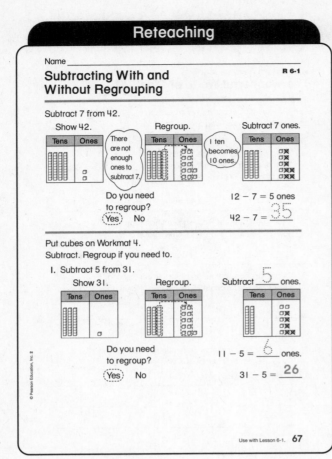

Show 42.

Tens	Ones

There are not enough ones to subtract 7.

Regroup.

Tens	Ones

1 ten becomes 10 ones.

Subtract 7 ones.

Tens	Ones

Do you need to regroup?
(Yes)   No

$12 - 7 = 5$ ones.

$42 - 7 = 35$

Put cubes on Workmat 4.
Subtract. Regroup if you need to.

1. Subtract 5 from 31.

Show 31.

Tens	Ones

Regroup.

Tens	Ones

Subtract 5 ones.

Tens	Ones

Do you need to regroup?
(Yes)   No

$11 - 5 = 6$ ones.

$31 - 5 = 26$

Use with Lesson 6-1. 67

Practice

Name _____   P 6-1

Subtracting With and Without Regrouping

Put cubes on Workmat 4.
Subtract. Regroup if you need to.

	Show	Subtract	Do you need to regroup?	Find the difference.
1.	47	9	yes	$47 - 9 = 38$
2.	52	6	yes	$52 - 6 = 46$
3.	38	5	no	$38 - 5 = 33$
4.	73	8	yes	$73 - 8 = 65$
5.	64	7	yes	$64 - 7 = 57$
6.	48	5	no	$48 - 5 = 43$
7.	27	4	no	$27 - 4 = 23$

Problem Solving *Visual Thinking*

8. The path is 30 inches long. How much farther does the worm need to crawl to get to the end?

Pokey crawled 14 inches. He needs to crawl _16_ inches farther.

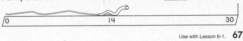

0   14   30

Use with Lesson 6-1. 67

Enrichment

Name _____   E 6-1
NUMBER SENSE

Pick A Number

Choose a number from the chart to subtract.
Cross out each number you choose.
Write the number in the box.
Decide if you need to regroup. Subtract.
You may use each number only once.

3	5	1	9	4	7	2	8	6

Answers will vary.

Did you regroup?

1. 62 - ☐ = ____   yes   no

2. 45 - ☐ = ____   yes   no

3. 71 - ☐ = ____   yes   no

4. 34 - ☐ = ____   yes   no

5. 82 - ☐ = ____   yes   no

6. 90 - ☐ = ____   yes   no

7. 58 - ☐ = ____   yes   no

Use with Lesson 6-1. 67

Problem Solving

Name _____   PS 6-1

Subtraction With and Without Regrouping

Subtract. Color the problems you regroup.

1. $45 - 8 = 37$	F	2. $62 - 7 = 55$	H
3. $91 - 5 = 86$	N	4. $24 - 6 = 18$	M
5. $53 - 7 = 46$	S	6. $39 - 3 = 36$	P
7. $34 - 8 = 26$	A	8. $81 - 9 = 72$	U
9. $57 - 4 = 53$	G	10. $71 - 2 = 69$	T
11. $21 - 4 = 17$	I	12. $57 - 6 = 51$	E

Solve the secret message. Write the letter that goes with each problem's answer.

M	A	T	H	I	S	F	U	N
18	26	69	55	17	46	37	72	86

13. Sandhya baked 25 muffins. She gave some muffins as a gift. How many muffins does she have left?

Sandhya has _16_ muffins left.

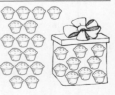

Use with Lesson 6-1. 67

Name _____

Recording Subtraction

R 6-2

Subtract 8 from 52.

Step 1	Step 2	Step 3
Think: There are not enough ones to subtract 8.	Regroup 1 ten as 10 ones. Write 12 ones. $12 - 8 = 4$ ones	Subtract the tens. $4 - 0 = 4$ tens

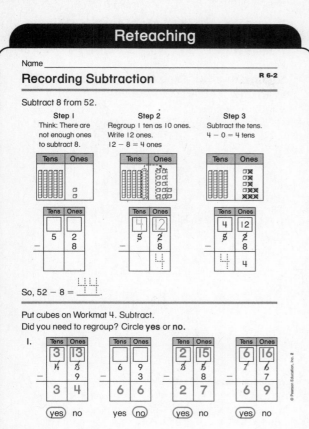

So, $52 - 8 = \underline{44}$.

Put cubes on Workmat 4. Subtract.
Did you need to regroup? Circle **yes** or **no**.

1.

Tens	Ones
3̶	13̶
4̶	3̶
	9
3	4

(yes) no

Tens	Ones
6	9
	3
6	6

yes (no)

Tens	Ones
2̶	15̶
3̶	5̶
	8
2	7

(yes) no

Tens	Ones
6̶	16̶
7̶	6̶
	7
6	9

(yes) no

Name _____

Recording Subtraction

P 6-2

Subtract. Regroup if you need to.
Use cubes and Workmat 4 if you need to.

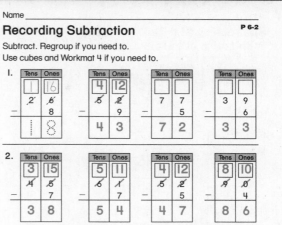

1.

Tens	Ones
1	16
2̶	6̶
	8
1	8

Tens	Ones
4	12
5̶	2̶
	9
4	3

Tens	Ones
7	7
	5
7	2

Tens	Ones
3	9
	6
3	3

2.

Tens	Ones
3	15
4̶	5̶
	7
3	8

Tens	Ones
5	11
6̶	1̶
	7
5	4

Tens	Ones
4	12
5̶	2̶
	5
4	7

Tens	Ones
8	10
9̶	0̶
	4
8	6

3.

Tens	Ones
7	6
	2
7	4

Tens	Ones
3	8
	3
3	5

Tens	Ones
5	13
6̶	3̶
	5
5	8

Tens	Ones
1	18
2̶	8̶
	9
1	9

Problem Solving *Reasonableness*

4. There are 45 students in the library.
Some of the students leave.
How many students could there be
left in the library now?

(37 students)

45 students

51 students

Name _____

Pet Stickers

E 6-2
REASONING

The children put pet stickers in notebooks.
Subtract to find how many stickers there are left.

Cats 42	Dogs 53	Birds 47	Fish 38	Snakes 45

Workspace

1. David chooses the dog stickers.
He puts 8 stickers in a book.
How many dog stickers are left?

_45_ dog stickers

	4	13
	5̶	3̶
−		8
	4	5

2. Hannah chooses the fish stickers.
She puts 9 stickers in a book.
How many fish stickers are left?

_29_ fish stickers

	2	18
	3̶	8̶
−		9
	2	9

3. Darren chooses the snake stickers.
He puts 7 stickers in a book.
How many snake stickers are left?

_38_ snake stickers

	3	15
	4̶	5̶
−		7
	3	8

4. Ari chooses the cat stickers.
He puts 6 stickers in a book.
How many cat stickers are left?

_36_ cat stickers

	3	12
	4̶	2̶
−		6
	3	6

Name _____

Recording Subtraction

PS 6-2

Read each problem.
Circle the correct answer.

1. There are 42 children on the
playground. 8 children go home.
How many children are left?   6   50   (34)

2. Lisa collects 56 leaves in the park.
She puts 9 leaves in an album.
How many leaves does she
have left?   (47)   65   10

3. Ravi collects 28 acorns.
He leaves 6 acorns for
the squirrels. How many acorns
does Ravi have left?   34   (22)   6

4. 24 children are playing a game
of tag. 7 of them quit the game.
How many children are left
playing the game?   3   31   (17)

5. There are 36 children eating lunch.
7 of them finish eating and go outside.
How many children are still eating?   (29)   31   43

6. 12 children are on the monkey bars.
Some of the children get off the bars.
Which number tells how many
children could still be on the bars?   (6)   12   15

Name _____

Subtracting Two-Digit Numbers With and Without Regrouping

Subtract 16 from 43.

Step 1
Think: There are not enough ones to subtract 6.

Step 2
Think: Do I need to regroup?

$13 - 6 = \underline{7}$ ones

Step 3
Think: Subtract the tens.

$3 - 1 = \underline{2}$ tens

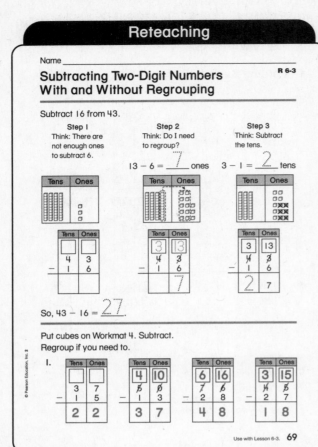

So, $43 - 16 = \underline{27}$.

Put cubes on Workmat 4. Subtract. Regroup if you need to.

1.

Tens	Ones
3	7
− 1	5
2	**2**

Tens	Ones
4	10
5̸	0̸
− 1	3
3	**7**

Tens	Ones
6	16
7̸	6̸
− 2	8
4	**8**

Tens	Ones
3	15
4̸	5̸
− 2	7
1	**8**

Name _____

Subtracting Two-Digit Numbers With and Without Regrouping

Subtract. Regroup if you need to.

1.

Tens	Ones
4	13
5̸	3̸
− 1	7
3	**6**

Tens	Ones
6	8
− 2	1
4	**7**

Tens	Ones
6	12
7̸	2̸
− 3	8
3	**4**

Tens	Ones
4	13
5̸	3̸
− 4	4
	9

2.

Tens	Ones
7	10
8̸	0̸
− 1	5
6	**5**

Tens	Ones
8	12
9̸	2̸
− 3	6
5	**6**

Tens	Ones
4	8
− 2	5
2	**3**

Tens	Ones
2	9
− 1	7
1	**2**

3.

Tens	Ones
2	18
3̸	8̸
− 1	9
1	**9**

Tens	Ones
5	11
6̸	1̸
− 2	7
3	**4**

Tens	Ones
7	15
8̸	5̸
− 4	6
3	**9**

Tens	Ones
6	15
7̸	5̸
− 4	7
2	**8**

Problem Solving *Mental Math*

Write the number that makes each number sentence true.

4. $90 - 30 = 80 - \underline{20}$

$80 - 70 = 20 - \underline{10}$

5. $70 - 40 = 60 - \underline{30}$

$60 - 10 = 90 - \underline{40}$

Name _____

Solve the Mystery

Use the numbers above each exercise to make the subtraction problem true. Write the numbers in the circles.

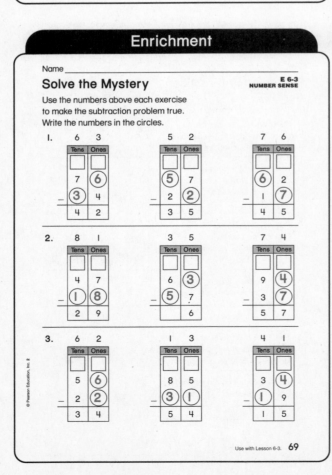

Name _____

Subtracting Two-Digit Numbers With and Without Regrouping

Help Mr. Potter sort the mail. Subtract.

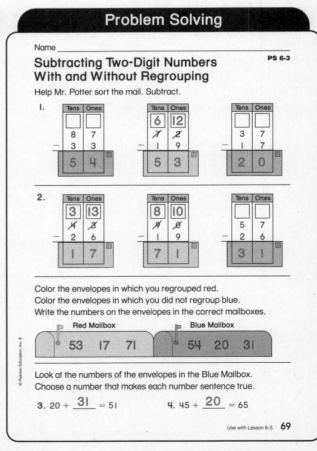

Color the envelopes in which you regrouped red.
Color the envelopes in which you did not regroup blue.
Write the numbers on the envelopes in the correct mailboxes.

Red Mailbox: 53 17 71

Blue Mailbox: 54 20 31

Look at the numbers of the envelopes in the Blue Mailbox.
Choose a number that makes each number sentence true.

3. $20 + \underline{31} = 51$

4. $45 + \underline{20} = 65$

Name_____

Practice with Two-Digit Subtraction

R 6-4

Remember the steps for subtracting:	Step 1: Look at the ones. Regroup if you need to. Step 2: Subtract the ones. Subtract the tens.

54 − 17
Regroup 1 ten as 10 ones.

Tens	Ones
4̶	1 4
5	4
− 1	7
3	7

38 − 13
You do **not** need to regroup 8 ones. Subtract the ones and tens.

Tens	Ones
3	8
− 1	3
2	5

Remember the steps for subtracting. Find the difference.

1.

64 − 18	37 − 14	45 − 26	73 − 25
Tens Ones 5 14 6̶ 4̶ − 1 8 4 6	Tens Ones 3 7 − 1 4 2 3	Tens Ones 3 15 4̶ 5̶ − 2 6 1 9	Tens Ones 6 13 7̶ 3̶ − 1 5 5 8

Problem Solving *Number Sense*

2. Use each number once.
Make the smallest sum.

5 3 2 4

Answer may also be 24 + 35.

Tens	Ones
2	5
+ 3	4
5	9

Name_____

Practice with Two-Digit Subtraction

P 6-4

Write the subtraction problem. Find the difference.

1.

64 − 39	45 − 16	72 − 31	56 − 29
Tens Ones 5 14 6̶ 4̶ − 3 9 2 5	Tens Ones 3 15 4̶ 5̶ − 1 6 2 9	Tens Ones 7 2 − 3 1 4 1	Tens Ones 4 16 5̶ 6̶ − 2 9 2 7

2.

84 − 29	34 − 15	96 − 48	43 − 27
Tens Ones 7 14 8̶ 4̶ − 2 9 5 5	Tens Ones 2 14 3̶ 4̶ − 1 5 1 9	Tens Ones 8 16 9̶ 6̶ − 4 8 4 8	Tens Ones 3 13 4̶ 3̶ − 2 7 1 6

Problem Solving *Number Sense*

For each problem, use each number only once. | 1 2 4 5 |

3. Make the greatest sum.

Tens	Ones
5	2
+ 4	1
9	3

or 51
+42
93

4. Make the greatest difference.

Tens	Ones
5	4
− 1	2
4	2

Name_____

5-Points

E 6-4
NUMBER SENSE

Play with a partner. Take turns. Choose two numbers. Subtract. The player with the greater difference gets 1 point. Cross out the numbers used. The first player to get 5 points wins.

15	46	14	73	27
67	23	65	98	50
35	77	80	41	79
12	61	43	54	85
92	39	29	31	96

Record the points	
1st Player	
2nd Player	

Name_____

Practice with Two-Digit Subtraction

PS 6-4

Write the subtraction problem. Find the difference.

1. Mike buys 65 baseball cards. Lois buys 23 baseball cards. How many more cards does Mike have than Lois?

____42____ more cards

Tens	Ones
6	5
− 2	3
4	2

2. Yuki has 72 blue beads and 37 red beads. How many more blue beads than red beads does Yuki have?

____35____ more blue beads

Tens	Ones
6	12
7̶	2̶
− 3	7
3	5

3. Josh has 43 bottle caps. He uses 28 caps to make an art project. How many bottle caps does Josh have left?

____15____ bottle caps

Tens	Ones
3	13
4̶	3̶
− 2	8
1	5

Look at the tens and the ones.

4. Which numbers could you subtract without regrouping?

0, 1, 2, 3, 4, 5, 6, 10, 11, 12, 13, 14, 15, 16

Name _____

PROBLEM-SOLVING STRATEGY   R 6-5

Write a Number Sentence

Read and Understand

Sue has 42 flowers. She gives 15 flowers to her sister.
How many flowers are left?

Plan and Solve

Look for clue words to decide whether to add
or subtract. "How many are left" tells you to
subtract. "How many in all" tells you to add.

Write a number sentence. Use the numbers
in the problem.

Tens	Ones
3	12
4	2
− 1	5
2	7

$42 \ominus 15 \ominus 27$ flowers left

Write a number sentence to solve the problem.

1. Paul has 37 marbles. He gives 18 marbles
   to a friend. How many marbles are left?

Tens	Ones
2	17
3	7
− 1	8
1	9

$37 \ominus 18 \ominus 19$ marbles left.

2. Tina has 23 crayons. She gets 27 more
   crayons. How many crayons does Tina
   have in all?

Tens	Ones
1	
2	3
+ 2	7
5	0

$23 \oplus 27 \ominus 50$ crayons.

Use with Lesson 6-5. 71

Name _____

PROBLEM-SOLVING STRATEGY   P 6-5

Write a Number Sentence

Write a number sentence to solve the problem.

1. Mel's pet store has 52 birds.
   24 of the birds are parrots.
   How many birds are not parrots?

Tens	Ones
4	12
5	2
− 2	4
2	8

$52 \ominus 24 \ominus 28$ birds

2. Mel orders 47 bags of cat food
   and 38 bags of dog food.
   How many bags does he order in all?

Tens	Ones
4	7
+ 3	8
8	5

$47 \oplus 38 \ominus 85$ bags

3. There are 78 containers of fish food.
   39 containers of food are sold.
   How many containers are left?

Tens	Ones
6	18
7	8
− 3	9
3	9

$78 \ominus 39 \ominus 39$ containers

4. The store has 59 dog toys and
   34 cat toys. How many more
   dog toys are there than cat toys?

Tens	Ones
5	9
− 3	4
2	5

$59 \ominus 34 \ominus 25$ more dog toys

Use with Lesson 6-5. 71

Name _____

E 6-5
DATA

Butterfly Collections

The chart shows the number of butterflies each child collects.
Write a number sentence to solve the problem.
Use the data in the chart. Show your work.

Number of Butterflies in a Collection					
Jimmy	Lucas	Anna	Mario	Yuki	Ruth
14	35	27	52	41	22

Workspace

1. How many more butterflies does Yuki
   have than Jimmy?

Tens	Ones

   $41 \ominus 14 = 27$ more butterflies

2. How many butterflies do Anna and
   Lucas have in all?

Tens	Ones

   $27 \oplus 35 = 62$ in all

3. Mario gives 16 butterflies to Ruth.
   How many butterflies does Mario have left?

Tens	Ones

   $52 \ominus 16 = 36$ butterflies left

Use with Lesson 6-5. 71

Name _____

PROBLEM-SOLVING STRATEGY   PS 6-5

Write a Number Sentence

There are 35 sleeping bags for the camping trip.
28 children use some of those sleeping bags.
How many sleeping bags are left?

Step 1: Which words help you decide whether to
add or subtract? __left__

Step 2: Will you add or subtract to
solve the problem? subtract

Tens	Ones
3	5
− 2	8
	7

Step 3: Write a number sentence.

$35 \ominus 28 \ominus 7$ sleeping bags

Write a number sentence to solve the problem.

1. 14 boys go on a hike. 18 girls go
   on the hike. How many children
   go on the hike in all?

Tens	Ones
1	
1	4
+ 1	8
3	2

$14 \oplus 18 \ominus 32$ children

2. There are 65 crackers in a bag.
   The children eat 27 crackers.
   How many crackers are left?

Tens	Ones
5	15
6	5
− 2	7
3	8

$65 \ominus 27 \ominus 38$ crackers

Using the page To help children **plan** and **solve** each problem, have them underline words that help them to decide whether to add or subtract.

Use with Lesson 6-5. 71

Subtracting Money

R 6-6

Subtracting money is the same as subtracting two-digit numbers.

5 1¢
− 2 2¢

Think of the pennies as ones and the dimes as tens.

Tens	Ones
4	11
5	1¢
− 2	2¢
2	9¢

Remember to write the cents sign in your answer.

Subtract to find the difference.

1.
					6	13	3	12
5	9¢	6	5¢	7	3¢	4	2¢
− 2	4¢	− 2	4¢	− 5	7¢	− 2	8¢
3	5¢	4	1¢	1	6¢	1	4¢

2.
7	10	6	12	5	10		
8	0¢	7	2¢	6	0¢	4	8¢
− 2	9¢	− 3	6¢	− 4	8¢	− 1	8¢
5	1¢	3	6¢	1	2¢	3	0¢

Problem Solving *Reasoning*

3. Greg has 58¢. He spends 25¢.
   How much money does Greg have left?

   Greg has __33¢__ left.

5	8¢
− 2	5¢
3	3¢

Subtracting Money

P 6-6

Subtract to find the difference.

1.
		4	14	7	16	6	10
6	8¢	5	4¢	8	6¢	7	9¢
− 2	3¢	− 1	5¢	− 2	8¢	− 1	6¢
4	5¢	3	9¢	5	8¢	5	4¢

2.
3	13	1	14			7	13
4	3¢	2	4¢	4	9¢	8	3¢
− 2	7¢	−	5¢	− 1	8¢	− 1	8¢
1	6¢	1	9¢	3	1¢	6	5¢

3.
6	12	4	17			2	16
7	2¢	5	7¢	6	8¢	3	6¢
− 6	3¢	− 1	9¢	− 3	1¢	− 1	9¢
	9¢	3	8¢	3	7¢	1	7¢

Problem Solving *Reasoning*

Solve. Show your work.

4. Mark has 33¢. He gives 8¢ to his sister.
   How much money does Mark have left? __25__ ¢

5. Jamal has 54¢. He wants to buy
   a toy that costs 70¢.
   How much more money does he need? __16__ ¢

Shopping Day

E 6-6
DECISION MAKING

Decide what each child will buy.
Subtract to find how much money is left.

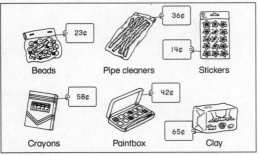

Beads — 23¢
Pipe cleaners — 36¢
Stickers — 14¢
Crayons — 58¢
Paintbox — 42¢
Clay — 65¢

Answers will vary.

Workspace

1. Bonnie has 47¢.

   She buys the _____.

   Bonnie has _____ left.

−	

2. Ricky has 59¢.

   He buys the _____.

   Ricky has _____ left.

−	

3. Which item is the one that neither child can buy? __clay__

Subtracting Money

PS 6-6

35¢
42¢
57¢
82¢
77¢
21¢

Subtract to find the difference.

1. Cara has 46¢.
   She buys the keychain.
   How much money does
   she have left?

   __11¢__

2. Dexter has 90¢.
   He buys the statue.
   How much money does
   he have left?

   __13¢__

3. Corey has 57¢.
   He buys the postcard.
   How much money does
   he have left?

   __15¢__

4. Zena has 75¢.
   She buys the snow globe.
   How much money does
   she have left?

   __18¢__

5. Jacy has these coins.
   Can he buy the pen? Explain.

   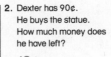

   __Yes, the coins__

   __equal 85¢.__

Name _____

Using Addition to Check Subtraction

R 6-7

When you subtract,
you start with the whole.
Then you take part away.
The other part is left.

$$37$$
$$-12$$
$$25$$

Tens	Ones

To check your work,
put the 2 parts back together.
Add. Your answer should be
the whole you started with.

$$25$$
$$+12$$
$$37$$

Tens	Ones

and   and

Subtract.
Check your answer by adding.

1.
$$\begin{array}{r} 4\ \ 14 \\ \not5\ \not4 \\ -1\ \ 9 \\ \hline 3\ \ 5 \end{array}$$
$$\begin{array}{r} 35 \\ +19 \\ \hline 54 \end{array}$$

2.
$$\begin{array}{r} 5\ \ 13 \\ \not6\ \not3 \\ -3\ \ 7 \\ \hline 2\ \ 6 \end{array}$$
$$\begin{array}{r} 26 \\ +37 \\ \hline 63 \end{array}$$

3.
$$\begin{array}{r} 7\ \ 16 \\ \not8\ \not6 \\ -\ \ \ 9 \\ \hline 7\ \ 7 \end{array}$$
$$\begin{array}{r} 77 \\ +\ \ 9 \\ \hline 86 \end{array}$$

4.
$$\begin{array}{r} \boxed{\ }\ \boxed{\ } \\ 3\ \ 3 \\ -2\ \ 1 \\ \hline 1\ \ 2 \end{array}$$
$$\begin{array}{r} 12 \\ +21 \\ \hline 33 \end{array}$$

Use with Lesson 6-7. 73

Name _____

Using Addition to Check Subtraction

P 6-7

Subtract. Check your answer by adding.

1.
$$\begin{array}{r} 5\ \ 12 \\ 6\ 2 \\ -1\ 8 \\ \hline 4\ 4 \end{array}$$
$$\begin{array}{r} 1 \\ 44 \\ +18 \\ \hline 62 \end{array}$$

2.
$$\begin{array}{r} 7\ 13 \\ 8\ 3 \\ -2\ 9 \\ \hline 5\ 4 \end{array}$$
$$\begin{array}{r} 1 \\ 54 \\ +29 \\ \hline 83 \end{array}$$

3.
$$\begin{array}{r} 6\ 13 \\ 7\ 3 \\ -3\ 7 \\ \hline 3\ 6 \end{array}$$
$$\begin{array}{r} 36 \\ +37 \\ \hline 73 \end{array}$$

4.
$$\begin{array}{r} 4\ 8 \\ -2\ 1 \\ \hline 2\ 7 \end{array}$$
$$\begin{array}{r} 27 \\ +21 \\ \hline 48 \end{array}$$

5.
$$\begin{array}{r} 8\ 14 \\ 9\ 4 \\ -2\ 8 \\ \hline 6\ 6 \end{array}$$
$$\begin{array}{r} 1 \\ 66 \\ +28 \\ \hline 94 \end{array}$$

6.
$$\begin{array}{r} 6\ 15 \\ 7\ 5 \\ -1\ 7 \\ \hline 5\ 8 \end{array}$$
$$\begin{array}{r} 1 \\ 58 \\ +17 \\ \hline 75 \end{array}$$

Problem Solving *Algebra*

Write the number that makes each number
sentence true.

7. $80 + 10 = 90 - \underline{0}$

   $10 + 30 = 70 - \underline{30}$

   $70 + 10 = 90 - \underline{10}$

8. $60 - 20 = 20 + \underline{20}$

   $50 - 40 = 10 + \underline{0}$

   $70 - 20 = 10 + \underline{40}$

Use with Lesson 6-7. 73

Name _____

At the Check-Out

E 6-7
NUMBER SENSE

Subtract. Check your answer by adding.

	Subtract	Check
1. Mei Ling has 71¢. She spent 25¢. How much money does Mei Ling have left?	$\begin{array}{r} 6\ 11 \\ 7\not1¢ \\ -25¢ \\ \hline 46¢ \end{array}$	$\begin{array}{r} 1 \\ 46¢ \\ +25¢ \\ \hline 71¢ \end{array}$
2. Eric has 62¢. He spent 33¢. How much money does Eric have left?	$\begin{array}{r} 5\ 12 \\ 6\not2¢ \\ -33¢ \\ \hline 29¢ \end{array}$	$\begin{array}{r} 1 \\ 29¢ \\ +33¢ \\ \hline 62¢ \end{array}$
3. Dennis has 51¢. He spent 32¢. How much money does Dennis have left?	$\begin{array}{r} 4\ 11 \\ 5\not1¢ \\ -32¢ \\ \hline 19¢ \end{array}$	$\begin{array}{r} 1 \\ 19¢ \\ +32¢ \\ \hline 51¢ \end{array}$
4. Raul has 99¢. He spent 49¢. How much money does Raul have left?	$\begin{array}{r} 99¢ \\ -49¢ \\ \hline 50¢ \end{array}$	$\begin{array}{r} 50¢ \\ +49¢ \\ \hline 99¢ \end{array}$

Use with Lesson 6-7. 73

Name _____

Using Addition to Check Subtraction

PS 6-7

Use the numbers in the basket to write a subtraction
problem. Then check your answer using addition.

Answers may vary. Sample answers are given.

1. 26 72 46
$$\begin{array}{r} 72 \\ -46 \\ \hline 26 \end{array}$$
$$\begin{array}{r} 26 \\ +46 \\ \hline 72 \end{array}$$

2. 63 26 37
$$\begin{array}{r} 63 \\ -26 \\ \hline 37 \end{array}$$
$$\begin{array}{r} 37 \\ +26 \\ \hline 63 \end{array}$$

3. 55 80 25
$$\begin{array}{r} 80 \\ -55 \\ \hline 25 \end{array}$$
$$\begin{array}{r} 25 \\ +55 \\ \hline 80 \end{array}$$

Write the number that makes each
number sentence true.

4. $80 - \underline{10} = 30 + 40$

   $70 - \underline{20} = 50 + 0$

   $60 - \underline{20} = 30 + 10$

5. $20 + \underline{20} = 40 + 0$

   $10 + \underline{80} = 20 + 70$

   $40 + \underline{50} = 60 + 30$

Use with Lesson 6-7. 73

Name _____

Estimating Differences

R 6-8

Remember, when you estimate, you find the closest 10.
Estimate the difference between 49 and 32.

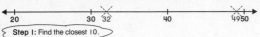

Step 1: Find the closest 10.

Find 49 on the number line.   49 is closest to __50__.

Find 32 on the number line.   32 is closest to __30__.

Step 2: Estimate.   Step 3: Solve.

```
  50            49
- 30          - 32
----          ----
 20            17
```

49 − 32 is about __20__.

Estimate the difference between 63 and 24.
Then solve and compare.

1. Find the closest ten.   Estimate.   Solve.

63 is closest to __60__.   60   5 13
                                       ⁶ ⅓
24 is closest to __20__.   − 20   − 2 4
                            ----   ------
63 − 24 is about __40__.   40   3 9

Name _____

Estimating Differences

P 6-8

Estimate the difference. Then solve and compare.

Find the closest 10	Estimate	Solve
1. 82 − 36 82 is closest to __80__. 36 is closest to __40__.	80 − 40 ---- 40 82 − 36 is about __40__.	7 12 8̶2̶ − 36 ---- 46 82 − 36 = __46__
2. 51 − 19 51 is closest to __50__. 19 is closest to __20__.	50 − 20 ---- 30 51 − 19 is about __30__.	4 11 5̶1̶ − 19 ---- 32 51 − 19 = __32__
3. 76 − 37 76 is closest to __80__. 37 is closest to __40__.	80 − 40 ---- 40 76 − 37 is about __40__.	6 16 7̶6̶ − 37 ---- 39 76 − 37 = __39__

Problem Solving *Estimation*

Circle the best estimate.

4. Andrew has 68 stickers.   about 30 stickers
He gives 32 stickers to his brother.
About how many stickers does   (about 40 stickers)
Andrew have left?   about 50 stickers

Name _____

Yard Sale

E 6-8
ESTIMATION

Teapot   Lunchbox   Vase   Pot
26¢   42¢   39¢   54¢

Choose the items each person buys at the yard sale.
Find the closest 10 to estimate how much money is left.

                                           Workspace

1. Don has 67¢. What does he buy?   **Answers may vary.**

_____

Don has about _____ ¢ left.

2. Millie has 80¢. What does she buy?

_____

Millie has about _____ ¢ left.

3. Stefan has 72¢. What does he buy?

_____

Stefan has about _____ ¢ left.

Name _____

Estimating Differences

PS 6-8

The children are selling tickets to a school play.
Use the chart to solve each exercise.

Number of Tickets Sold

Betty	Kenji	Ellis	Gina	Juan
57	13	72	48	34

Estimate the difference.

1. About how many more tickets
did Ellis sell than Juan?

about __40__ more tickets

2. About how many more tickets
did Betty sell than Kenji?

about __50__ more tickets

3. About how many more tickets does Gina need
to sell to get to 90?

about __40__ more tickets

4. About how many more tickets does Juan need
to sell to get to 50?

about __20__ more tickets

5. There are 42 people in the first row at the play.
There are 28 people in the second row. Estimate
how many more people are in the first row.

about __10__ more people

© Pearson Education, Inc. 2

Name _____

Ways to Subtract

R 6-9

Remember there are 4 ways you can subtract.

Use **mental math** to subtract. $75 - 20$
Think: Count back 2 tens to subtract. 75, 65, 55 $75 - 20 = \underline{55}$

Use **cubes** to subtract. $38 - 12$

Show 38. Take away 1 ten.
Then take away 2 ones.

Tens	Ones

$38 - 12 = \underline{26}$

Use **paper and pencil** to subtract. $60 - 23$
Think: Regroup 1 ten as 10 ones.

5	10

$$\begin{array}{r} \cancel{6}\ \cancel{0} \\ -\ 2\ 3 \\ \hline \end{array}$$ $60 - 23 = \underline{37}$

Use a **calculator** to subtract. $85 - 59$
Press 8 5 − 5 9 = $85 - 59 = \underline{26}$

Circle the better way to solve the problem. Then subtract.

1.
$$\begin{array}{r} 7\ 5 \\ -\ 1\ 0 \\ \hline 6\ 5 \end{array}$$
paper and pencil
(mental math)

2.
$$\begin{array}{r} 4\ 9 \\ -\ 2\ 2 \\ \hline 2\ 7 \end{array}$$
(cubes)
mental math

3.
$$\begin{array}{r} 6\ 7 \\ -\ 1\ 9 \\ \hline 4\ 8 \end{array}$$
mental math
(paper and pencil)

4.
$$\begin{array}{r} 8\ 3 \\ -\ 3\ 0 \\ \hline 5\ 3 \end{array}$$
calculator
(mental math)

Use with Lesson 6-9. **75**

© Pearson Education, Inc. 2

Name _____

Ways to Subtract

P 6-9

Write the letter that tells how you will solve the problem. Then subtract and write the difference.

a. mental math	b. cubes
c. paper and pencil	d. calculator

Letter answers may vary. Accept reasonable responses. Possible letter answers are given.

1.
$$\begin{array}{r} 5\ 10 \\ \cancel{6}\ \cancel{0} \\ -\ 3\ 5 \\ \hline 2\ 5 \end{array}$$
b, c, or d

2.
$$\begin{array}{r} 5\ 12 \\ \cancel{6}\ \cancel{2} \\ -\ \ \ 9 \\ \hline 5\ 3 \end{array}$$
b, c, or d

3.
$$\begin{array}{r} 4\ 9 \\ -\ \ \ 7 \\ \hline 4\ 2 \end{array}$$
a, b, c, or d

4.
$$\begin{array}{r} 7\ 13 \\ \cancel{8}\ \cancel{3} \\ -\ 3\ 7 \\ \hline 4\ 6 \end{array}$$
b, c, or d

5.
$$\begin{array}{r} 5\ 3 \\ -\ 2\ 0 \\ \hline 3\ 3 \end{array}$$
a

6.
$$\begin{array}{r} 6\ 15 \\ \cancel{7}\ \cancel{5} \\ -\ 2\ 6 \\ \hline 4\ 9 \end{array}$$
b, c, or d

7.
$$\begin{array}{r} 3\ 16 \\ \cancel{4}\ \cancel{6} \\ -\ 1\ 8 \\ \hline 2\ 8 \end{array}$$
b, c, or d

8.
$$\begin{array}{r} 5\ 7 \\ -\ 3\ 1 \\ \hline 2\ 6 \end{array}$$
a, b, c, or d

Problem Solving *Writing in Math*

Answers will vary.

9. Write 2 new subtraction problems that you would use pencil and paper to solve.

Use with Lesson 6-9. **75**

© Pearson Education, Inc. 2

Name _____

Secret Numbers

E 6-9
ALGEBRA

Use the numbers in the chart to solve each problem.
Did you use mental math, cubes, paper and pencil, or a calculator? Write the way you solved the problem.

□ = 40	☆ = 72	○ = 56
△ = 34	☺ = 91	☀ = 67
☾ = 25	⇧ = 18	◈ = 85

Methods may vary.

1. ○ − ⇧
$\underline{56} - \underline{18} = \underline{38}$
I used _____.

2. ◈ − ☾
$\underline{85} - \underline{25} = \underline{60}$
I used _____.

3. ☺ − △
$\underline{91} - \underline{34} = \underline{57}$
I used _____.

4. ☆ − □
$\underline{72} - \underline{40} = \underline{32}$
I used _____.

5. Use the shapes in the chart. Write your own secret number sentence. Then solve. Answers will vary.

____ − ____   ____ − ____ = ____

Use with Lesson 6-9. **75**

© Pearson Education, Inc. 2

Name _____

Ways to Subtract

PS 6-9

Solve. Write how you solved the problem.

Methods used may vary.

mental math	cubes	paper and pencil	calculator

1. A coloring book has 45 pages. Ted colors 30 of the pages. How many pages are left?
   $\underline{15}$ pages are left
   I solved by using _____
   _____

2. Abbey has 82 crayons. Kevin has 38 crayons. How many more crayons does Abbey have?
   $\underline{44}$ more crayons
   I solved by using _____
   _____

3. A large box has 38 pencils. A small box has 12 pencils. How many more pencils are in the large box?
   $\underline{26}$ more pencils
   I solved by using _____
   _____

Writing in Math

4. Gabby solved this problem using cubes. Write sentences to explain how she did this. Then find the difference.
$$\begin{array}{r} 2\ 8 \\ -\ 1\ 3 \\ \hline 1\ 5 \end{array}$$
   Possible answer: Gabby showed 2 tens and 8 ones.
   Then she took away 3 ones and 1 ten to get 15.

Use with Lesson 6-9. **75**

© Pearson Education, Inc. 2

© Pearson Education, Inc. 2

Name _____

Extra Information

Sometimes there is extra information that you do not need to answer the question.

There are 4 children on a bowling team. Mike bowls a score of 65. Sherry bowls a score of 33. How much higher is Mike's score?

> What is the question asking?

How much higher is Mike's score than Sherry's score?

> Which information do you need to answer the question?

Mike bowls a score of 65. Sherry bowls a score of 33.

> Which information doesn't tell about the scores?

There are 4 children on a bowling team.

$$\begin{array}{r} 65 \\ -\ 33 \\ \hline 32 \end{array}$$

32 points higher

Cross out the extra information. Then solve the problem.   Solve

1. There are 78 adults at the bowling alley.
   There are 39 children at the bowling alley.
   ~~Mark bowls a score of 82.~~
   How many more adults than children are there?

   $$\begin{array}{r} \overset{6\ 18}{7\cancel{8}} \\ -\ 39 \\ \hline 39 \end{array}$$

   39 more adults

2. In the first game, Sari bowls a score of 57.
   ~~Her brother bowls a score of 48.~~
   In the second game, Sari bowls a score of 38.
   What is Sari's total score for the two games?

   $$\begin{array}{r} \overset{1}{}57 \\ +\ 38 \\ \hline 95 \end{array}$$

   95 points

Name _____

Extra Information

Cross out the extra information. Then solve the problem.

1. 45 people ride on the Ferris wheel.
   ~~The Ferris wheel is 38 feet tall.~~
   63 people ride the bumper cars.
   How many more people ride the bumper cars than the Ferris wheel?

   $$\begin{array}{r} \overset{5\ 13}{\cancel{6}\cancel{3}} \\ -\ 45 \\ \hline 18 \end{array}$$

   18 more people

2. 26 boys and 32 girls ride the water slide.
   ~~44 adults watch the water slide.~~
   How many children in all ride the water slide?

   $$\begin{array}{r} 26 \\ +\ 32 \\ \hline 58 \end{array}$$

   58 children

3. 72 children are waiting to ride the roller coaster. 48 of them get on the next ride.
   ~~The roller coaster has 24 cars.~~
   How many children did not get on the ride?

   $$\begin{array}{r} \overset{6\ 12}{7\cancel{2}} \\ -\ 48 \\ \hline 24 \end{array}$$

   24 children

4. A man sells 53 hot dogs and 87 hamburgers.
   ~~He also sells 45 pretzels.~~
   How many more hamburgers than hot dogs are sold?

   $$\begin{array}{r} 87 \\ -\ 53 \\ \hline 34 \end{array}$$

   34 more hamburgers

Name _____

Meet Me at the Crafts Fair

Three classes made crafts for the fair.
Cross out the extra information in the chart.
Then solve the problems.

Class	Potholders	Necklaces	Bird Feeders	Puppets
Mr. Mark's	17	42	13	~~11~~
Miss Brown's	21	18	~~18~~	12
Mrs. Cruz's	25	~~32~~	31	18

Workspace

1. How many more beaded necklaces did Mr. Mark's class make than Miss Brown's class?

   $$\begin{array}{r} \overset{3\ 12}{4\cancel{2}} \\ -\ 18 \\ \hline 24 \end{array}$$

   24 more necklaces

2. How many potholders did Miss Brown's class and Mrs. Cruz's class make altogether?

   $$\begin{array}{r} 21 \\ +\ 25 \\ \hline 46 \end{array}$$

   46 potholders

3. How many more bird feeders did Mrs. Cruz's class make than Mr. Mark's class?

   $$\begin{array}{r} \overset{2\ 11}{3\cancel{1}} \\ -\ 13 \\ \hline 18 \end{array}$$

   18 more bird feeders

4. How many potholders did Mr. Mark's class and Miss Brown's class make in all?

   $$\begin{array}{r} 17 \\ +\ 21 \\ \hline 38 \end{array}$$

   38 potholders

Name _____

Extra Information

35 children ride the merry-go-round.
~~There are 23 children that wait in line.~~
18 children ride the Ferris wheel.
How many more children ride the merry-go-round than the Ferris wheel?

Solve.

$$\begin{array}{r} 35 \\ -\ 18 \\ \hline 17 \end{array}$$

17 more children

> What information is not needed? Cross out the information you do not need.

Cross out the information you do not need. Then solve the problem.

1. A man sells 47 red balloons.
   Later he sells 26 blue balloons.
   ~~The man also sells 13 puppets.~~
   How many more red balloons than blue balloons does the man sell?

   21 more red balloons

2. The ball toss has 60 stuffed animals as prizes.
   ~~Billy knocks over 12 pins with balls.~~
   35 of the stuffed animals are given away as prizes.
   How many stuffed animals are left?

   25 stuffed animals

Using the page To help children *look back* and check each problem, have them identify the information that they used to solve each problem. Then have them identify the information that they did not use.

Reteaching

Name

PROBLEM-SOLVING APPLICATIONS   R 6-11

Here Kitty, Kitty!

Subtract to **compare numbers.**

A mother lion has 30 teeth.
Her baby cub has only 14 teeth.
How many more teeth does the
mother lion have?

 Regroup 1 ten as 10 ones.

 Subtract.

Tens	Ones		Tens	Ones

Step 1
Regroup. Subtract the ones.

$$\begin{array}{r} 2\ 10 \\ \cancel{3}\ \cancel{0} \\ -\ 1\ 4 \\ \hline 6 \end{array}$$

Step 2
Subtract the tens.

$$\begin{array}{r} 2\ 10 \\ \cancel{3}\ \cancel{0} \\ -\ 1\ 4 \\ \hline 16 \end{array}$$

Solve. Show your work.

1. A tiger is 87 inches long. A lion
   is 76 inches long. How much
   longer is the tiger than the lion?

   $$\begin{array}{r} 87 \\ -\ 76 \\ \hline 11 \end{array}$$ __11__ inches longer

2. There are 27 lions in a pride.
   9 of the lions are cubs. How
   many adult lions are in the pride?

   $$\begin{array}{r} {}^{1\ 17} \\ \cancel{27} \\ -\ \ 9 \\ \hline 18 \end{array}$$ __18__ adult lions

3. There are 17 lions in a group.
   10 lions leave the group.
   How many lions are left?

   $$\begin{array}{r} 17 \\ -\ 10 \\ \hline 7 \end{array}$$ __7__ lions are left.

Use with Lesson 6-11. **77**

Practice

Name

PROBLEM-SOLVING APPLICATION   P 6-11

Here Kitty, Kitty!

Fun Fact
The cheetah is the fastest animal on land.
It can run up to 70 miles per hour.

1. A cheetah runs at a speed of 70 miles per hour.
   A bus has a speed of 35 miles per hour on a street.
   How much faster is the cheetah's speed than the bus's speed?

   __70__ ⊖ __35__ = __35__ miles per hour faster

2. There are 22 lions that live in a pride.
   13 of the lions are cubs.
   How many of the lions are not cubs?

   __9__ lions are not cubs.

3. Estimate how much longer the lion is.

   82 is closest to __80__ .

   68 is closest to __70__ .

Animal	Length
Lion	About 82 inches
Cheetah	About 68 inches

   So a good estimate of the difference

   would be __10__ inches.

Writing in Math

4. Write a subtraction story about cheetahs.

   Stories will vary.

Use with Lesson 6-11. **77**

Enrichment

Name

Animal Safari
                                        E 6-11
                                        NUMBER SENSE

Mr. and Mrs. Santos went
on an African safari. Use the
information in the chart to
answer the questions.

Number of Animals Seen		
	Day 1	Day 2
Giraffes	65	27
Elephants	9	32
Lions	16	25
Zebras	11	48

1. How many more giraffes did the Santos's
   see on Day 1 than on Day 2?

   __65__ ⊖ __27__ = __38__ more giraffes

2. How many more elephants than giraffes
   did they see on Day 2?

   __32__ ⊖ __27__ = __5__ more elephants

3. Which number would be the
   most reasonable estimate for the
   number of lions they saw in all?

   30   (40)   50

4. How many more zebras than lions did
   they see on Day 2?

   __48__ ⊖ __25__ = __23__ more zebras

Use with Lesson 6-11. **77**

Problem Solving

Name

PROBLEM-SOLVING APPLICATIONS   PS 6-11

Here Kitty, Kitty!

A tiger cub named Russell weighs 72 pounds.
His sister, Asha, weighs 56 pounds.
How many more pounds does Russell weigh?

(What is the question asking?)

How much more does Russell
weigh than Asha?

(Subtract to solve.)

 72 ⊖ 56 ⊖ 16 more pounds

Solve.

1. A mother tiger eats 68 pounds of meat. Her cub
   eats 13 pounds. How many more pounds of meat
   does the mother tiger eat?

   __68__ ⊖ __13__ = __55__ more pounds

2. There are 47 tigers in one group.
   19 of the tigers are adults.
   The rest are tiger cubs.
   How many of the tigers are cubs?

   __47__ ⊖ __19__ = __28__ are cubs

Using the page Have students *read* the problem. Ask them to state the problem in their own words to show that
they *understand* the question.

Use with Lesson 6-11. **77**

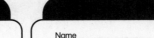

Name _____

Flat Surfaces, Vertices, and Edges

R 7-1

Flat surface
2 flat surfaces meet at an edge.
2 or more edges meet at a vertex.

A cube has __6__ flat surfaces.

A cube has __12__ edges.

A cube has __8__ vertices.

A cube has the same shape as a

Circle the object with the same shape.
Write how many flat surfaces, vertices, and edges.
Use solid figures to help you.

1.

A pyramid has __5__ flat surfaces, __5__ vertices, and __8__ edges.

2.

A rectangular prism has __6__ flat surfaces, __8__ vertices,

and __12__ edges.

78 Use with Lesson 7-1.

© Pearson Education, Inc. 2

Name _____

Flat Surfaces, Vertices, and Edges

P 7-1

Write how many flat surfaces, vertices, and edges.
Then circle the objects that have the same shape.

1. A cube has __6__ flat surfaces, __8__ vertices, and __12__ edges.

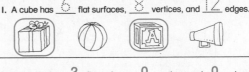

2. A cylinder has __2__ flat surfaces, __0__ vertices, and __0__ edges.

3. A rectangular prism has __6__ flat surfaces, __8__ vertices,

and __12__ edges.

Problem Solving *Visual Thinking*

Circle the answer.

4. Which shapes could roll if you turned them on their side?

78 Use with Lesson 7-1.

© Pearson Education, Inc. 2

Name _____

Two Solids Make One

E 7-1
VISUAL THINKING

Circle the 2 solid figures that make the first object.
Draw the missing edge that connects the solids.

1.

2.

3.

4.

78 Use with Lesson 7-1.

© Pearson Education, Inc. 2

Name _____

Flat Surfaces, Vertices, and Edges

PS 7-1

Name the solid figure for each description.
Then go on a treasure hunt.   Drawings will vary.
Find and draw one object with the same shape.

1. I have no flat surfaces, vertices, or edges.	2. I have 6 flat surfaces. They are all squares.
I am a ___sphere___.	I am a ___cube___.
3. I have two flat surfaces that are circles. You can roll me.	4. I have 6 flat surfaces. 4 of these surfaces are rectangles. Draw my shape.
I am a ___cylinder___	Children should draw a rectangular prism.

78 Use with Lesson 7-1.

© Pearson Education, Inc. 2

---

78   Use with Chapter 7, Lesson 1.

© Pearson Education, Inc. **2**

Reteaching

Name _____

Relating Plane Shapes to Solid Figures   R 7-2

If you trace the flat surfaces of this box, you will get these shapes.

Use the solid figures in your classroom.
Trace one flat surface. Draw the shape on the page.

1.

○

2.

△ or ▢

3.

▢

4.

○

Practice

Name _____

Relating Plane Shapes to Solid Figures   P 7-2

Circle the solid figure or figures you can trace
to make the plane shape.

1.

square

2.

triangle

3.

rectangle

4.

circle

Problem Solving *Algebra*

5. Count the number of vertices.
   Write a number sentence.

   $\underline{8}$ + $\underline{5}$ = $\underline{13}$

Enrichment

Name _____

A Shape Graph   E 7-2 DATA

Count the number of circles, squares, rectangles,
and triangles that are made by tracing each flat
surface of each solid. Color one box in the graph
for every plane shape you count.

Number of Plane Shapes Found in Solids										
○										
▢										
△										
▭										
	1	2	3	4	5	6	7	8	9	10

Answer the questions.

1. Write the total number of plane shapes counted.

   $\underline{3}$ circles $\underline{9}$ squares

   $\underline{4}$ rectangles $\underline{4}$ triangles

2. Which plane shape was counted the most? __square__

3. Which plane shape was counted the least? __circle__

Problem Solving

Name _____

Relating Plane Shapes to Solid Figures   PS 7-2

Write the name of the solid figure.
Then answer the questions.

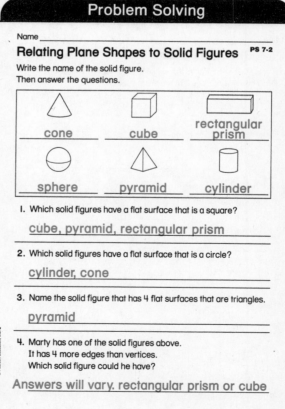

cone   cube   rectangular prism

sphere   pyramid   cylinder

1. Which solid figures have a flat surface that is a square?

   __cube, pyramid, rectangular prism__

2. Which solid figures have a flat surface that is a circle?

   __cylinder, cone__

3. Name the solid figure that has 4 flat surfaces that are triangles.

   __pyramid__

4. Marty has one of the solid figures above.
   It has 4 more edges than vertices.
   Which solid figure could he have?

   __Answers will vary. rectangular prism or cube__

Name _____

PROBLEM-SOLVING SKILL   R 7-3

Use Data from a Picture

A net is a pattern that makes
a solid figure when folded.

Count the faces of the net.

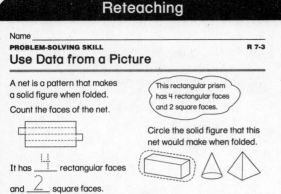

This rectangular prism
has 4 rectangular faces
and 2 square faces.

Circle the solid figure that this
net would make when folded.

It has __4__ rectangular faces

and __2__ square faces.

Circle the solid figure that the net makes when folded.
Use the clues to help you.

1.

It has 4 triangular faces
and 1 square face.

2.

It has 6 square faces.

80   Use with Lesson 7-3.

Name _____

PROBLEM-SOLVING SKILL   P 7-3

Use Data from a Picture

Circle the solid figure that the net will
make if you fold it and tape it together.

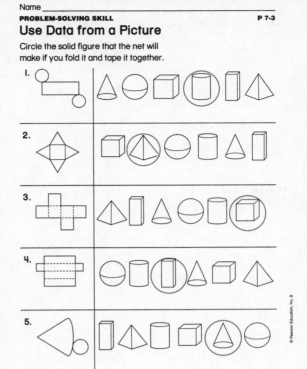

1.

2.

3.

4.

5.

80   Use with Lesson 7-3.

Name _____

All Kinds of Nets   E 7-3
                                                  REASONING

Write the name of the solid figure you could form
from each net. Then answer the questions.

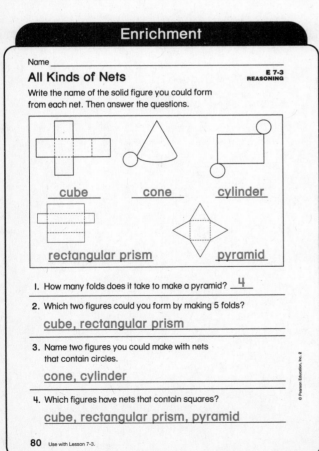

    cube   cone   cylinder

    rectangular prism   pyramid

1. How many folds does it take to make a pyramid? __4__

2. Which two figures could you form by making 5 folds?

   cube, rectangular prism

3. Name two figures you could make with nets
   that contain circles.

   cone, cylinder

4. Which figures have nets that contain squares?

   cube, rectangular prism, pyramid

80   Use with Lesson 7-3.

Name _____

PROBLEM-SOLVING SKILL   PS 7-3

Use Data from a Picture

Janet has a glass figure collection.
She wants to wrap each figure.
Which net would make the best wrap?

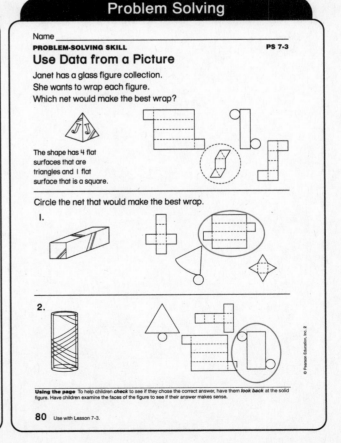

The shape has 4 flat
surfaces that are
triangles and 1 flat
surface that is a square.

Circle the net that would make the best wrap.

1.

2.

Using the page To help children *check* to see if they chose the correct answer, have them *look back* at the solid
figure. Have children examine the faces of the figure to see if their answer makes sense.

80   Use with Lesson 7-3.

Name _____

Making New Shapes

R 7-4

You can make a larger shape from smaller shapes.
Use pattern blocks.

trapezoid   hexagon

2 trapezoids make 1 hexagon.

The larger shape has
__6__ sides and __6__ angles.

Use the pattern blocks shown to make the larger shapes.
Trace the shapes to show all the sides.

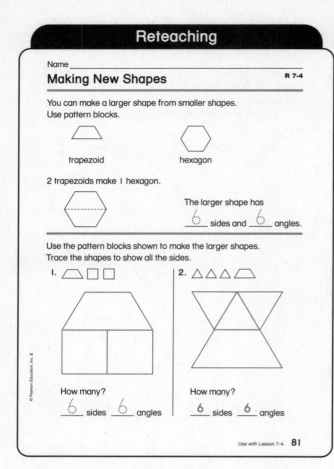

1.

How many?
__6__ sides __6__ angles

2.

How many?
__6__ sides __6__ angles

Use with Lesson 7-4. 81

Name _____

Making New Shapes

P 7-4

Sample answers are given.

Use pattern blocks to make the shape.
Trace and color to show one way to make it.
Write the number of sides and the number of angles.

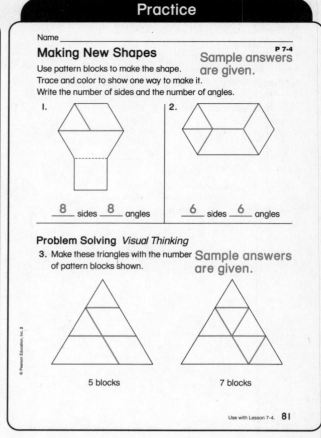

1.

__8__ sides __8__ angles

2.

__6__ sides __6__ angles

Problem Solving Visual Thinking

3. Make these triangles with the number   Sample answers
of pattern blocks shown.   are given.

5 blocks   7 blocks

Use with Lesson 7-4. 81

Name _____

Make a Shape

E 7-4
PATTERNS

Use pattern blocks to make the shape.
Trace and color to show one way.

1. Use 6 blocks.   Possible answers shown.

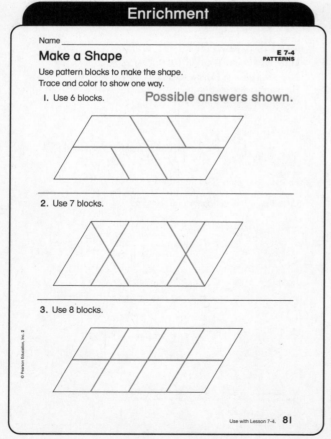

2. Use 7 blocks.

3. Use 8 blocks.

Use with Lesson 7-4. 81

Name _____

Making New Shapes

PS 7-4

Write the number of sides and angles.
Then draw lines to make new shapes.

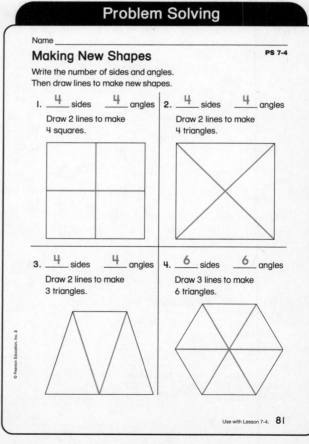

1. __4__ sides __4__ angles
Draw 2 lines to make
4 squares.

2. __4__ sides __4__ angles
Draw 2 lines to make
4 triangles.

3. __4__ sides __4__ angles
Draw 2 lines to make
3 triangles.

4. __6__ sides __6__ angles
Draw 3 lines to make
6 triangles.

Use with Lesson 7-4. 81

Name _____

Congruence

R 7-5

These rectangles are not the same shape.

These rectangles are not the same size.

These rectangles are the same shape and same size.

They are not congruent.

They are not congruent.

They are congruent.

Are the shapes congruent? Circle **Yes** or **No**.

	Same Shape	Same Size	Congruent
1.	(Yes) / No	(Yes) / No	(Yes) / No
2.	(Yes) / No	Yes / (No)	Yes / (No)
3.	(Yes) / No	(Yes) / No	(Yes) / No
4.	Yes / (No)	(Yes) / No	Yes / (No)

82 Use with Lesson 7-5.

© Pearson Education, Inc. 2

Name _____

Congruence

P 7-5

Draw a shape that is congruent.

1.

2.

3.

4.

Draw shapes that are congruent.

5.

6. Check children's drawings.

Problem Solving *Algebra*

Draw the shape that makes each number sentence true.

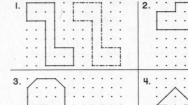

□ = 7   ○ = 8   △ = 9

7. 8 + △ = 17

8. 6 + □ = 13

82 Use with Lesson 7-5.

© Pearson Education, Inc. 2

Name _____

Same and Different

E 7-5
DECISION MAKING

Draw 2 shapes that are congruent.   **Answers will vary.**

1. Draw triangles.

2. Draw trapezoids.

Shapes should be the same size and shape.

Draw 2 shapes that are not congruent.

3. Draw hexagons.

4. Draw parallelograms.

Shapes should not be the same size and/or shape.

82 Use with Lesson 7-5.

© Pearson Education, Inc. 2

Name _____

Congruence

PS 7-5

Draw a shape that is congruent. Then draw a different shape that is **not** congruent.

1.

2.

Check children's drawings. Noncongruent shape should have a different shape.

Draw a shape that is congruent. Then draw the same shape in a different size that is **not** congruent.

3.

4.

Check children's drawings. Noncongruent shape should be a different size only.

5. Solve.

 = 5   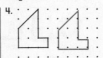 = 7

 +  = __10__

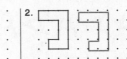 + 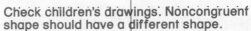 = __14__

82 Use with Lesson 7-5.

© Pearson Education, Inc. 2

Name _____

Slides, Flips, and Turns

R 7-6

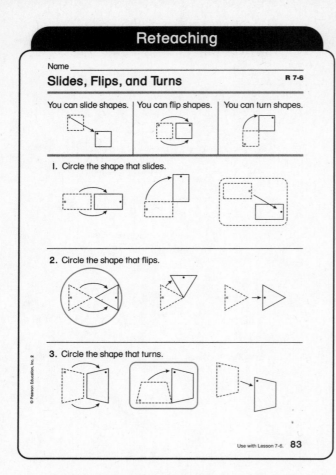

You can slide shapes. | You can flip shapes. | You can turn shapes.

1. Circle the shape that slides.

2. Circle the shape that flips.

3. Circle the shape that turns.

Use with Lesson 7-6. **83**

Name _____

Slides, Flips, and Turns

P 7-6

Is it a slide, a flip, or a turn?
Circle the answer.

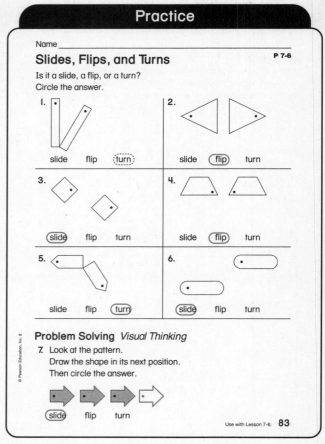

1. slide   flip   (turn)

2. slide   (flip)   turn

3. (slide)   flip   turn

4. slide   (flip)   turn

5. slide   flip   (turn)

6. (slide)   flip   turn

Problem Solving *Visual Thinking*

7. Look at the pattern.
Draw the shape in its next position.
Then circle the answer.

(slide)   flip   turn

Use with Lesson 7-6. **83**

Name _____

Crazy Letters

E 7-6
VISUAL THINKING

Do the letters show a flip, a slide, or a turn?
Circle what comes next.

1. turn

2. flip

3. turn

4. slide

5. flip

Use with Lesson 7-6. **83**

Name _____

Slides, Flips, and Turns

PS 7-6

Write **slide**, **flip**, or **turn** to tell how the first shape
moved. Then circle the position that shows the same
move for the next shape.

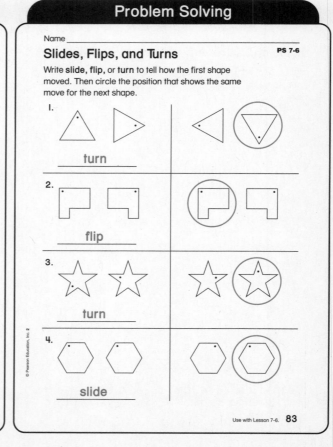

1. turn

2. flip

3. turn

4. slide

Use with Lesson 7-6. **83**

Reteaching

Name _____

Symmetry   R 7-7

Both parts match. This shape has a line of symmetry.

The parts do not match. This shape does not have a line of symmetry.

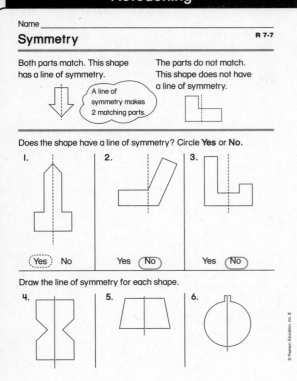

A line of symmetry makes 2 matching parts.

Does the shape have a line of symmetry? Circle **Yes** or **No**.

1.   (Yes)   No
2.   Yes   (No)
3.   Yes   (No)

Draw the line of symmetry for each shape.

4.   5.   6.

84 Use with Lesson 7-7.

© Pearson Education, Inc. 2

Practice

Name _____

Symmetry   P 7-7

Draw the matching part to make the shape symmetrical.

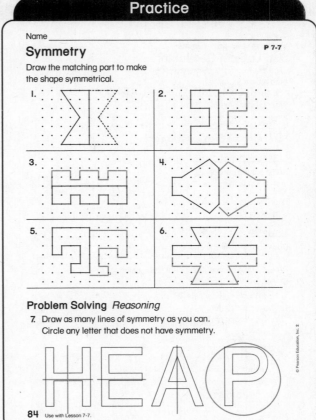

1.   2.

3.   4.

5.   6.

Problem Solving *Reasoning*

7. Draw as many lines of symmetry as you can. Circle any letter that does not have symmetry.

HEAP

84 Use with Lesson 7-7.

© Pearson Education, Inc. 2

Enrichment

Name _____

Name Symmetry   E 7-7
                                   REASONING

Many letters have a line of symmetry.
Draw a line of symmetry if you can.
Some letters have two lines of symmetry.

1. A G H P W X

2. Write the letters of your first and last name in capitals.
   Draw lines of symmetry for the letters.

Check students' work.

3. Which of the letters in your name have 1 line of symmetry?

   Answers will vary.

4. Which of the letters in your name have no lines of symmetry?

   Answers will vary.

84 Use with Lesson 7-7.

© Pearson Education, Inc. 2

Problem Solving

Name _____

Symmetry   PS 7-7

The first piece of paper is folded in half. Draw what this shape will look like when you unfold the paper.

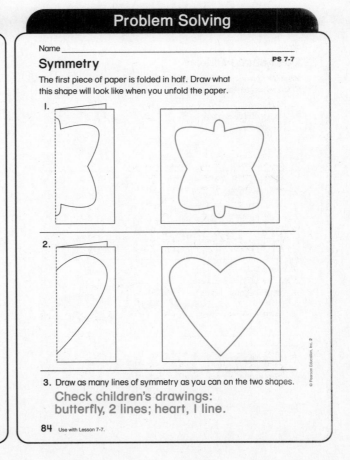

1.

2.

3. Draw as many lines of symmetry as you can on the two shapes.

   Check children's drawings:
   butterfly, 2 lines; heart, 1 line.

84 Use with Lesson 7-7.

© Pearson Education, Inc. 2

Name _____

PROBLEM-SOLVING STRATEGY   R 7-8
Use Logical Reasoning

I am not a square.
I do not have 4 sides.
Which shape am I?

Read and Understand

Find the shape that answers the question.

Plan and Solve

Cross out the shapes
that do not fit the clues.

Which shape is not
crossed out?

1st Clue: I am not
a square. So, cross
out the square.

2nd Clue: I do not have
4 sides. So, cross out
any shape with 4 sides.

Look Back and Check

Does your answer match the clues?

Cross out the shapes that do not fit the clues.
Circle the shape that is left. Answer the questions.

1. I do not have 5 angles.
   I am not a rectangle.
   Which shape am I?
   <u>triangle</u>

   How many angles do I have?
   <u>3</u>

2. I do not have 6 sides.
   I am not a circle.
   Which shape am I?
   <u>parallelogram</u>

   How many angles do I have?
   <u>4</u>

Use with Lesson 7-8. **85**

© Pearson Education, Inc. 2

Name _____

PROBLEM-SOLVING STRATEGY   P 7-8
Use Logical Reasoning

Cross out the shapes that do not fit the clues.
Circle the shape that answers the question.

1. Who am I?
   I have 4 angles.
   I have only 1 line
   of symmetry.

2. Who am I?
   I have 2 lines
   of symmetry.
   I have 4 angles.

3. Who am I?
   I have more than 3 angles.
   I have 6 lines
   of symmetry.

Problem Solving *Writing in Math*

4. Write a riddle about one of
   these solid shapes.
   Have a friend solve your riddle.

   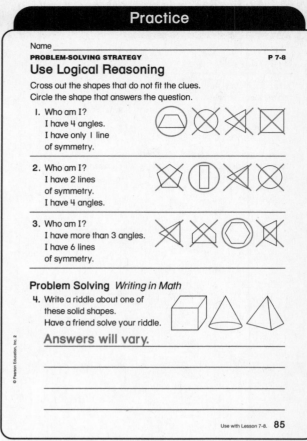

   <u>Answers will vary.</u>

   _____

   _____

Use with Lesson 7-8. **85**

© Pearson Education, Inc. 2

Name _____

Solid Shape Riddles   E 7-8
                                                REASONING

Read the clues.
Circle the solid shape that answers the question.

1. Who am I?
   My flat surfaces are circles.
   I have 0 edges.

2. Who am I?
   One of my flat surfaces
   is a square.
   I have 5 vertices.

3. Who am I?
   My flat surface is a circle.
   I have 0 edges.

4. Who am I?
   I have more than 8 edges.
   Only 2 of my faces are squares.

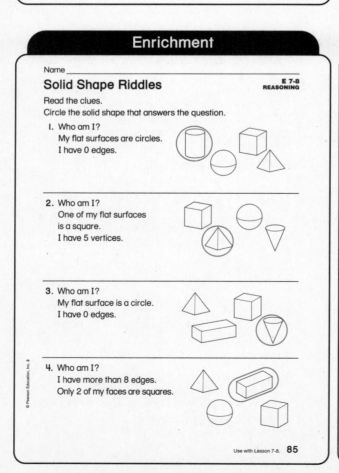

Use with Lesson 7-8. **85**

© Pearson Education, Inc. 2

Name _____

PROBLEM-SOLVING STRATEGY   PS 7-8
Use Logical Reasoning

Who am I? I have less than 5 sides. I am not a square.

Read and Understand

Read the clues carefully to find
out what you need to look for.

Plan and Solve

Cross out the shapes that have 5 or more sides.
Cross out the shapes with square faces.
The shape that is left answers the question.

Look Back and Check

Does the shape have less than 5 sides?   (yes)   no

Is it a square?   yes   (no)

Cross out the shapes that do not match the clues.
Circle the shape that answers the question.

1. Who am I?
   I have more than
   4 angles. I have less
   than 6 sides.

2. Who am I?
   I have less than
   5 sides. I have
   one line of symmetry.

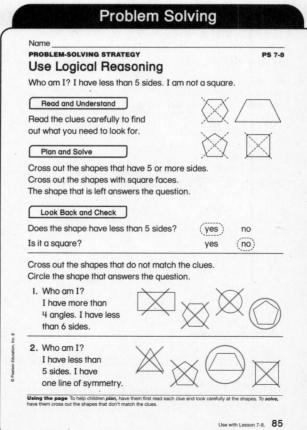

Using the page To help children *plan*, have them first read each clue and look carefully at the shapes. To *solve*, have them cross out the shapes that don't match the clues.

Use with Lesson 7-8. **85**

© Pearson Education, Inc. 2

Use with Chapter 7, Lesson 8. **85**

Name

Equal Parts   R 7-9

Equal parts are the same shape and size.

 equal parts | equal parts | equal parts

(halves) / thirds / fourths   halves / (thirds) / fourths   halves / thirds / (fourths)

How many equal parts? Write the number of parts or circle halves, thirds, or fourths.

1. _3_ equal parts   2. _2_ equal parts   3. _4_ equal parts

 halves / (thirds) / fourths   (halves) / thirds / fourths   halves / thirds / (fourths)

4. _2_ equal parts   5. _3_ equal parts   6. _4_ equal parts

 (halves) / thirds / fourths   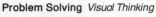 halves / (thirds) / fourths   halves / thirds / (fourths)

Problem Solving *Visual Thinking*

Draw lines to show 2 equal parts.

     Answers may vary.

Name

Equal Parts   Sample answers are given.   P 7-9

Draw a line or lines to show equal parts.

1. fourths   2. halves

3. thirds   4. fourths

Does the picture show halves, thirds, or fourths? Circle your answer.

5. (halves) / thirds / fourths   6. halves / thirds / (fourths)

7. halves / (thirds) / fourths   8. (halves) / thirds / fourths

Problem Solving *Visual Thinking*

9. Draw one more line to show fourths.

Name

Let's Share Lunch   E 7-9 VISUAL THINKING

1. Two children want to share a small pizza. Draw two ways to split the pizza into halves.

2. Three children want to share a tray of apple crisp. Draw two ways to split the apple crisp into thirds.

3. Four children want to share an apple pie. Draw lines to split the pie into fourths.

Possible answer given.

Name

Equal Parts   PS 7-9

Read each story.
Draw 1 or more lines to show equal parts.   **Sample answers given.**

1. Justino and Donna baked a pine-tree shaped cookie. Now they each want to eat part of the cookie.

2. Barry, Kika, Oliver, and James share a flower garden. Show each part of the garden.

3. Samantha, Charlie, and Mariko each look out a different part of a window. What might the window look like?

4. An old sign broke in half. Marissa glued the pieces back together. Show Marissa's sign.

5. Biku has three brothers. All 4 children have the same birthday. Show how they shared their birthday cake.

6. 3 friends made a fruit smoothie. Show how much each friend drank.

---

86   Use with Chapter 7, Lesson 9.

Reteaching

Name

Unit Fractions

R 7-10

A fraction can name one of the equal parts of a whole shape.

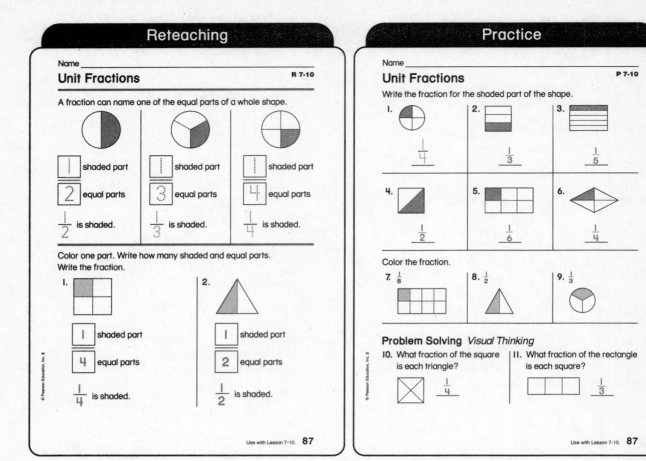

| | 1 shaded part | | 1 shaded part | | 1 shaded part |
| 2 equal parts | | 3 equal parts | | 4 equal parts |

$\frac{1}{2}$ is shaded. $\frac{1}{3}$ is shaded. $\frac{1}{4}$ is shaded.

Color one part. Write how many shaded and equal parts.
Write the fraction.

1.
1 shaded part
4 equal parts
$\frac{1}{4}$ is shaded.

2.
1 shaded part
2 equal parts
$\frac{1}{2}$ is shaded.

© Pearson Education, Inc. 2

Use with Lesson 7-10. **87**

Practice

Name

Unit Fractions

P 7-10

Write the fraction for the shaded part of the shape.

1. $\frac{1}{4}$ 2. $\frac{1}{3}$ 3. $\frac{1}{5}$

4. $\frac{1}{2}$ 5. $\frac{1}{6}$ 6. $\frac{1}{4}$

Color the fraction.

7. $\frac{1}{8}$ 8. $\frac{1}{2}$ 9. $\frac{1}{3}$

Problem Solving *Visual Thinking*

10. What fraction of the square is each triangle? $\frac{1}{4}$

11. What fraction of the rectangle is each square? $\frac{1}{3}$

© Pearson Education, Inc. 2

Use with Lesson 7-10. **87**

Enrichment

Name

Shapes of Color

E 7-10
NUMBER SENSE

Each shape is divided into equal parts.
Color 1 part red.
Write the fraction for the part that is red.

Any 1 part in each shape should be colored. Possible responses shown.

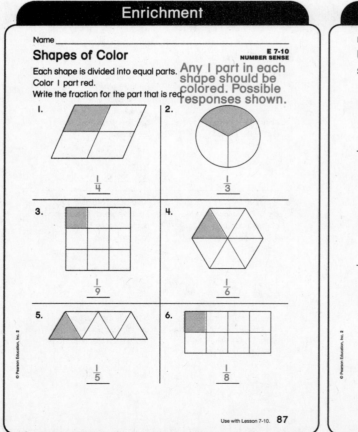

1. $\frac{1}{4}$

2. $\frac{1}{3}$

3. $\frac{1}{9}$

4. $\frac{1}{6}$

5. $\frac{1}{5}$

6. $\frac{1}{8}$

© Pearson Education, Inc. 2

Use with Lesson 7-10. **87**

Problem Solving

Name

Unit Fractions

PS 7-10

Solve.

1. Marge cuts a pie into 4 equal parts. She eats one part. What fraction of the pie did she eat? $\frac{1}{4}$

2. Tony cuts an apple into 6 equal parts. He eats one part. What fraction of the apple did Tony eat? $\frac{1}{6}$

3. Becky ate $\frac{1}{6}$ of a pizza.
Which picture shows the slice of pizza Becky ate?

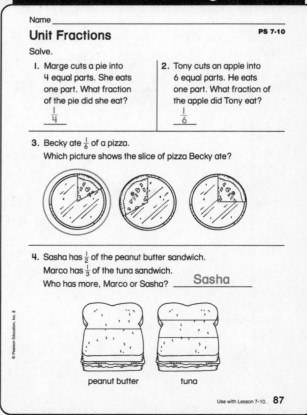

4. Sasha has $\frac{1}{2}$ of the peanut butter sandwich.
Marco has $\frac{1}{3}$ of the tuna sandwich.
Who has more, Marco or Sasha?   Sasha

peanut butter   tuna

© Pearson Education, Inc. 2

Use with Lesson 7-10. **87**

Name _____

Non-Unit Fractions

R 7-11

A fraction can name two or more equal parts of a whole shape.

 [2] shaded parts [3] equal parts $\frac{2}{3}$ is shaded.

Color the parts red.
Write the fraction for the shaded part.

1. Color 4 parts.

[4] parts are red.
[6] equal parts $\frac{4}{6}$ is red.

2. Color 2 parts.

[2] parts are red.
[4] equal parts $\frac{2}{4}$ is red.

3. Color 5 parts.

[5] parts are red.
[8] equal parts $\frac{5}{8}$ is red.

4. Color 3 parts.

[3] parts are red.
[5] equal parts $\frac{3}{5}$ is red.

88 Use with Lesson 7-11.

© Pearson Education, Inc. 2

Name _____

Non-Unit Fractions

P 7-11

Write the fraction for the shaded part of the shape.

1. $\frac{2}{4}$

2. $\frac{8}{10}$

3. $\frac{3}{6}$

4. $\frac{7}{8}$

5. $\frac{2}{3}$

6. $\frac{4}{5}$

Color to show the fraction.

7. $\frac{2}{5}$

8. $\frac{2}{6}$

9. $\frac{3}{4}$

Problem Solving *Visual Thinking*

10. Draw 1 line to show $\frac{2}{4}$.

11. Draw 2 lines to show $\frac{4}{8}$.

Sample answers are given.

88 Use with Lesson 7-11.

© Pearson Education, Inc. 2

Name _____

It's All in the Parts

E 7-11
NUMBER SENSE

Color the parts.
Write the fraction for the parts you color.

Possible answers given.

1. Color $\frac{1}{8}$ yellow.
Then color another $\frac{2}{8}$ yellow.
Color the rest green.
What part is green?

$\frac{5}{8}$

2. Color $\frac{2}{5}$ red.
Then color another $\frac{1}{5}$ red.
Color the rest blue.
What part is blue?

$\frac{2}{5}$

3. Color $\frac{1}{6}$ pink.
Then color another $\frac{3}{6}$ pink.
Color the rest yellow.
What part is yellow?

$\frac{2}{6}$

4. Color $\frac{4}{10}$ green.
Then color another $\frac{2}{10}$ green.
Color the rest purple.
What part is purple?

$\frac{4}{10}$

88 Use with Lesson 7-11.

© Pearson Education, Inc. 2

Name _____

Non-Unit Fractions

PS 7-11

Solve.

1. Ken cut a sandwich into four equal parts. Show how he cut the sandwich. Color 2 pieces. How much of the sandwich is colored? Write the fraction.

$\frac{2}{4}$

2. Billy cut the tray of brownies into 8 equal parts. Show how he cut the brownies. Color 6 parts. How much of the tray of brownies is colored? Write the fraction.

$\frac{6}{8}$

3. Maria cut a pizza into six equal parts. Show how she cut the pizza. Color 5 parts. How much of the pizza is colored? Write the fraction.

$\frac{5}{6}$

88 Use with Lesson 7-11.

© Pearson Education, Inc. 2

Name _____

Estimating Fractions

R 7-12

To estimate fractions, think about the number of equal parts in the whole.

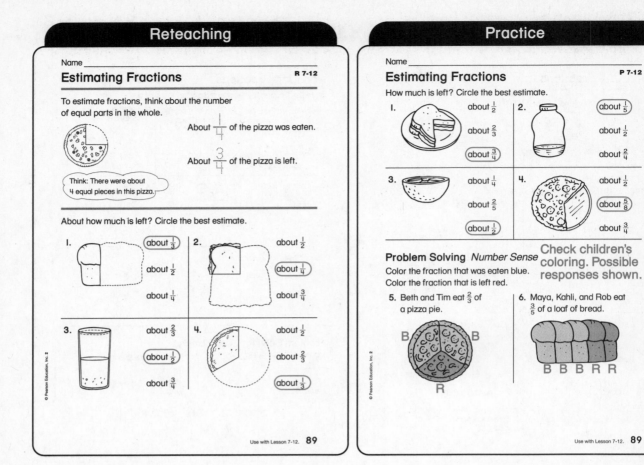

About $\frac{1}{4}$ of the pizza was eaten.

About $\frac{3}{4}$ of the pizza is left.

Think: There were about 4 equal pieces in this pizza.

About how much is left? Circle the best estimate.

1. (about $\frac{1}{3}$) / about $\frac{1}{2}$ / about $\frac{1}{4}$

2. about $\frac{1}{2}$ / (about $\frac{1}{4}$) / about $\frac{3}{4}$

3. about $\frac{2}{3}$ / (about $\frac{1}{2}$) / about $\frac{3}{4}$

4. about $\frac{1}{2}$ / about $\frac{2}{3}$ / (about $\frac{1}{3}$)

© Pearson Education, Inc. 2

Use with Lesson 7-12. **89**

Name _____

Estimating Fractions

P 7-12

How much is left? Circle the best estimate.

1. about $\frac{1}{2}$ / about $\frac{2}{3}$ / (about $\frac{3}{4}$)

2. (about $\frac{1}{5}$) / about $\frac{1}{2}$ / about $\frac{2}{4}$

3. about $\frac{1}{4}$ / about $\frac{2}{5}$ / (about $\frac{1}{2}$)

4. about $\frac{1}{2}$ / (about $\frac{5}{8}$) / about $\frac{3}{4}$

Problem Solving *Number Sense*

Color the fraction that was eaten blue.
Color the fraction that is left red.

Check children's coloring. Possible responses shown.

5. Beth and Tim eat $\frac{2}{3}$ of a pizza pie.

6. Maya, Kahli, and Rob eat $\frac{3}{5}$ of a loaf of bread.

B B B R R

© Pearson Education, Inc. 2

Use with Lesson 7-12. **89**

Name _____

Oodles of Noodles

E 7-12
ESTIMATION

About how much is needed to fill each jar to the fill line? Circle your answer.

1. ($\frac{2}{3}$) / $\frac{2}{5}$ / $\frac{1}{2}$

2. $\frac{3}{4}$ / ($\frac{1}{2}$) / $\frac{1}{3}$

3. ($\frac{2}{5}$) / $\frac{5}{6}$ / $\frac{2}{3}$

4. $\frac{3}{4}$ / ($\frac{1}{6}$) / $\frac{3}{5}$

5. $\frac{2}{5}$ / $\frac{2}{3}$ / ($\frac{1}{4}$)

6. $\frac{1}{3}$ / ($\frac{3}{4}$) / $\frac{2}{5}$

© Pearson Education, Inc. 2

Use with Lesson 7-12. **89**

Name _____

Estimating Fractions

PS 7-12

Circle the best estimate.

1. Eddie ate part of a loaf of bread. About how much of the bread is left?

about $\frac{1}{2}$ about $\frac{3}{4}$ (about $\frac{2}{3}$)

2. Tina poured some juice. About how much juice is left in the pitcher?

about $\frac{3}{4}$ about $\frac{1}{2}$ (about $\frac{1}{5}$)

3. Cindy made a pie. About how much of the pie is left?

(about $\frac{2}{3}$)   about $\frac{1}{6}$ about $\frac{3}{10}$

4. Paco made some soup. About how much of the soup is left?

about $\frac{3}{6}$ (about $\frac{1}{4}$)   about $\frac{2}{3}$

5. Tad made some sauce.

Write the fraction for how much of the jar is filled with sauce. $\frac{4}{5}$

About how much sauce does Tad need to fill the jar?

(about $\frac{1}{5}$)   about $\frac{1}{3}$ about $\frac{3}{4}$

6. Rosa made a pizza.

Write the fraction for the part that she gave her brother. $\frac{1}{3}$

How much pizza does Rosa have left?

(about $\frac{2}{3}$)   about $\frac{1}{3}$ about $\frac{3}{4}$

© Pearson Education, Inc. 2

Use with Lesson 7-12. **89**

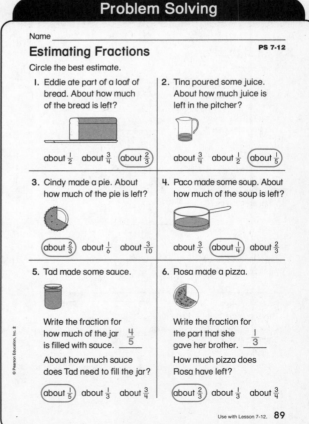

Use with Chapter 7, Lesson 12. **89**

Name _____

Fractions of a Set
R 7-13

A fraction can name the equal parts of a set or a group.

  ⎡2⎤ shaded balls $\frac{2}{5}$ of the balls are shaded.
 ⎣5⎦ balls in all

Color the parts.
Write the fraction for the part you color.

1. Color 2 parts blue.

 ⎡2⎤ blue stars $\frac{2}{6}$ of the stars are blue.
⎣6⎦ stars in all

2. Color 3 parts green.

 ⎡3⎤ green balloons $\frac{3}{4}$ of the balloons are green.
⎣4⎦ balloons in all

3. Color 5 parts red.

 ⎡5⎤ red apples $\frac{5}{8}$ of the apples are red.
⎣8⎦ apples in all

Name _____

Fractions of a Set
P 7-13
Write the fraction of the group that is shaded.

1. $\frac{3}{4}$ 2. $\frac{2}{6}$

3. 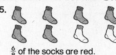 $\frac{4}{8}$ 4. $\frac{1}{3}$

Color to show the fraction. **Check children's coloring.**

5. $\frac{6}{8}$ of the socks are red.   6. $\frac{7}{10}$ of the mittens are red.

7. $\frac{1}{2}$ of the shoes are red.   8.  $\frac{3}{6}$ of the shorts are red.

Problem Solving *Number Sense*
Solve.

9. Sue has 9 baseball cards.
She gives 4 cards to her brother.

How many cards does Sue have left? __5__

What fraction of the cards does Sue have? $\frac{5}{9}$

Name _____

Making Fruit Salad
E 7-13
DECISION MAKING

Make fruit salad. Color a part of each group of fruit. Write the fraction. Then write your recipe for fruit salad below.

Answers will vary.

 _____   _____

  _____   _____

Tell how many of each fruit you chose. Write the fraction.

My Recipe for Fruit Salad

_____ bananas   _____ grapes

_____ strawberries   _____ cherries

Name _____

Fractions of a Set
PS 7-13
Color the objects. Then solve.

1. Olin has 8 buttons. 3 of the buttons are red and the rest are blue. What fraction of the buttons are blue?

$\frac{5}{8}$ are blue.

2. Mike has 9 counters. 7 of the counters are red. The rest are yellow. What fraction of the counters are yellow?

$\frac{2}{9}$ are yellow.

3. Solve. Abbey tosses 10 pennies on a table. 4 of the pennies turn up heads. The rest turn up tails. What fraction of the pennies are tails?

$\frac{6}{10}$ are tails.

© Pearson Education, Inc. 2

---

90 Use with Chapter 7, Lesson 13.

Name _____

PROBLEM SOLVING APPLICATIONS   R 7-14

Under the Sea

Some shells have a line of symmetry.
Some shells do not have a line of symmetry.

This shell does not have   This shell has
a line of symmetry.   a line of symmetry.

Both parts do not match.   Both parts match.

Does the shell have a line of symmetry?
Circle **Yes** or **No**.

1.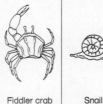

   Yes (No)   (Yes) No

2.

   (Yes) No   Yes (No)

Writing in Math   Answers will vary.

Choose one of the shells
that has a line of symmetry.
Circle the shell.
Write a sentence
to describe the shell.

© Pearson Education, Inc. 2

Use with Lesson 7-14. **91**

Name _____

PROBLEM-SOLVING APPLICATIONS   P 7-14

Under the Sea

1. Here is a type of shell that is
   found in deep water. This shell
   can get up to 3 inches long.
   What shape do you think of
   when you look at this shell?
   I think of a

   _____cone_____

2. This shell is called a bi-valve.
   It means that there are two
   half-shells. How many lines
   of symmetry can you draw
   on the shells?
   Draw them.

   ___I___ line of symmetry

Writing in Math

3. Draw a picture of a shell that you have found
   or would like to find. Then write a sentence
   that describes its shape.

   Drawings and descriptions will vary.

   _____

   _____

© Pearson Education, Inc. 2

Use with Lesson 7-14. **91**

Name _____

Shell Shaped Animals   E 7-14
                                       VISUAL THINKING

Some animals have shells that
protect their bodies.
Use the animals in the pictures
to answer your questions.

Fiddler crab	Snail	Turtle	Horseshoe crab

1. Draw a line of symmetry for each animal that you can.
   Which animals are symmetrical?
   turtle, horseshoe crab

2. Which animals have a rounded shape?
   snail, horseshoe crab, turtle

3. Which animals have shells shaped like an oval? ⬭
   turtle, horseshoe crab

4. Which animal has legs that are shaped like cylinders?
   fiddler crab

© Pearson Education, Inc. 2

Use with Lesson 7-14. **91**

Name _____

PROBLEM-SOLVING APPLICATIONS   PS 7-14

Under the Sea

Solve.

1. Carrie found 27 shells.   Do you need to add or subtract
   18 of the shells have a line   to solve the problem?
   of symmetry. How many   (subtract)   add
   shells do not have a line
   of symmetry?   27 ⊝ 18 = 9

2. A lobster is a kind of shellfish with 8 small legs
   and 2 large legs called claws. If Sam catches
   5 lobsters, how many legs are there in all?   10
   (Hint: How many legs does 1 lobster have?)   ___ legs

   __50__ legs in all

3. Jim likes shells that have a cone shape.
   Circle the shells he might add to his shell collection.

4. Draw a shell that you might like to add to a
   shell collection. Tell what shape your shell is.

   Drawings will vary.

© Pearson Education, Inc. 2

Using the page To help students **understand** the problem, have them **read** each problem first. Then have them
plan the strategy they need to use to solve the problem.

Use with Lesson 7-14. **91**

© Pearson Education, Inc. 2

Name _____

Telling Time to Five Minutes

R 8-1

It takes five minutes for the minute hand to move from number to number.

To tell time to five minutes count by 5s for every number.

The time is 5:15

Count by 5s. Write the time.

1.  7:15

2.  10:40

3.  1:35

4.  4:50

Problem Solving *Reasoning*

5. The time is 6:10. Is the hour hand closer to 6 or 7? Why?

It is closer to the 6 because it is only 10 minutes past 6 o'clock.

92 Use with Lesson 8-1.

Name _____

Telling Time to Five Minutes

P 8-1

Draw the clock hands for each time.

1.   3:25

2.  10:20

3. 2:45

4. 5:10

5. 12:30

6.  4:55

Problem Solving *Reasoning*

7. The time is 5:15. Is the hour hand closer to the 5 or the 6? Why?

It is closer to 5 because it is only 15 minutes after 5 o'clock.

92 Use with Lesson 8-1.

Name _____

Just 5 More Minutes

E 8-1
VISUAL THINKING

Draw hands on the clock to show the time 5 minutes later. Then write the time.

1.  4:30

2.   7:50

3.   2:45

4. 8:15

5.   1:05

6.   1:00

92 Use with Lesson 8-1.

Name _____

Telling Time to Five Minutes

PS 8-1

At what time might each of these activities take place? Draw the hands on the clock. Write the time. Answers will vary.

1.   ___:___

2.  ___:___

3. ___:___

4.  ___:___

5. Look at the pattern. Write the time that comes next.

  5:15

92 Use with Lesson 8-1.

© Pearson Education, Inc. 2

Name _____

Telling Time After the Hour

R 8-2

There are different ways to say time after the hour.

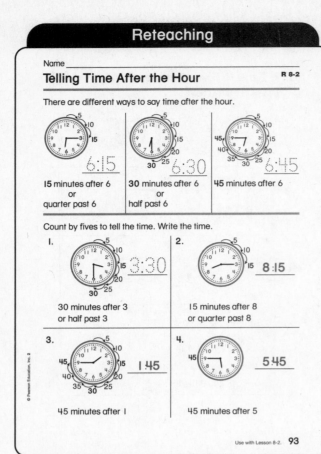

15 minutes after 6
or
quarter past 6

30 minutes after 6
or
half past 6

45 minutes after 6

Count by fives to tell the time. Write the time.

1. 3:30
30 minutes after 3
or half past 3

2. 8:15
15 minutes after 8
or quarter past 8

3. 1:45
45 minutes after 1

4. 5:45
45 minutes after 5

© Pearson Education, Inc. 2

Name _____

Telling Time After the Hour

P 8-2

Write the time or draw the minute hand to show
the time. Circle another way to say the time.

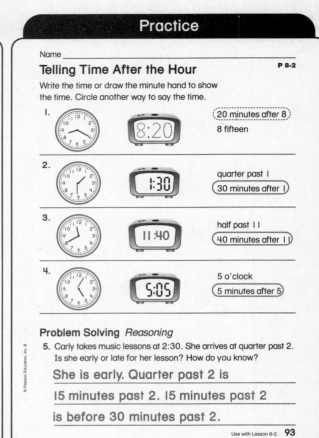

1. 8:20   (20 minutes after 8)
             8 fifteen

2. 1:30   quarter past 1
             (30 minutes after 1)

3. 11:40   half past 11
             (40 minutes after 11)

4. 5:05   5 o'clock
             (5 minutes after 5)

Problem Solving *Reasoning*

5. Carly takes music lessons at 2:30. She arrives at quarter past 2.
   Is she early or late for her lesson? How do you know?

   She is early. Quarter past 2 is

   15 minutes past 2. 15 minutes past 2

   is before 30 minutes past 2.

© Pearson Education, Inc. 2

Name _____

What's the Time?

E 8-2
PATTERNS

Look for a pattern.
Write the missing time. Then write
another way to say the time.

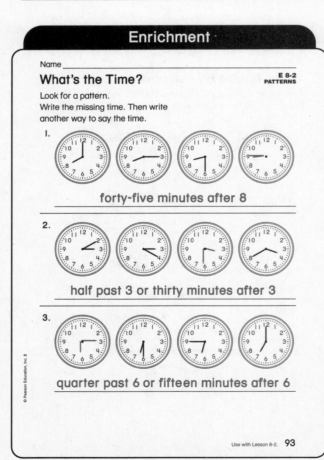

1. forty-five minutes after 8

2. half past 3 or thirty minutes after 3

3. quarter past 6 or fifteen minutes after 6

Name _____

Telling Time After the Hour

PS 8-2

Underline the words in each problem that tell the time.
Then draw the hands on the clock and write the time.

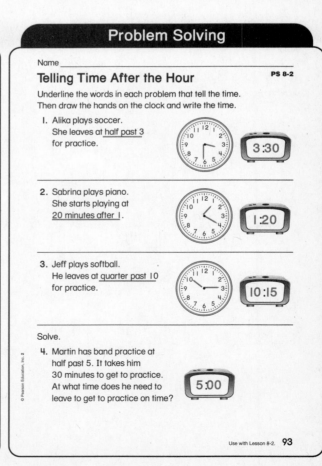

1. Alika plays soccer.
   She leaves at half past 3
   for practice.   3:30

2. Sabrina plays piano.
   She starts playing at
   20 minutes after 1.   1:20

3. Jeff plays softball.
   He leaves at quarter past 10
   for practice.   10:15

Solve.

4. Martin has band practice at
   half past 5. It takes him
   30 minutes to get to practice.
   At what time does he need to   5:00
   leave to get to practice on time?

© Pearson Education, Inc. 2

Reteaching

Name _____

Telling Time Before the Hour

R 8-3

Count by 5s from the 12 to the minute hand to say or write the time **after** the hour.	Count by 5s from the minute hand to the 12 to say or write the time **before** the hour.

35 minutes **after** 2   is the same as   25 minutes **before** 3

Write the time or draw the minute hand to show the time.
Write the time before the hour.

1. 6:50   10 minutes before 7

2. 10:40   20 minutes before 11

94 Use with Lesson 8-3.

Practice

Name _____

Telling Time Before the Hour

P 8-3

Write the time or draw the minute hand to show the time. Write the time before the hour.

1. 7:45   quarter to 8

2. 5:35   25 minutes before 6

3. 4:50   10 minutes before 5

4. 1:55   5 minutes before 2

Problem Solving *Writing in Math*

5. Write two ways to say the time shown.   3:35

35 minutes past 3

25 minutes before 4

94 Use with Lesson 8-3.

Enrichment

Name _____

Early, Late, or On Time?

E 8-3
NUMBER SENSE

Write the time.
Then answer each question.

1. Nancy arrives at 10 minutes before 8.
7:50

School starts at

Is Nancy early or late?
early

2. Sean arrives at quarter to 7.
6:45

Dinner starts at

Is Sean early or late?
late

3. Chris arrives at 20 minutes before 1:00.
12:40

Lunch starts at

Is Chris early or late?
early

4. Cory arrives at 5 minutes before 10.
9:55

Practice starts at

Is Cory early or late?
early

94 Use with Lesson 8-3.

Problem Solving

Name _____

Telling Time Before the Hour

PS 8-3

	Leaves	Arrives Park City
Bus A	6:45	7:35
Bus B	12:40	1:55
Bus C	3:50	5:45

Read the sentences. Write the times in the bus schedule.

1. Bus A leaves at quarter to 7.
It gets to Park City at 25 minutes before 8.

2. Bus B leaves at 20 minutes before 1.
It gets to Park City at 5 minutes before 2.

3. Bus C leaves at 10 minutes before 4.
It gets to Park City at 15 minutes before 6.

4. Nate wants to get to Park City by 6:00.
Which bus should he take? _____ Bus C

Writing in Math

5. Write 3 ways to say the time shown.

Answers will vary. Sample answers are given.

half past one

30 minutes before two

30 minutes after one

94 Use with Lesson 8-3.

---

94   Use with Chapter 8, Lesson 3.

© Pearson Education, Inc. 2

Name _____

Estimating Time

R 8-4

About how long does it take to wash your face?

(about 1 minute) — Is 1 minute reasonable? Yes.

about 1 hour — Is 1 hour reasonable? No, it's too long.

about 1 day — Is 1 day reasonable? No, it's too long.

Circle the amount of time each activity will take.

1. Drinking milk
- (about 1 minute)
- about 1 hour
- about 1 day

2. Watching a TV show
- about 1 minute
- (about 1 hour)
- about 1 day

3. Going on a picnic
- about 2 minutes
- (about 2 hours)
- about 2 days

4. Going on a trip
- about 5 minutes
- about 5 hours
- (about 5 days)

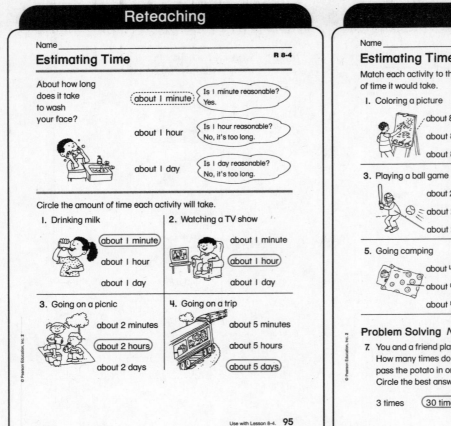

© Pearson Education, Inc. 2

Use with Lesson 8-4. **95**

Name _____

Estimating Time

P 8-4

Match each activity to the amount of time it would take.

1. Coloring a picture
- about 8 minutes
- about 8 days
- about 8 hours

2. Watering a garden
- about 10 minutes
- about 10 days
- about 10 hours

3. Playing a ball game
- about 2 minutes
- about 2 days
- about 2 hours

4. Making a sandwich
- about 5 minutes
- about 5 days
- about 5 hours

5. Going camping
- about 4 minutes
- about 4 days
- about 4 hours

6. Visiting a friend
- about 3 minutes
- about 3 days
- about 3 hours

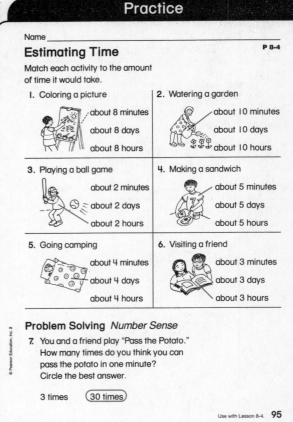

Problem Solving *Number Sense*

7. You and a friend play "Pass the Potato." How many times do you think you can pass the potato in one minute? Circle the best answer.

3 times   (30 times)

© Pearson Education, Inc. 2

Use with Lesson 8-4. **95**

Name _____

What Would You Do?

E 8-4
ESTIMATION

Draw a picture of an activity you would like to do that takes the amount of time shown.

1. About 1 hour

2. About 10 minutes

Answers will vary. Check children's drawings.

3. About 3 days

4. About 5 hours

© Pearson Education, Inc. 2

Use with Lesson 8-4. **95**

Name _____

Estimating Time

PS 8-4

Solve.

1. Kim builds a birdhouse. Sue puts birdseed in the birdhouse. Who takes about 1 minute to do her activity?

Kim   (Sue)

2. Billy plants a garden. Kenji waters the garden. Who takes about 2 days to do his activity?

(Billy)   Kenji

3. Sara builds a bookshelf. Rachel puts books on the shelf. Who takes about 2 days to do her activity?

Rachel   (Sara)

4. Juan brushes his hair while Matt takes a bath. Who takes about 1 minute to do his activity?

(Juan)   Matt

5. Ned paints his house. Berto paints the front door. Who takes about 5 days to do his activity?

(Ned)   Berto

6. Francine goes to a movie at the mall. Judy buys a yogurt at the mall and leaves. Who takes about 2 hours to do her activity?

Judy   (Francine)

7. Mimi sets the table. Lara helps make dinner. Who takes about 5 minutes to do her activity?

(Mimi)   Lara

8. Rodrigo makes lasagna. Devin eats the lasagna. Who takes about 1 hour to do his activity?

Devin   (Rodrigo)

© Pearson Education, Inc. 2

Use with Lesson 8-4. **95**

© Pearson Education, Inc. 2

Use with Chapter 8, Lesson 4. **95**

Name _____

Elapsed Time

R 8-5

Count the number of hours to find out how much time has passed.

Count from the start time to the end time.

Starts	Ends	Starts	Ends
3:00	5:00	7:00	10:00
(2 hours)	3 hours	2 hours	(3 hours)

Write the times. Then circle how many hours have passed.

1.
Starts	Ends
6:00	7:00
(1 hour)	2 hours

2.
Starts	Ends
1:00	4:00
7 hours	(3 hours)

3.
Starts	Ends
9:00	12:00
(3 hours)	4 hours

4.
Starts	Ends
2:00	8:00
5 hours	(6 hours)

Name _____

Elapsed Time

P 8-5

Draw the clock hands and write the end time for each. Use a clock if you need to.

1. Cook dinner.

	Starts	Lasts	Ends
		1 hour	
	5:00		6:00

2. Make your bed.

	Starts		Ends
		15 minutes	
	8:00		8:15

Problem Solving *Number Sense*

3. Ricky leaves his house at 4:30.
   He rides his bike to the store for 15 minutes.

   What time does he get to the store? __4:45__

Name _____

City Sights

E 8-5
DATA

A Tour of the City

Event	Time
Bus trip around the city	9:15
Visit the museum	10:30
Buggy ride in the park	12:45
Science Center dinosaur movie	2:15
Dinner at the harbor	5:30
Go to a play	7:00

Use the chart to answer the questions.

1. The museum visit lasts 2 hours. What time does it end? Draw the clock hands.

   12:30

2. The play lasts for 1 hour and 30 minutes. What time does it end? Draw the clock hands.

   8:30

3. Maggie gets to the park at 12:00. How long does she wait to take the buggy ride?

   __45 minutes__

4. Vinnie leaves his house at 1:15. How much time does he have to get to the Science Center before the dinosaur movie begins?

   __1 hour__

Name _____

Elapsed Time

PS 8-5

Draw hands on the clock to show the start time. Write the end time in the digital clock.

1. Maria walks the dog at 7:00. The walk lasts for 30 minutes. At what time does she finish?

Starts	Ends
	7:30

2. Ronnie starts to cook dinner at 5:00. He cooks for one hour. At what time is dinner ready?

    6:00

3. Betsy gets on the bus at 10:00. She rides for 2 hours. At what time does the bus trip end?

    12:00

Solve.

4. Zack starts work at 8:30. He leaves for work at 8:00 and travels for one hour. Will he be early or late?

   early   (late)

5. The concert starts at 2:00. Kirk leaves for the concert at 1:30 and walks for 15 minutes. Is he early or late?

   (early)   late

© Pearson Education, Inc. 2

Name _____

A.M. and P.M.

R 8-6

There are two 12:00s in one day.

12:00 A.M.
Most of us are asleep.

12:00 P.M.
Most of us are eating lunch.

A.M. starts at 12:00 midnight. It ends at noon.
P.M. starts at 12:00 noon. It ends at midnight.

Is it A.M. or P.M.?

3:00 A.M. (P.M.)

8:00 A.M. P.M.

9:00 A.M. P.M.

Circle A.M. or P.M. to tell the time.

1. 8:00 A.M. (P.M.)

2. 7:00 A.M. P.M.

3. 10:00 (A.M.) P.M.

Use with Lesson 8-6. 97

© Pearson Education, Inc. 2

Name _____

A.M. and P.M.

P 8-6

Draw lines to match the events to the times.

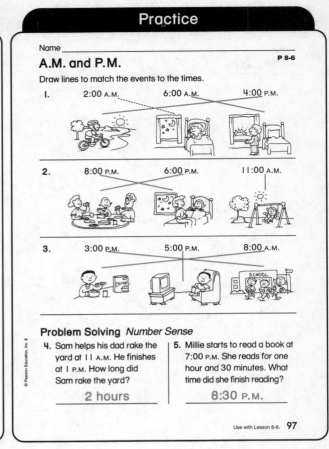

1. 2:00 A.M.   6:00 A.M.   4:00 P.M.

2. 8:00 P.M.   6:00 P.M.   11:00 A.M.

3. 3:00 P.M.   5:00 P.M.   8:00 A.M.

Problem Solving *Number Sense*

4. Sam helps his dad rake the yard at 11 A.M. He finishes at 1 P.M. How long did Sam rake the yard?

   2 hours

5. Millie starts to read a book at 7:00 P.M. She reads for one hour and 30 minutes. What time did she finish reading?

   8:30 P.M.

Use with Lesson 8-6. 97

© Pearson Education, Inc. 2

Name _____

A.M. or P.M.?

E 8-6
DECISION MAKING

You are spending the summer at the beach. Decide what time you will do each activity. Write A.M. or P.M. next to each time.

Answers will vary. Each response should include A.M. or P.M.

Play Frisbee with the dog. _____

Have a cookout. _____

Watch the sunset. _____

Build a sandcastle. _____

Roast marshmallows. _____

Go swimming. _____

Eat breakfast. _____

Tell ghost stories. _____

Collect seashells. _____

Watch the sunrise. _____

Sing songs around the campfire. _____

Go fishing. _____

Use with Lesson 8-6. 97

© Pearson Education, Inc. 2

Name _____

A.M. and P.M.

Answers will vary. PS 8-6

1. Draw a picture of something you do in the A.M. Draw the hands on the clock and write the time.

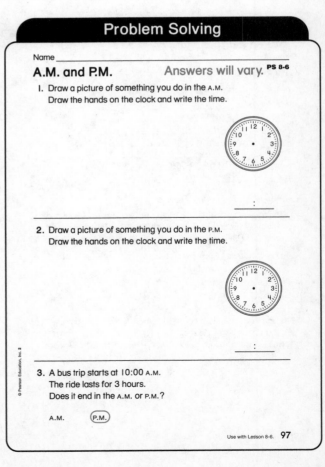

   ___ : ___

2. Draw a picture of something you do in the P.M. Draw the hands on the clock and write the time.

   ___ : ___

3. A bus trip starts at 10:00 A.M. The ride lasts for 3 hours. Does it end in the A.M. or P.M.?

   A.M.   (P.M.)

Use with Lesson 8-6. 97

© Pearson Education, Inc. 2

Name _____

Using a Calendar

R 8-7

There are 12 months in one year.
March is the 3rd month of the year.

Days of the week

Name of the month

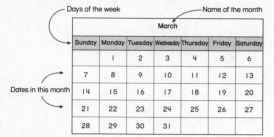

March						
Sunday	Monday	Tuesday	Wednesday	Thursday	Friday	Saturday
	1	2	3	4	5	6
7	8	9	10	11	12	13
14	15	16	17	18	19	20
21	22	23	24	25	26	27
28	29	30	31			

Dates in this month

Look at the last date in the month
to find how many days in March.

Use the calendar to answer the questions.

1. What day is the first day of March? **Monday**

2. What day is the 16th? **Tuesday**

3. What is the day after Wednesday? **Thursday**

4. What is the date of the third Friday? **19th**

5. How many days are in March altogether? **31**

Name _____

Using a Calendar

P 8-7

Use the calendar to answer the questions.

1. What month comes just before April? **March**

2. How many months have 31 days? **7**

3. What month is the ninth month of the year? **September**

4. What day of the week is December 3rd
on this calendar? **Saturday**

5. What date follows June 30? **July 1**

Problem Solving *Reasoning*

Use the calendar to solve.

6. Sara's birthday is in a month that has 5 Thursdays.
Her birthday is on a Thursday, and is the
23rd of the month. What month is her birthday? **June**

Name _____

It's a Date

E 8-7
NUMBER SENSE

January						
S	M	T	W	T	F	S
1	2	3	4	5	6	7
8	9	10	11	12	13	14
15	16	17	18	19	20	21
22	23	24	25	26	27	28
29	30	31				

February						
S	M	T	W	T	F	S
			1	2	3	4
5	6	7	8	9	10	11
12	13	14	15	16	17	18
19	20	21	22	23	24	25
26	27	28				

March						
S	M	T	W	T	F	S
			1	2	3	4
5	6	7	8	9	10	11
12	13	14	15	16	17	18
19	20	21	22	23	24	25
26	27	28	29	30	31	

Use the calendars to answer each question.

1. It is February 26th. Juan
has a game on March 5th.
How many more days until
Juan's game?

   7 days

2. Trish went to a party
on January 28th. It is
February 7th. How many days
have passed since the party?

   10 days

3. It is February 17th. In
14 days, Tonya has a piano
recital. What is the date of
Tonya's recital?

   March 3rd

4. Bill went ice skating on
January 30th. One week later,
the ice melted. What was the
date the ice melted?

   February 6th

Name _____

Using a Calendar

PS 8-7

July						
Sunday	Monday	Tuesday	Wednesday	Thursday	Friday	Saturday
			1	2	3	4
5	6	7	8	9	10	11
12	13	14	15	16	17	18
19	20	21	22	23	24	25
26	27	28	29	30	31	

Solve.

1. Olin starts summer camp
on July 5. She goes to camp
for 14 days. What is the last
day of camp?

   July 18

2. Nell arrives at the beach on
July 24. She is at the beach
for 7 days. On what day of
the week does she leave
the beach?

   Thursday

3. Brian goes to soccer camp
on July 15. He returns home
on Saturday of the next
week. What is the date he
comes home?

   July 25

4. Mick goes fishing on July 3.
Monique goes fishing on
July 5. Both stay for 5 days.
Who comes home first?

   Mick

Reteaching

Name

Equivalent Times

R 8-8

Starts	Ends

is __15__ minutes or one quarter hour

11:45 to 12:00

Starts	Ends

is __30__ minutes or one half hour

12:00 to 12:30

Starts	Ends

is __60__ minutes or one hour

12:30 to 1:30

> Equivalent time is another way to say the same time.

Circle the equivalent time.

1. Mario reads from 12:00 to 12:30.

   (30 minutes)   60 minutes   15 minutes

2. Jamal sings for 15 minutes.

   (one quarter hour)   one half hour   one hour

Use with Lesson 8-8. **99**

© Pearson Education, Inc. 2

Practice

Name

Equivalent Times

P 8-8

Afternoon Schedule	
12:15–12:45	Music
12:45–1:45	Science
1:45–2:00	Recess
2:00–2:15	Story Time
2:15–2:45	Social Studies
2:45–3:00	Clean Up

Use the schedule to answer the questions.

1. Which two activities are one half hour long?

   __music and social studies__

2. How many hours long is Science? __1 hour__

3. Name other activities that are as long as Recess.

   __story time and clean up__

4. How long are Story Time and Social Studies together?

   __45 minutes__

Problem Solving *Visual Thinking*

5. Look at each clock. What activity takes place between these times?

   __music__

Use with Lesson 8-8. **99**

© Pearson Education, Inc. 2

Enrichment

Name

Family Day

E 8-8
DATA

Use the schedule to answer the questions.

Family Day

Events	Starts	Ends
Sack races	1:00	2:00
Relay races	2:00	2:30
Swimming races	2:30	3:30
Arts and Crafts Show	2:00	3:30
Science Show	1:00	2:00

1. Which races last for exactly one hour each?

   __sack races and swimming races__

2. How long does the Arts and Crafts Show last?

   __one hour and 30 minutes__

3. How many events last exactly 60 minutes? __3__

4. Which event lasts the longest?

   __arts and crafts show__

5. Which event lasts exactly one half hour? __relay races__

Use with Lesson 8-8. **99**

© Pearson Education, Inc. 2

Problem Solving

Name

Equivalent Times

PS 8-8

Use the schedule to answer the questions.
The shaded boxes show when children have band practice.

Band Practice

	Jason	Alex	Janey	Elisa	Corey
12:00–12:45	▓			▓	
12:45–1:30		▓			
1:30–2:30			▓		▓

1. Which children go to band practice for 45 minutes?

   __Jason, Alex, and Elisa__

2. Which two children go to band practice for one hour?

   __Janey and Corey__

3. Ginny has band practice from 12:45 to 1:30. What other child goes to practice during this time?

   __Alex__

4. Alice has band practice at the time shown. Who else starts band practice at the same time?

   __Jason, Elisa__

Use with Lesson 8-8. **99**

© Pearson Education, Inc. 2

Name _____

Make a Table

Sasha had a box of school supplies.
How many of each kind of school supply are there?

Read and Understand

What are the supplies?
How many of each are there?

Plan and Solve

Think: What do I need to find out?

Complete the table. Count the objects.
Use one tally mark for each object.

Look Back and Check

How does the table help you
organize information?

Answers will vary.
Possible response:
Each tally mark in
the table counts as
one item.

School Supplies	
Kinds	Number
Crayons	¦¦
Tape	¦
Pencils	ⵏⵏ
Erasers	ⵏⵏ ¦

Now use the table to answer the questions.

1. How many crayons are there? __2__

2. How many pencils are there? __5__

3. Are there more crayons or pencils? __pencils__

4. How many more erasers are there than pencils? __1__

100 Use with Lesson 8-9.

Name _____

Make a Table

The second grade class drew pictures of their
favorite pets. Complete the table. Use tally marks.

Favorite Pets	
Rabbit	¦¦
Dog	¦¦¦¦
Hamster	¦
Cat	ⵏⵏ ¦
Bird	¦¦¦

1. How many children drew
   dogs as their favorite pet? __4__ children

2. Do more children like hamsters or birds? __birds__
   How many more? __2__ children

3. What pet is the favorite of most children? __cats__

4. Which pet did 1 child name as the favorite? __hamster__

5. How many children are in this class? __16__ children

6. What if some children drew these pictures
   as their favorite pets? Draw the tally marks
   there would be for turtles. __ⵏⵏ ¦¦__

100 Use with Lesson 8-9.

Name _____

All About Shapes

Ask some classmates to choose
their favorite shape below.

Draw each shape they choose.

Shapes will vary.

Make a table. Use tally marks to show
how many of each shape.

1. Which shape do children
   like the most?

   _____

2. How many children chose
   the triangle as their favorite
   shape?

   _____

3. Which shape do children
   like the least?

   _____

4. Do more children like
   circles or squares?

   _____

Answers will vary.

Favorite Shapes	
○	
△	
▢	
▭	

100 Use with Lesson 8-9.

Name _____

Make a Table

Grade 2 has a school supply drawer.
There are 4 crayons, 3 erasers, 6 pencils,
5 paper clips, and 1 ruler.

Read the story again and complete the table.
Use tally marks.

The correct number
of tally marks will
show that you
understand what
you read.

School Supplies	
Crayons	¦¦¦¦
Erasers	¦¦¦
Pencils	ⵏⵏ ¦
Paper clips	ⵏⵏ
Rulers	¦

1. How many more pencils than rulers are there? __5__ more pencils

2. Which school supply has the most items? __pencils__

3. Which school supply has 5 items? __paper clips__

Write the number shown by the tally marks.

4. ¦ __1__   5. ⵏⵏ ¦ __6__

Using the page Have children *read* the words carefully. Ask them to state the problems in their own words to
show that they *understand* what they've read.

100 Use with Lesson 8-9.

© Pearson Education, Inc. **2**

Name _____

Recording Data from a Survey

R 8-10

Take a **survey** to collect information. Information is called **data**. Make tally marks to record this **data**.

What is your favorite flavor?

vanilla!

chocolate!

strawberry!

Favorite Frozen Yogurt Flavors

Vanilla	Chocolate	Strawberry
JHT I	JHT II	III

Use the survey to answer the questions.

1. Which flavor is the favorite of the greatest number of children?

   chocolate

2. Which flavor did the least number of children choose?

   strawberry

3. How many children in all answered the survey? 16

4. How many more children chose vanilla than strawberry? 3

Use with Lesson 8-10. 101

© Pearson Education, Inc. 2

Name _____

Recording Data from a Survey

P 8-10

Use the survey to answer the questions.

Favorite Foods	
Food	Number of Children
Spaghetti	JHT JHT IIII
Hot dogs	JHT JHT JHT IIII
Cereal	JHT JHT I

1. How many children chose hot dogs? 19 children

2. Which food is the favorite of
   the greatest number of children? hot dogs

3. How many more children chose
   spaghetti than cereal? 3 children

4. Which food did the least number
   of children choose? cereal

Problem Solving *Number Sense*

Solve.

5. If 7 more children choose spaghetti,
   what will the new total be for spaghetti? 21 children

Use with Lesson 8-10. 101

© Pearson Education, Inc. 2

Name _____

Favorite Colors

E 8-10
DATA

Here is a survey that was taken in Grades 1 and 2.
Use this survey to answer the questions.

Our Favorite Colors

Color	Grade 1	Grade 2
Red	JHT IIII	JHT I
Blue	JHT III	IIII
Green	II	JHT II
Yellow	JHT	III
Pink	JHT I	IIII
Purple	III	III

1. Which color did more children choose as
   their favorite? red

2. Do more children like green or yellow? green

3. How many children like pink the best? 10 children

4. Do more children like blue in Grade 1
   or Grade 2? Grade 1

5. Which color does the same number of
   children like in both grades? purple

Use with Lesson 8-10. 101

© Pearson Education, Inc. 2

Name _____

Recording Data from a Survey

PS 8-10

Ricardo asked the children in his school
about their favorite kinds of TV shows.

Use tally marks to help Ricardo
record his data in the chart.

Favorite Kinds of TV Shows	
Animal	JHT JHT IIII
Action	JHT JHT I
Comedy	JHT JHT III
Cartoons	JHT JHT II
Movies	JHT JHT

1. 14 children chose animal shows.

2. There were 11 children who liked action shows.

3. 2 more children chose comedy shows
   than action shows.

4. 1 less child chose cartoons than comedy shows.

5. 15 children said they liked movies the best.
   Then 5 children changed their minds.

6. Suppose 3 more children
   chose comedy.
   What would be the new total? 16 children

Use with Lesson 8-10. 101

© Pearson Education, Inc. 2

Name _____

Using a Venn Diagram

R 8-11

A Venn diagram can be used to collect and show information. It can show how many people like different things and how many people like both things.

Do you like hot dogs, hamburgers, or both?

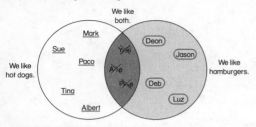

Use the diagram to answer the questions.

1. Draw a line under the names of children who like only hot dogs.

2. Circle the names of children who like only hamburgers.

3. Draw an X over the names of children who like both hot dogs and hamburgers.

4. How many children like hamburgers? _____7_____ children

5. How many children were surveyed altogether? _____12_____ children

Name _____

Using a Venn Diagram

P 8-11

Ask 8 children the question below. Record the data using their names.

Do you like cats or dogs or both?

I like cats.

I like dogs.

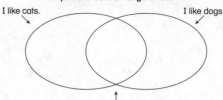

I like both cats and dogs.

Use the diagram to answer the questions. **Answers will vary.**

1. How many children like cats? _____ children

2. How many children like cats but not dogs? _____ children

3. How many children like dogs? _____ children

4. How many children like dogs but not cats? _____ children

Problem Solving *Writing in Math*

5. How can you use the diagram to tell how many children like both cats and dogs?

I can count the number of names in the part of the diagram that overlaps.

Name _____

Cubes, Cylinders, or Cones?

E 8-11
VISUAL THINKING

Gray Shapes   Cones

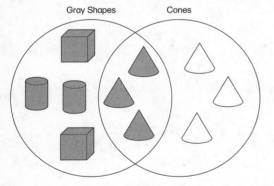

Use the Venn Diagram to answer the questions.

1. How many gray shapes are there? _____7_____

2. How many cones are there? _____6_____

3. How many gray cones are there? _____3_____

4. How many shapes are gray but not cones? _____4_____

5. How many shapes are cones but not gray? _____3_____

Name _____

Using a Venn Diagram

PS 8-11

Do you like math, reading, or both?

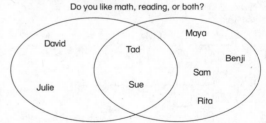

I like math.   I like both.   I like reading.

Add your name to the diagram. Then answer the questions. **Answers may vary by I more.**

1. How many children like math? _____4_____

2. How many children like math but not reading? _____2_____

3. How many children like reading? _____6_____

4. How many children like reading but not math? _____4_____

5. Write a question that you could use with the Venn diagram. Show your results.

Answers will vary.

_____

Name
Pictographs

R 8-12

A pictograph uses pictures or symbols to show information.
Write how many children chose each snack.

Each 😊 = 1 child

> There are 9 symbols for popcorn. So 9 children chose popcorn.

Favorite Snacks

Popcorn	😊😊😊😊😊😊😊😊😊	9
Fruit Cups	😊😊😊😊	4
Yogurt	😊😊😊😊😊😊😊	7
Cheese and Crackers	😊😊😊😊😊😊😊😊😊😊	10

Use the graph to answer the questions.

1. How many children like cheese and crackers the best? __10__ children

2. How many children like yogurt the best? __7__ children

3. Which snack is the least favorite? __fruit cups__

4. Which snack is favored by most children? __cheese and crackers__

5. How many more children like yogurt than fruit cups? __3__ children

6. How many more children like cheese and crackers than yogurt? __3__ children

© Pearson Education, Inc. 2

Use with Lesson 8-12. 103

Name
Pictographs

P 8-12

Use the graphs to answer the questions.

Favorite TV Show

Animal Stories	🖥️🖥️🖥️🖥️ 🖥️🖥️🖥️
Sports	🖥️🖥️🖥️
Cartoons	🖥️🖥️🖥️🖥️ 🖥️🖥️🖥️ 🖥️🖥️

Each 🖥️ = 1 child

1. Which show is favored by most children?
   __cartoons__

2. How many children like Animal Stories best? __7__

3. Which show is the favorite of 3 children? __sports__

Favorite Colors

Red	Blue	Green
	😊	
😊	😊	
😊	😊	
😊	😊	😊
😊	😊	😊

Each 😊 = 2 children

4. Which color is favored by most children?
   __blue__

5. How many children like red best?
   😊 😊 😊 😊
   2 4 6 8

Problem Solving *Number Sense*

6. If 4 more children choose green, write a number sentence that tells how many children like green now. Solve.

$4 + 4 = 8$

© Pearson Education, Inc. 2

Use with Lesson 8-12. 103

Name
At the Book Store

E 8-12
VISUAL THINKING

Use the key and the pictograph to answer the questions.

Books Sold Last Week

Cartoon Books	📖📖📖📖
Coloring Books	📖📖📖📖📖📖📖
Picture Books	📖📖📖
Animal Books	📖📖📖📖📖📖📖📖📖

Each 📖 = 5 books sold

1. Which kind of book was sold the most? __animal__

2. How many coloring books were sold? __35__

3. How many animal books were sold? __45__

4. How many more animal books than coloring books were sold? __10__

5. 5 more picture books are sold. How many more book symbols would you draw on the graph? __1__

© Pearson Education, Inc. 2

Use with Lesson 8-12. 103

Name
Pictographs

PS 8-12

Draw a picture symbol next to your favorite subject.
Then use the graph to answer the questions.

Favorite School Subjects

Math	👤👤👤👤👤👤
Reading	👤👤👤👤
Art	👤👤👤👤👤👤👤👤
Music	👤👤👤👤👤

Each 👤 = 1 person.

Answers may vary by 1 more.

1. How many children like math best? __6__ children

2. How many children like music best? __5__ children

3. Which subject is favored by the most children? __Art__

4. Which subject is favored by the least children? __Reading__

5. Write a number sentence to show how many more children like art than reading.

$8 - 4 = 4$

6. Write a number sentence to show how many more children like math than music.

$6 - 5 = 1$

© Pearson Education, Inc. 2

Use with Lesson 8-12. 103

Name _____

Bar Graphs

R 8-13

A bar graph uses bars to show information.
The name of the graph tells the kind of information.

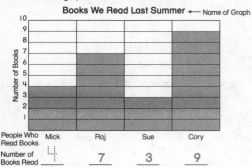

Books We Read Last Summer ← Name of Graph

People Who Read Books	Mick	Raj	Sue	Cory
Number of Books Read	4	7	3	9

Count the number of colored boxes and write the number.
These numbers tell how many books each person read.

Use the graph to answer the questions.

1. How many books did Mick read last summer? _4_ books

2. How many books did Sue and Raj read last summer? _10_ books

3. Who read the most books? _Cory_

4. Who read the least books? _Sue_

Name _____

Bar Graphs

P 8-13

1. Take a survey. Ask classmates what they like to do inside.
Make tally marks to keep track of what each classmate says.

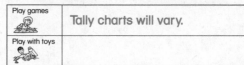

Play games	Tally charts will vary.
Play with toys	

2. Make a bar graph. Color one box for each time an activity was chosen.   **Bar graphs will vary.**

Favorite Inside Activities

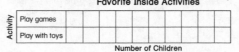

Activity	Play games	
	Play with toys	

Number of Children

Use the graph to answer each question. **Answers will vary.**

3. Which activity is favored by the most children? _____

4. Which activity is favored by the least children? _____

Problem Solving *Writing in Math*

5. Explain how you read the information in the bar graph.

For each activity, count the number of colored squares in the row to tell how many children chose the activity.

Name _____

The School Play

E 8-13
MENTAL MATH

The table shows how many tickets
the children sold for the school play.

Tickets Sold

Name	Number of Tickets
Ken	70
Lisa	30
Paul	90
Yuki	50

Make a bar graph. Color one box
for each 10 tickets sold.

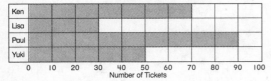

Tickets Sold

Ken								
Lisa								
Paul								
Yuki								

0 10 20 30 40 50 60 70 80 90 100
Number of Tickets

Use the bar graph and mental math
to answer each question.

1. Who sold the greatest number of tickets? _Paul_

2. How many more tickets did Paul sell than Lisa? _60_

3. Who sold fewer tickets, Lisa or Yuki? _Lisa_

   How many fewer? _20_

4. How many tickets did Yuki and Lisa sell in all? _80_

5. How many more tickets did Ken sell than Yuki? _20_

Name _____

Bar Graphs

PS 8-13

This chart shows the materials children
like to use most in art class.

Favorite Art Materials	
Paint	|||| ||
Crayons	|||| ||||
Clay	|||
Beads	||||

1. Use the tally chart to make a bar graph.
Color one box for each time an art material is chosen.

Favorite Art Materials

Paint									
Crayons									
Clay									
Beads									

0 1 2 3 4 5 6 7 8 9

Writing in Math

2. Do you think the chart or the graph is better
for showing the information? Why?

Answers will vary.

_____

Name _____

Line Plots
R 8-14

A line plot is another way to show how many.
Look at the parts of the line plot.

each X = 1 child

Children's Crayons

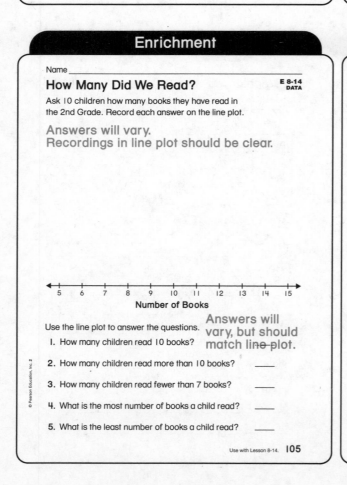

The numbers tell how many.

The name tells what the numbers stand for.

Look above the number 4. There are 3 Xs.

This line plot shows that ___3___ children have
4 crayons each.

Look above the number 6. There are 4 Xs. This line plot

shows that ___4___ children have 6 crayons each.

Use the line plot to answer the questions.

1. How many children have 3 crayons? ___3___ children

2. How many children have 1 crayon? ___3___ children

3. How many children have 0 crayons? ___1___ child

4. How many crayons did
   the most number of children have? ___5___ crayons

Use with Lesson 8-14. **105**

Name _____

Line Plots
P 8-14

Use the line plot to answer the questions.

Number of Letters in Our Names

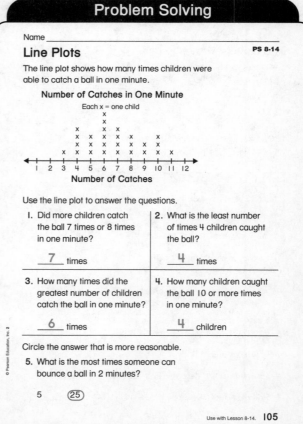

Number of Letters

1. How many children have
   15 letters in their name?
   ___4___ children

2. What is the greatest number
   of letters in a child's name?
   ___21___ letters

3. How many children
   have 17 or more letters
   in their name?
   ___10___ children

4. How many children have
   15 or fewer letters in
   their name?
   ___18___ children

Problem Solving *Reasonableness*
Circle the answer that is more reasonable.

5. Susan's last name has fewer
   letters than her first name.
   How many letters are in her
   name in all?

   5   (9)

6. Marshall has more letters in
   his last name than his first
   name. How many letters are
   in his name in all?

   8   (20)

Use with Lesson 8-14. **105**

Name _____

How Many Did We Read?
E 8-14
DATA

Ask 10 children how many books they have read in
the 2nd Grade. Record each answer on the line plot.

Answers will vary.
Recordings in line plot should be clear.

◄─┼──┼──┼──┼──┼──┼──┼──┼──┼──┼──►
   5 6 7 8 9 10 11 12 13 14 15

Number of Books

Use the line plot to answer the questions.

1. How many children read 10 books? ____

Answers will vary, but should match line plot.

2. How many children read more than 10 books? ____

3. How many children read fewer than 7 books? ____

4. What is the most number of books a child read? ____

5. What is the least number of books a child read? ____

Use with Lesson 8-14. **105**

Name _____

Line Plots
PS 8-14

The line plot shows how many times children were
able to catch a ball in one minute.

Number of Catches in One Minute

Each x = one child

```
                x
                x
         x      x
   x  x  x  x  x  x        x
   x  x  x  x  x  x  x
   x  x  x  x  x  x  x  x
◄──┼──┼──┼──┼──┼──┼──┼──┼──┼──┼──┼──┼──►
   1  2  3  4  5  6  7  8  9  10 11 12
```

Number of Catches

Use the line plot to answer the questions.

1. Did more children catch
   the ball 7 times or 8 times
   in one minute?
   ___7___ times

2. What is the least number
   of times 4 children caught
   the ball?
   ___4___ times

3. How many times did the
   greatest number of children
   catch the ball in one minute?
   ___6___ times

4. How many children caught
   the ball 10 or more times
   in one minute?
   ___4___ children

Circle the answer that is more reasonable.

5. What is the most times someone can
   bounce a ball in 2 minutes?

   5   (25)

Use with Lesson 8-14. **105**

Use with Chapter 8, Lesson 14. **105**

Name _____

Coordinate Graphs

R 8-15

Coordinate graphs show where things are located.

The ordered pair (B, 1) names the location of the fish on the graph.

Where is the mouse?
Start at 0 and go to A.
From A, go up.
Count the spaces.
The mouse is located at (A , 2).

Where is the fly?
Start at 0 and go to B.
From B, go up.
Count the spaces.
The fly is located at (B , 2).

Write the ordered pair where each animal is located.

1. (A , 3)

2. (B , 1)

3.  (C , 2)

© Pearson Education, Inc. 2

Name _____

Coordinate Graphs

P 8-15

Find the Wild Animals

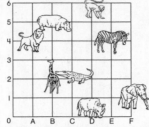

Write the ordered pair where each animal is located.

1. (B, 5)   2. (C, 2)
3. (A, 4)   4. (F, 1)

Problem Solving *Writing in Math*

5. Tell how you would find the ordered pair that tells the location of the lion.

Sample answer: Start at 0. Move to A.
Move up 4 spaces to the lion: The ordered
pair is (A, 4).

© Pearson Education, Inc. 2

Name _____

Where Will You Draw the Shapes?

E 8-15
ALGEBRA

Look at the ordered pairs below.
Then draw the shapes on the graph.

1. Draw a triangle on (D, 3).	2. Draw a square on (A, 5).
3. Draw a circle on (E, 1).	4. Draw a rectangle on (B, 2).
5. Draw a triangle on (C, 4).	6. Draw a circle on (F, 6).

© Pearson Education, Inc. 2

Name _____

Coordinate Graphs

PS 8-15

1. Color the circles at these ordered pairs red.
(A, 5) (C, 3) (A, 3) (C, 5)

2. Color the circles at these ordered pairs blue.
(B, 0) (E, 4) (F, 1)

3. Connect the red circles. What shape do you see?

   square

4. Connect the blue circles. What shape do you see?

   triangle

Writing in Math

5. Write a question using some of the leftover circles.

Answers will vary. Possible answer:
Connect (D, 2), (E, 3), (E, 1). What shape
do you see?

© Pearson Education, Inc. 2

Reteaching

Name _____

PROBLEM-SOLVING SKILL   R 8-16

Use Data from a Graph

A graph shows us information.

How many animals are there?

Animals We Have

(bar graph: Number of Children vs Animals — Cat, Dog, Horse, Guinea Pig)

Cat 2
Dog 3
Horse 1
Guinea Pig 4

Use the graph to answer the questions.

1. How many sports cards does each child have?

John 3

Maria 4

Dia 1

Ahmad 2

Sports Cards

(bar graph: Number of Cards vs Children — John, Maria, Dia, Ahmad)

2. Who has the most sports cards? **Maria**

3. Who has the fewest? **Dia**

Use with Lesson 8-16. **107**

Practice

Name _____

PROBLEM-SOLVING SKILL   P 8-16

Use Data from a Graph

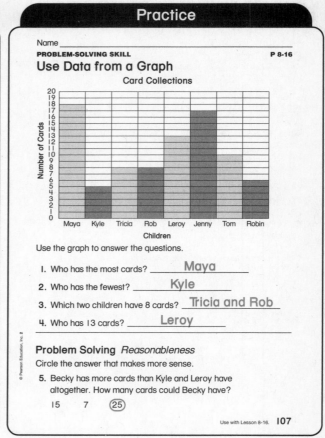

Use the graph to answer the questions.

1. Who has the most cards? **Maya**

2. Who has the fewest? **Kyle**

3. Which two children have 8 cards? **Tricia and Rob**

4. Who has 13 cards? **Leroy**

Problem Solving *Reasonableness*

Circle the answer that makes more sense.

5. Becky has more cards than Kyle and Leroy have altogether. How many cards could Becky have?

   15   7   (25)

Use with Lesson 8-16. **107**

Enrichment

Name _____

At the Amusement Park

E 8-16
DATA

Tickets at the amusement park come in books of 10. The graph shows how many books of tickets each child has.

Tickets We Have

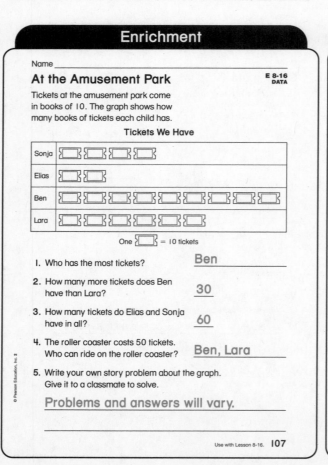

One 🎟 = 10 tickets

1. Who has the most tickets? **Ben**

2. How many more tickets does Ben have than Lara? **30**

3. How many tickets do Elias and Sonja have in all? **60**

4. The roller coaster costs 50 tickets. Who can ride on the roller coaster? **Ben, Lara**

5. Write your own story problem about the graph. Give it to a classmate to solve.

   Problems and answers will vary.

   _____

Use with Lesson 8-16. **107**

Problem Solving

Name _____

PROBLEM-SOLVING SKILL   PS 8-16

Use Data from a Graph

Homeruns Hit This Season

Paul	○○○
Jennifer	○○○○○
Denzel	○○○○○○
Megan	○○○○

Each ○ = 5 homeruns.

How many homeruns did Paul hit? Count by 5s to count the number of balls.

5, 10, 15

Paul hit 15 homeruns.

Use the graph to answer the questions. Count by 5s to help you.

1. Megan hit 20 homeruns. Draw the rest of the balls in the graph to show how many homeruns she hit.

2. Who hit the most homeruns? **Denzel**

3. How many more homeruns did Jennifer hit than Megan? **5** more homeruns

4. How many homeruns did Paul and Denzel hit in all? **45**

5. Who hit more homeruns than Megan?

   Jennifer and Denzel

Using the page To help children *plan and solve* each problem, have them count by 5s then write the total number at the end of each row in the graph.

Use with Lesson 8-16. **107**

© Pearson Education, Inc. 2

Use with Chapter 8, Lesson 16. **107**

Reteaching

Name _____

PROBLEM-SOLVING APPLICATIONS   R 8-17

Fly, Butterfly, Fly!

The short hand tells the hour 1:_____.

The long hand tells the minutes _____:30.

The time is **1:30**

Write the time.

1. The butterfly rests on a flower.

   11:00

2. The butterfly leaves the flower.

   11:15

3. How long did the butterfly stay on the flower?

   15 minutes

Writing in Math

4. Write a sentence about what the butterfly did next. Tell how long it took and show the time on the clock.

Answers will vary. Clock should reflect elapsed time.

108 Use with Lesson 8-17.

Practice

Name _____

PROBLEM-SOLVING APPLICATIONS   P 8-17

Fly, Butterfly, Fly!

Solve.

1. A butterfly landed on a plant at 3:00. It stayed there for 10 minutes. Then it flew away.

   It flew away at ___**3:10**___.

2. There are 17 butterflies in a garden. 8 more butterflies come to join them. How many butterflies are in the garden now?

   17 + **8** = **25** butterflies

3. Linda has 23 butterflies in a collection. She gives away 6 butterflies. How many butterflies are in her collection now?

   23 ⊖ **6** = **17** butterflies

Writing in Math

Write a story about a butterfly.

Stories will vary.

_____

_____

_____

108 Use with Lesson 8-17.

Enrichment

Name _____

All About Butterflies   E 8-17
REASONABLENESS

Circle the time that is the most reasonable.

1. Jane colored a picture of a butterfly. About how long did it take her?

   1 minute   (10 minutes)   100 minutes

2. Malik spent the afternoon going butterfly watching. About how long was he watching for butterflies?

   (3 hours)   1 hour   30 hours

3. A butterfly takes about one month to complete its growth. About how long does it take the butterfly to grow?

   1 week   (4 weeks)   10 weeks

4. A caterpillar stays in its pupa for a couple of weeks. About how long does the caterpillar stay in the pupa?

   1 day   50 days   (14 days)

5. Leon made a paper model of a butterfly. About how long did it take him?

   (2 hours)   10 hours   20 hours

108 Use with Lesson 8-17.

Problem Solving

Name _____

PROBLEM-SOLVING APPLICATIONS   PS 8-17

Fly, Butterfly, Fly!

1. A butterfly starts to fly at 3:00. It flies for 15 minutes.

   Find how much time has passed.

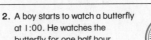

   It stops flying at **3:15**.

2. A boy starts to watch a butterfly at 1:00. He watches the butterfly for one half hour.

   He stops watching at **1:30**.

3. A butterfly started to dry its wings at 9:00. It takes 2 hours for the wings to dry.

   The wings are dry at **11:00**.

4. A butterfly rests on a flower for one quarter of an hour. Write the time in another way.

   15 minutes

Using the page Have students *look back* at their answers, using an analog clockface to help them *check* the times.

108 Use with Lesson 8-17.

Reteaching

Name _____

Understanding Length and Height

R 9-1

Height is how tall an object is.
You can use cubes to measure height.
Line up the cubes with the ends
of the object.

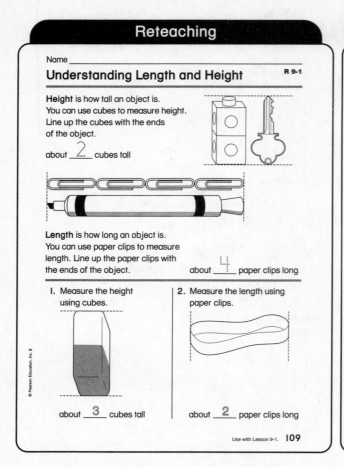

about __2__ cubes tall

Length is how long an object is.
You can use paper clips to measure
length. Line up the paper clips with
the ends of the object.

about __4__ paper clips long

1. Measure the height
using cubes.

about __3__ cubes tall

2. Measure the length using
paper clips.

about __2__ paper clips long

Use with Lesson 9-1. 109

Practice

Name _____

Understanding Length and Height

P 9-1

Measure each classroom object using cubes or paper
clips. Circle the word or words that make sense.

Answers will vary.

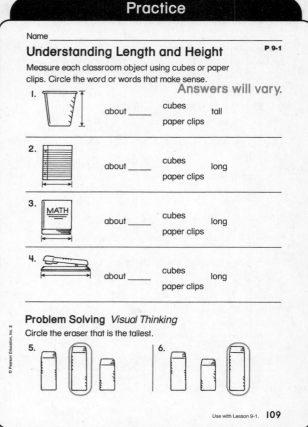

1. about _____ cubes / paper clips — tall

2. about _____ cubes / paper clips — long

3. MATH about _____ cubes / paper clips — long

4. about _____ cubes / paper clips — long

Problem Solving *Visual Thinking*
Circle the eraser that is the tallest.

5.

6.

Use with Lesson 9-1. 109

Enrichment

Name _____

Hands Up!

E 9-1
VISUAL THINKING

You can use your hand to measure.

Answers will vary.

Use your hand to measure the objects below.

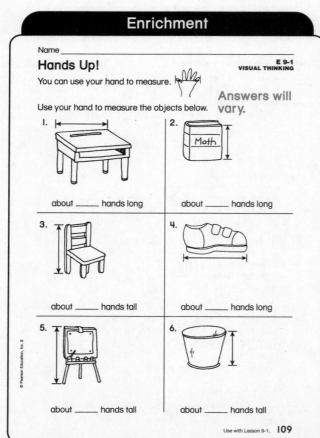

1. about _____ hands long

2. Math — about _____ hands long

3. about _____ hands tall

4. about _____ hands long

5. about _____ hands tall

6. about _____ hands tall

Use with Lesson 9-1. 109

Problem Solving

Name _____

Understanding Length and Height

PS 9-1

Solve. Use 🖇 and 🎲.

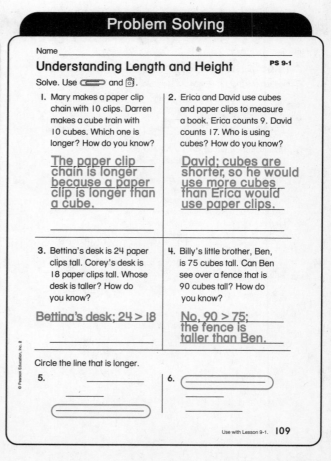

1. Mary makes a paper clip
chain with 10 clips. Darren
makes a cube train with
10 cubes. Which one is
longer? How do you know?

**The paper clip
chain is longer
because a paper
clip is longer than
a cube.**

2. Erica and David use cubes
and paper clips to measure
a book. Erica counts 9. David
counts 17. Who is using
cubes? How do you know?

**David; cubes are
shorter, so he would
use more cubes
than Erica would
use paper clips.**

3. Bettina's desk is 24 paper
clips tall. Corey's desk is
18 paper clips tall. Whose
desk is taller? How do
you know?

Bettina's desk; 24 > 18

4. Billy's little brother, Ben,
is 75 cubes tall. Can Ben
see over a fence that is
90 cubes tall? How do
you know?

**No, 90 > 75;
the fence is
taller than Ben.**

Circle the line that is longer.

5.

6.

Use with Lesson 9-1. 109

Reteaching

Name _____

Inches and Feet   R 9-2

Use a ruler to measure inches or feet.

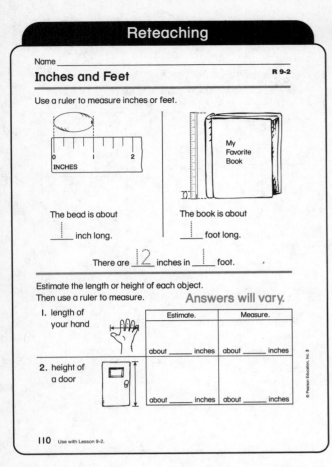

The bead is about

___1___ inch long.

The book is about

___1___ foot long.

There are __12__ inches in __1__ foot.

Estimate the length or height of each object.
Then use a ruler to measure.   **Answers will vary.**

	Estimate.	Measure.
1. length of your hand	about _____ inches	about _____ inches
2. height of a door	about _____ inches	about _____ inches

110 Use with Lesson 9-2.

Practice

Name _____

Inches and Feet   P 9-2

Estimate the length or height of each object.
Then use a ruler to measure.

Answers will vary.

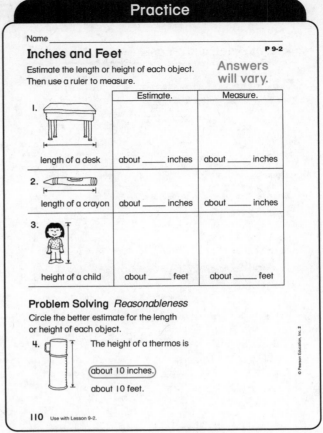

	Estimate.	Measure.
1. length of a desk	about _____ inches	about _____ inches
2. length of a crayon	about _____ inches	about _____ inches
3. height of a child	about _____ feet	about _____ feet

Problem Solving *Reasonableness*
Circle the better estimate for the length
or height of each object.

4. The height of a thermos is

(about 10 inches.)

about 10 feet.

110 Use with Lesson 9-2.

Enrichment

Name _____

Pathways Through the Park   E 9-2
                                        VISUAL THINKING

Estimate the length of each path through the park.
Then use your inch ruler to measure. **Estimates will vary.**

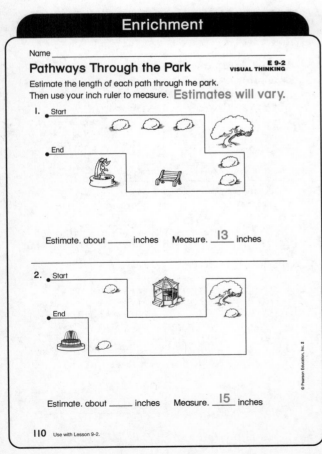

1.

Estimate. about _____ inches   Measure. __13__ inches

2.

Estimate. about _____ inches   Measure. __15__ inches

110 Use with Lesson 9-2.

Problem Solving

Name _____

Inches and Feet   PS 9-2

Use the clues to complete the table.
Then answer the questions.

Pets We Have		Length in Inches
	Rabbit	12
	Ferret	12
	Dog	36
	Snake	24
	Turtle	20

1. The ferret is the same length as the rabbit.

2. The dog is 24 inches longer than the rabbit.

3. The snake is one foot shorter than the dog.

4. The turtle is 8 inches longer than the ferret.

5. Which animal is the longest? ____dog____

6. How much longer is the snake than the turtle? __4 inches__

7. Laura has a cat that is 13 inches long.
   Jimmy has a cat that is one foot long.
   Who has the longer cat? How do you know?

   Laura; 12 inches equals 1 foot, and
   13 inches is longer than one foot.

110 Use with Lesson 9-2.

© Pearson Education, Inc. 2

---

110 Use with Chapter 9, Lesson 2.

Name _____

Inches, Feet, and Yards

R 9-3

Use inches to measure short lengths.
Use feet to measure medium-sized lengths.
Use **yards** to measure long lengths.

> Remember:
> 3 feet = 1 yard
> 36 inches = 1 yard

about ⋯3⋯ inches about ⋯4⋯ feet about ⋯4⋯ yards

Estimate. Then use a ruler to measure. **Answers will vary.**

	Estimate.	Measure.
1.	about _____ inches	about _____ inches
2.	about _____ feet	about _____ feet

Estimate. Then use a yardstick to measure.

	Estimate.	Measure.
3.	about _____ yards	about _____ yards

Use with Lesson 9-3. 111

© Pearson Education, Inc. 2

Name _____

Inches, Feet, and Yards

P 9-3

Estimate the width, height, or length of each object.
Then use a ruler or a yardstick to measure.

Answers will vary.

	Estimate.	Measure.
1. length of a chalkboard	about _____ feet	about _____ feet
2. height of a door	about _____ yards	about _____ yards
3. width of a chair	about _____ inches	about _____ inches

Problem Solving *Reasonableness*
Circle inches, feet, or yards.

4. The bicycle is about 3 ~~inches~~ **(feet)** tall.

5. The swing set is about 3 ~~feet~~ **(yards)** long.

Use with Lesson 9-3. 111

© Pearson Education, Inc. 2

Name _____

What's the Measure?

E 9-3
DECISION MAKING

Find three objects and measure their length or height.
Draw a picture or write the name of each object.
Then measure one using inches, one using feet, and
one using yards. **Answers will vary.**

1.

about _____ inches

2.

about _____ feet

3.

about _____ yards

Use with Lesson 9-3. 111

© Pearson Education, Inc. 2

Name _____

Inches, Feet, and Yards

PS 9-3

Circle the best estimate.

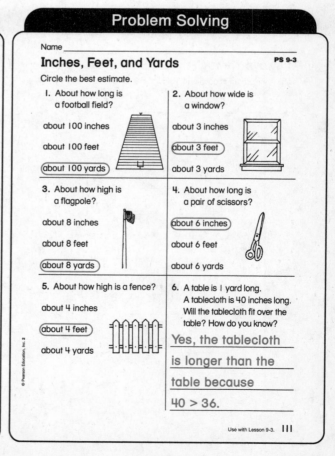

1. About how long is
   a football field?

   about 100 inches

   about 100 feet

   (about 100 yards)

2. About how wide is
   a window?

   about 3 inches

   (about 3 feet)

   about 3 yards

3. About how high is
   a flagpole?

   about 8 inches

   about 8 feet

   (about 8 yards)

4. About how long is
   a pair of scissors?

   (about 6 inches)

   about 6 feet

   about 6 yards

5. About how high is a fence?

   about 4 inches

   (about 4 feet)

   about 4 yards

6. A table is 1 yard long.
   A tablecloth is 40 inches long.
   Will the tablecloth fit over the
   table? How do you know?

   Yes, the tablecloth

   is longer than the

   table because

   40 > 36.

Use with Lesson 9-3. 111

© Pearson Education, Inc. 2

© Pearson Education, Inc. 2

Name _____

Centimeters and Meters

R 9-4

Centimeters are used to measure short lengths.
Meters are used to measure long lengths.

There are 100 centimeters in 1 meter.

CENTIMETERS

about ⸱3⸱ centimeters   about ⸱1⸱ meter

Estimate longer or shorter than 1 meter.
Then use a ruler to measure. Circle your answers.

Estimates may vary.

	Estimate.	Measure.
1.	longer than 1 meter	longer than 1 meter
	shorter than 1 meter	(shorter than 1 meter)
2.	longer than 1 meter	(longer than 1 meter)
	shorter than 1 meter	shorter than 1 meter
3.	longer than 1 meter	(longer than 1 meter)
	shorter than 1 meter	shorter than 1 meter

© Pearson Education, Inc. 2

Name _____

Centimeters and Meters

P 9-4

Estimate the length or height of each object.
Then use a ruler to measure.   **Answers will vary.**

		Estimate.	Measure.
1.	 length of a calendar	about _____ cm	about _____ cm
2.	height of the wall	about _____ m	about _____ m
3.	width of a pencil box	about _____ cm	about _____ cm

Problem Solving   *Writing in Math*

4. Should Carla measure the length of the pool in centimeters or meters? Tell why you think so.

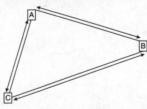

Meters are better to measure very wide
or very long items.

© Pearson Education, Inc. 2

Name _____

Race to the Cheese

E 9-4
VISUAL THINKING

Help the mice get to the cheese. Use a centimeter
ruler to draw straight lines through each maze.
Record the lengths. Then answer the questions.

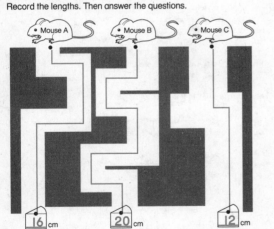

16 cm   20 cm   12 cm

Answers will vary. Possible answers given.

1. Which mouse had the longest path to the cheese?

Mouse B _____

2. Which mouse had the shortest path to the cheese?

Mouse C _____

© Pearson Education, Inc. 2

Name _____

Centimeters and Meters

PS 9-4

A ──→ B

C ↙

Use a ruler to measure each distance.

1. From A to B is __7__ centimeters long.

2. From B to C is __9__ centimeters long.

3. From A to C is __5__ centimeters long.

4. The total distance from A to B to C

and back to A is __21__ centimeters long.

5. If 1 centimeter stands for 1 meter, what is
the total distance in meters from A to B to C? __16__ meters

Writing in Math

6. A bookcase is 1 meter wide. Will it fit in a space
that is 75 cm wide? How do you know?

No. There are 100 cm in 1 m; the

bookcase is too wide, because 75 < 100.

© Pearson Education, Inc. 2

Name _____

PROBLEM-SOLVING STRATEGY   R 9-5

Act It Out

Find the perimeter and area of the shape.

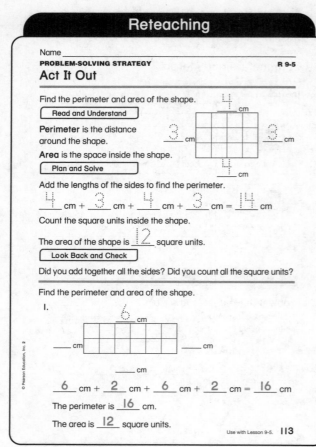

| Read and Understand |

Perimeter is the distance around the shape.

Area is the space inside the shape.

| Plan and Solve |

Add the lengths of the sides to find the perimeter.

$\underline{4}$ cm + $\underline{3}$ cm + $\underline{4}$ cm + $\underline{3}$ cm = $\underline{14}$ cm

Count the square units inside the shape.

The area of the shape is $\underline{12}$ square units.

| Look Back and Check |

Did you add together all the sides? Did you count all the square units?

Find the perimeter and area of the shape.

1.

$\underline{6}$ cm + $\underline{2}$ cm + $\underline{6}$ cm + $\underline{2}$ cm = $\underline{16}$ cm

The perimeter is $\underline{16}$ cm.

The area is $\underline{12}$ square units.

Use with Lesson 9-5.   113

© Pearson Education, Inc. 2

Name _____

PROBLEM-SOLVING STRATEGY   P 9-5

Act It Out

Find the perimeter and area of each shape.

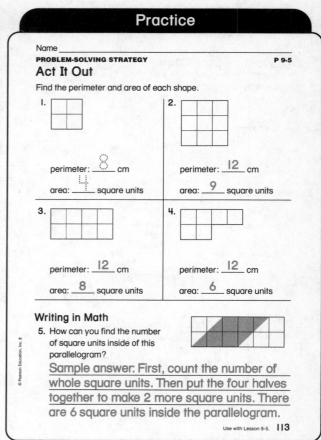

1.

perimeter: $\underline{8}$ cm

area: $\underline{4}$ square units

2.

perimeter: $\underline{12}$ cm

area: $\underline{9}$ square units

3.

perimeter: $\underline{12}$ cm

area: $\underline{8}$ square units

4.

perimeter: $\underline{12}$ cm

area: $\underline{6}$ square units

Writing in Math

5. How can you find the number of square units inside of this parallelogram?

Sample answer: First, count the number of whole square units. Then put the four halves together to make 2 more square units. There are 6 square units inside the parallelogram.

Use with Lesson 9-5.   113

© Pearson Education, Inc. 2

Name _____

In and Around the Shapes

E 9-5
VISUAL THINKING

Find the perimeter and area of each shape.

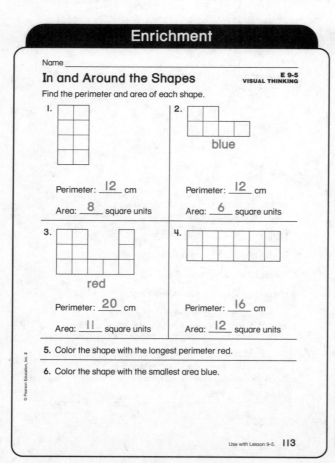

1.

Perimeter: $\underline{12}$ cm

Area: $\underline{8}$ square units

2.

blue

Perimeter: $\underline{12}$ cm

Area: $\underline{6}$ square units

3.

red

Perimeter: $\underline{20}$ cm

Area: $\underline{11}$ square units

4.

Perimeter: $\underline{16}$ cm

Area: $\underline{12}$ square units

5. Color the shape with the longest perimeter red.

6. Color the shape with the smallest area blue.

Use with Lesson 9-5.   113

© Pearson Education, Inc. 2

Name _____

PROBLEM-SOLVING STRATEGY   PS 9-5

Act It Out

Find the perimeter and area of the shape

To find the perimeter, you need to measure each side of the shape. Use a centimeter ruler or count. Write the numbers below.

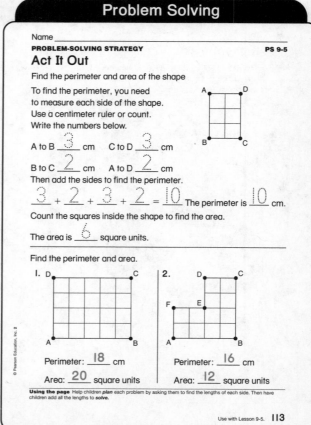

A to B $\underline{3}$ cm   C to D $\underline{3}$ cm

B to C $\underline{2}$ cm   A to D $\underline{2}$ cm

Then add the sides to find the perimeter.

$\underline{3}$ + $\underline{2}$ + $\underline{3}$ + $\underline{2}$ = $\underline{10}$ The perimeter is $\underline{10}$ cm.

Count the squares inside the shape to find the area.

The area is $\underline{6}$ square units.

Find the perimeter and area.

1.

Perimeter: $\underline{18}$ cm

Area: $\underline{20}$ square units

2.

Perimeter: $\underline{16}$ cm

Area: $\underline{12}$ square units

Using the page Help children *plan* each problem by asking them to find the lengths of each side. Then have children add all the lengths to *solve*.

Use with Lesson 9-5.   113

© Pearson Education, Inc. 2

© Pearson Education, Inc. 2

Name _____

Understanding Capacity

R 9-6

Capacity is the amount a container holds.
A large object holds more.
A small object holds less.

Which object holds more? | Which object holds less?

Circle the object that holds more.

1.

Circle the object that holds less.

2.

Circle the object that holds more.

3.

Name _____

Understanding Capacity

P 9-6

Circle the object that holds the most.

1.

2.

3.

Circle the object that holds the least.

4.

5.

Problem Solving *Writing in Math*

6. Sally wants to water her garden. Circle the container she should use. Tell why.

Sample answer is given. The bucket holds more water than the sandpail.

Name _____

Double Measures

E 9-6
VISUAL THINKING

Circle the two containers that hold about the same amount.

1.

2.

3.

4.

5.

Name _____

Understanding Capacity

PS 9-6

Choose the best container.

1. Tom wants to give his dog water.

2. Fiona wants to make soup for the family.

3. Shayna gives her puppy some medicine.

4. Bruce brings juice to a picnic.

Writing in Math

5. Write your own problem with 3 containers. Then draw the containers.

Problems will vary.   Pictures will vary.

_____

_____

Name _____

Cups, Pints, and Quarts

Use **cups**, **pints**, and **quarts** to measure capacity.

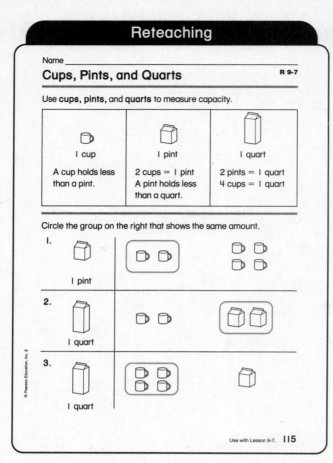

I cup	I pint	I quart
A cup holds less than a pint.	2 cups = I pint A pint holds less than a quart.	2 pints = I quart 4 cups = I quart

Circle the group on the right that shows the same amount.

1. I pint

2. I quart

3. I quart

Use with Lesson 9-7. 115

© Pearson Education, Inc. 2

Name _____

Cups, Pints, and Quarts

Circle the containers that hold the same amount.

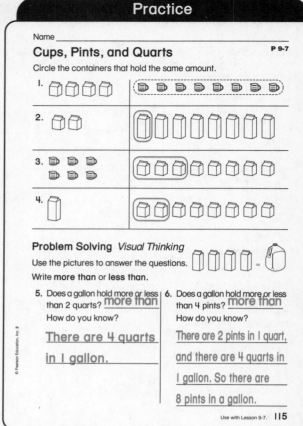

Problem Solving *Visual Thinking*

Use the pictures to answer the questions.
Write **more than** or **less than**.

5. Does a gallon hold more or less than 2 quarts? more than

How do you know?

There are 4 quarts in 1 gallon.

6. Does a gallon hold more or less than 4 pints? more than

How do you know?

There are 2 pints in 1 quart, and there are 4 quarts in 1 gallon. So there are 8 pints in a gallon.

Use with Lesson 9-7. 115

© Pearson Education, Inc. 2

Name _____

Cooking with Cups

2 cups = I pint
4 cups = 2 pints = I quart

Use the table above to rewrite the recipes.

1. Rewrite the recipe using only cups.

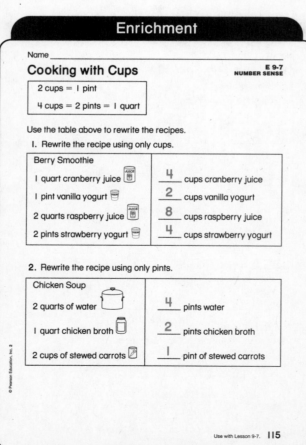

Berry Smoothie	
I quart cranberry juice	4 cups cranberry juice
I pint vanilla yogurt	2 cups vanilla yogurt
2 quarts raspberry juice	8 cups raspberry juice
2 pints strawberry yogurt	4 cups strawberry yogurt

2. Rewrite the recipe using only pints.

Chicken Soup	
2 quarts of water	4 pints water
I quart chicken broth	2 pints chicken broth
2 cups of stewed carrots	I pint of stewed carrots

Use with Lesson 9-7. 115

© Pearson Education, Inc. 2

Name _____

Cups, Pints, and Quarts

2 cups = I pint	4 cups = 2 pints = I quart

Solve.

1. Jenna needs 2 pints of milk to make pudding. She has a 1-cup container. How many cups will she use?

4 cups

2. Mrs. Ling needs 2 quarts of juice to make punch. She has a 1-pint container. How many pints will she use?

4 pints

3. Enrico needs a pot that will hold 6 cups of soup. He has a 1-pint container. How can he figure out which pot will hold 6 cups?

If he can pour 3 pints into a pot, the pot will hold 6 cups; 3 pints equal 6 cups.

4. Deena has 5 cups of milk. Troy has 2 pints of milk. Who has more milk? How do you know?

Deena; there are 2 cups in 1 pint, so Troy has 4 cups. 5 cups is more than 4 cups.

Use the pictures to solve. Color to show your answer.

5.

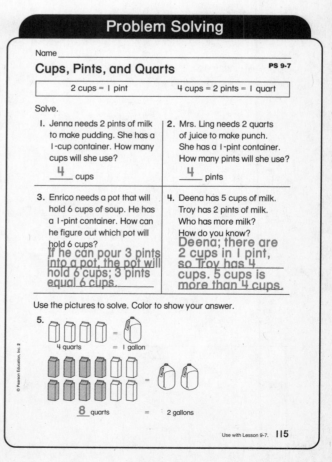

4 quarts = 1 gallon

8 quarts = 2 gallons

Use with Lesson 9-7. 115

© Pearson Education, Inc. 2

Name _____

Liters

Liters are used to measure capacity.

1 liter

This bottle of juice holds 1 liter.

This glass of juice holds _less_ than 1 liter.

Circle the container that holds more than 1 liter.

1.

Circle the container that holds less than 1 liter.

2.

Juice

Circle the container that holds more than 1 liter.

3.

116 Use with Lesson 9-8.

Name _____

Liters

About how many liters does the object hold?
Circle the better estimate.

1. about 30 liters
(about 3 liters)

2. (about 10 liters)
about 2 liters

3. about 28 liters
(about 2 liters)

4. about 9 liters
(about 90 liters)

Problem Solving *Number Sense*

Solve.

5. How many 2 liter bottles of water can the cooler hold?

___6___ bottles

12 liters   2 liters

116 Use with Lesson 9-8.

Name _____

How Much Do You Use?

Circle the most reasonable answer.

1. Liza makes a pitcher of lemonade for her family. Does she use more or less than one liter of water?

(more than one liter)

less than one liter

2. Maria makes a cup of tea for her friend. Does she use more or less than one liter of water?

more than one liter

(less than one liter)

3. Edmund fills a tub to take a bath. Does he use 40 liters or 4 liters?

(40 liters)

4 liters

4. Carlos fills a goldfish bowl. Does he use 3 liters or 30 liters?

(3 liters)

30 liters

5. Ari helps clean the classroom tables. Does he use 1 liter of water or 10 liters of water?

(1 liter)

10 liters

6. Bonnie fills a washtub to wash her dog. Does she use 5 liters or 25 liters of water?

5 liters

(25 liters)

116 Use with Lesson 9-8.

Name _____

Liters

The chart shows how many liters of water some containers can hold.

Capacity in Liters

Container	Pitcher	Vase	Watering Can	Fish Tank	Sink	Tub
Number of Liters	1	5	10	15	23	40

Solve.

1. How many liters of water does it take to fill the watering can and the tub?

___50___ liters

2. How many liters of water does it take to fill the pitcher and the sink?

___24___ liters

3. How many more liters does it take to fill the tub than the vase?

___35___ liters

4. How many vases could you fill with water from the fish tank?

___3___ vases

5. How many watering cans could you fill with water from the tub?

___4___ watering cans

6. How could you use the pitcher and the watering can to fill the sink?

Fill 2 watering cans and 3 pitchers to make 23 liters.

116 Use with Lesson 9-8.

© Pearson Education, Inc. 2

Reteaching

Name _____

Understanding Volume

R 9-9

Volume is the amount of space inside an object.
Use cubes to measure volume.

Count how many cubes fill this box.

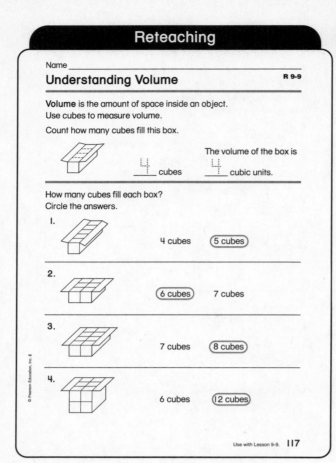

__4__ cubes

The volume of the box is
__4__ cubic units.

How many cubes fill each box?
Circle the answers.

1.

     4 cubes   (5 cubes)

2.

    (6 cubes)   7 cubes

3.

     7 cubes   (8 cubes)

4.

     6 cubes   (12 cubes)

Practice

Name _____

Understanding Volume

P 9-9

Circle the number of cubes in each box.

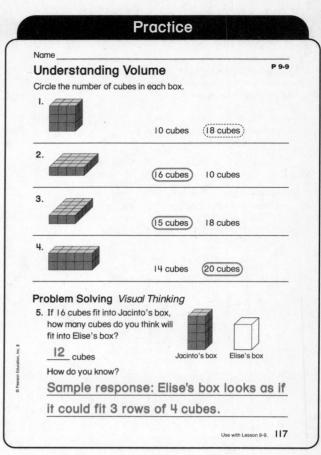

1.

     10 cubes   (18 cubes)

2.

    (16 cubes)   10 cubes

3.

    (15 cubes)   18 cubes

4.

     14 cubes   (20 cubes)

Problem Solving *Visual Thinking*

5. If 16 cubes fit into Jacinto's box,
how many cubes do you think will
fit into Elise's box?

  __12__ cubes

Jacinto's box   Elise's box

How do you know?

Sample response: Elise's box looks as if
it could fit 3 rows of 4 cubes.

Enrichment

Name _____

Finding Cubic Units

E 9-9
ALGEBRA

Use the data in the chart to fill each box with cubes.
Then complete the chart.

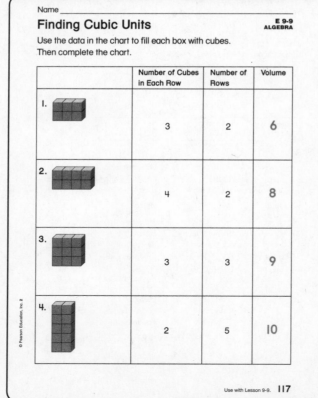

	Number of Cubes in Each Row	Number of Rows	Volume
1.	3	2	6
2.	4	2	8
3.	3	3	9
4.	2	5	10

Problem Solving

Name _____

Understanding Volume

PS 9-9

How many more cubes are needed to fill each box?

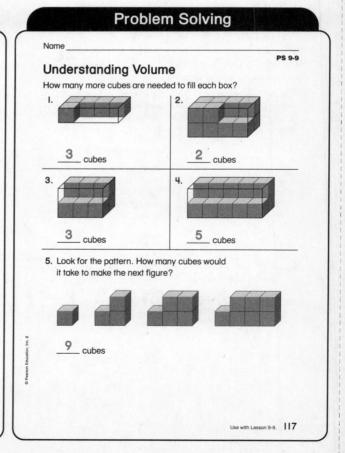

1. __3__ cubes   2. __2__ cubes

3. __3__ cubes   4. __5__ cubes

5. Look for the pattern. How many cubes would
it take to make the next figure?

__9__ cubes

© Pearson Education, Inc. 2

Name _____

Understanding Weight

R 9-10

Weight tells how heavy something is.
You can use a balance scale to measure
weight. The balance scale shows which
object is heavier. The heavier object weighs
more and is lower on the scale.

The heavier side of the scale is lower.

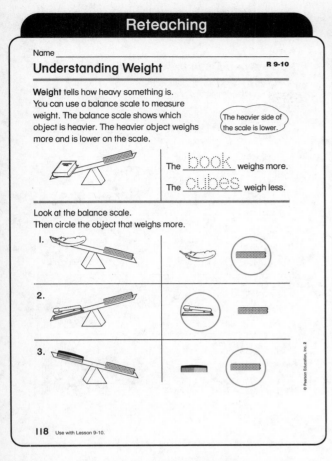

The _book_ weighs more.

The _cubes_ weigh less.

Look at the balance scale.
Then circle the object that weighs more.

1.

2.

3.

Name _____

Understanding Weight

P 9-10

Circle the object that weighs more.

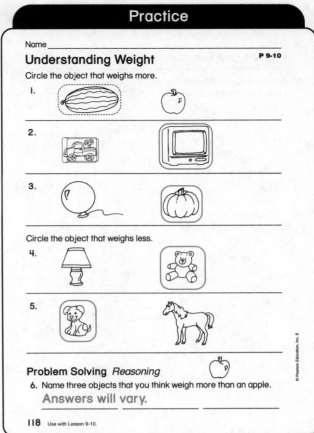

1.

2.

3.

Circle the object that weighs less.

4.

5.

Problem Solving *Reasoning*

6. Name three objects that you think weigh more than an apple.

   Answers will vary.

Name _____

A Balancing Act

E 9-10
REASONABLENESS

Circle the object that would make the scale balance.

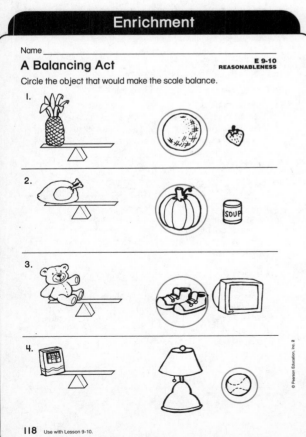

1.

2.

3.

4.

Name _____

Understanding Weight

PS 9-10

Look at the pictures. Balance each scale
by drawing the correct weights on each side.

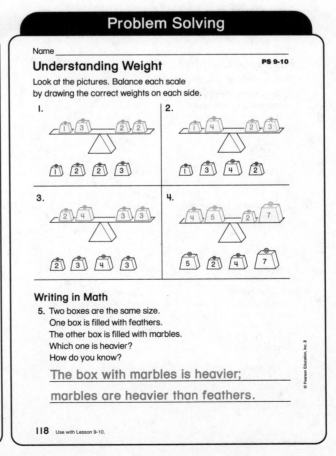

1.   2.

3.   4.

Writing in Math

5. Two boxes are the same size.
   One box is filled with feathers.
   The other box is filled with marbles.
   Which one is heavier?
   How do you know?

   The box with marbles is heavier;

   marbles are heavier than feathers.

Reteaching

Name _____

Pounds and Ounces

R 9-11

Ounces are used to measure light things.
Pounds are used to measure heavier things.

Remember:
1 pound = 16 ounces.

The book weighs about 1 pound.

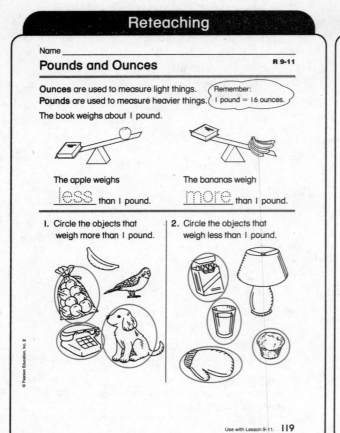

The apple weighs

___less___ than 1 pound.

The bananas weigh

___more___ than 1 pound.

1. Circle the objects that weigh more than 1 pound.

2. Circle the objects that weigh less than 1 pound.

Use with Lesson 9-11. **119**

Practice

Name _____

Pounds and Ounces

P 9-11

About how much does each object weigh?
Circle the better estimate.

1. (about 1 ounce) / about 1 pound

2. about 2 ounces / (about 2 pounds)

3. (about 4 ounces) / about 4 pounds

4. about 12 ounces / (about 12 pounds)

5. about 6 ounces / (about 6 pounds)

6. (about 10 ounces) / about 10 pounds

7. about 9 ounces / (about 9 pounds)

8. about 5 ounces / (about 5 pounds)

Problem Solving *Algebra*
Solve.

9. 1 pound is 16 ounces. How many ounces are in 2 pounds?

1 pound = 16 ounces
2 pounds = ? ounces

___16 + 16 = 32 ounces___

Use with Lesson 9-11. **119**

Enrichment

Name _____

Pounds or Ounces?

E 9-11
REASONABLENESS

Circle the most reasonable answer.

1. Dana makes a peanut butter sandwich. Does she use 1 ounce or 1 pound of peanut butter?

   (1 ounce)

   1 pound

2. Enrico makes a glass of fruit drink. Does he use 5 ounces or 5 pounds of fruit for the drink?

   (5 ounces)

   5 pounds

3. Eric buys apples to make an apple pie. Does he get 3 ounces or 3 pounds of apples?

   3 ounces

   (3 pounds)

4. Steven makes hamburgers for a party. Does each hamburger weigh 4 ounces or 4 pounds?

   (4 ounces)

   4 pounds

5. Sonya makes a pizza with cheese. Does she use 10 ounces or 10 pounds of cheese?

   (10 ounces)

   10 pounds

6. Megan wants to weigh her baby kitten. Does the kitten weigh 16 ounces or 16 pounds?

   (16 ounces)

   16 pounds

Use with Lesson 9-11. **119**

Problem Solving

Name _____

Pounds and Ounces

PS 9-11

Circle the correct answers.
Remember, there are 16 ounces in 1 pound.

1. Anna puts 1 pound of bananas and some apples on the scale. Altogether they weigh more than 2 pounds. Which fruit weighs more?

   bananas (apples)

2. Freddy wants to make some sauce. Does he use 5 pounds or 5 ounces of tomatoes?

   (5 pounds) 5 ounces

3. Jake puts 18 ounces of carrots in a pot of soup and a pound of celery. Which weighs more, the carrots or the celery?

   (carrots) celery

4. Dixie makes a pumpkin pie. Does she use a 10-pound pumpkin or a 10-ounce pumpkin?

   (10-pound) 10-ounce

5. Carla needs 2 pounds of flour to make some dough. She has a 30-ounce bag. Does she have enough flour? Tell how you know.

   16 ounces = 1 pound

   ___32___ ounces = 2 pounds

   ___No. She needs 32 ounces___

   ___to make 2 pounds.___

Use with Lesson 9-11. **119**

Grams and Kilograms

Name_____

R 9-12

Grams are used to measure light things.
Kilograms are used to measure heavier things.

Remember:
1,000 grams = 1 kilogram.

The shoe measures about 1 kilogram.

The balloon measures
less than 1 kilogram.

The clock measures
more than 1 kilogram.

1. Circle the objects that measure more than 1 kilogram.

2. Circle the objects that measure less than 1 kilogram.

120 Use with Lesson 9-12.

Grams and Kilograms

Name_____

P 9-12

About how much does each object measure?
Circle the better estimate.

1.
about 3 grams
(about 3 kilograms)

2.
(about 60 grams)
about 60 kilograms

3.
about 20 grams
(about 20 kilograms)

4.
(about 400 grams)
about 400 kilograms

5.
about 30 grams
(about 30 kilograms)

6.
about 8 grams
(about 8 kilograms)

Problem Solving *Number Sense*
Solve.

7. Circle the weight that will make both sides of the scale even.

1,000 g = 1 kg

1 kg   4 kg   (2 kg)

120 Use with Lesson 9-12.

Animal Measures

Name_____

E 9-12
REASONING

Does each animal measure less than 1 kilogram, about 1 kilogram, or more than 1 kilogram? Write the name of the animal in the chart under its measure. Then think of another animal you can add to each measure.

frog   pig   turtle   goldfish

guinea pig   seal   mouse   kitten   wolf

Answers will vary.

Less than 1 kilogram	About 1 kilogram	More than 1 kilogram
frog	turtle	pig
goldfish	guinea pig	seal
mouse	kitten	wolf
My choice:	My choice:	My choice:

120 Use with Lesson 9-12.

Grams and Kilograms

Name_____

PS 9-12

Circle the correct answers.

1. A cat measures about 6 kilograms. Which two animals together measure about the same as the cat?

Cat 6 kg | Squirrel 2 kg   Rabbit 3 kg   Dog 15 kg

2. A dog measures about 15 kilograms. Which two animals together measure about the same as the dog?

Dog 15 kg | Raccoon 8 kg   Deer 22 kg   Fox 7 kg

3. A mouse measures about 50 grams. Which two animals together measure about the same as the mouse?

Mouse 50 g | Parakeet 23 g   Toad 27 g   Turtle 1,000 g

4. A marble measures about 1 gram. About how many marbles would it take to make $\frac{1}{2}$ of a kilogram?

1,000 g = 1 kg

_500_ marbles

120 Use with Lesson 9-12.

---

120 Use with Chapter 9, Lesson 12.

© Pearson Education, Inc. 2

Name _____

Temperature: Fahrenheit and Celsius

R 9-13

Temperature tells how hot or how cold.
You can measure temperature in **Fahrenheit**.

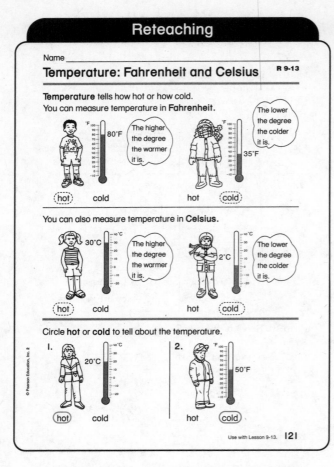

You can also measure temperature in **Celsius.**

Circle **hot** or **cold** to tell about the temperature.

1.

2.

Name _____

Temperature: Fahrenheit and Celsius

P 9-13

Color to show the temperature.
Circle **hot** or **cold** to tell about the temperature.

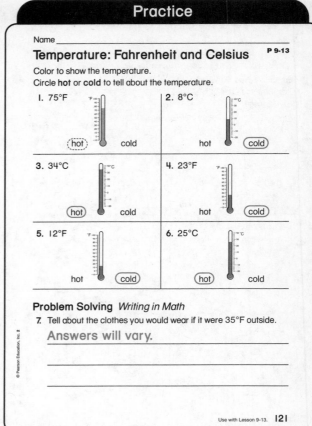

1. 75°F   (hot)   cold
2. 8°C   hot   (cold)
3. 34°C   (hot)   cold
4. 23°F   hot   (cold)
5. 12°F   hot   (cold)
6. 25°C   (hot)   cold

Problem Solving *Writing in Math*

7. Tell about the clothes you would wear if it were 35°F outside.

Answers will vary.

Name _____

Let's Play Outdoors

E 9-13
REASONING

Draw a picture of the clothes you might
wear outdoors for each temperature.

Answers may
vary. Possible
responses given.

1. 85°F

swimsuit,
shorts, T-shirt

2. 25°F

winter coat,
hat, gloves,
scarf, boots

3. 25°C

shorts,
summer dress,
sandals, visor

4. 5°C

jacket,
long pants,
gloves, hat

Name _____

Temperature: Fahrenheit and Celsius

PS 9-13

Use the Celsius thermometer to answer each question.

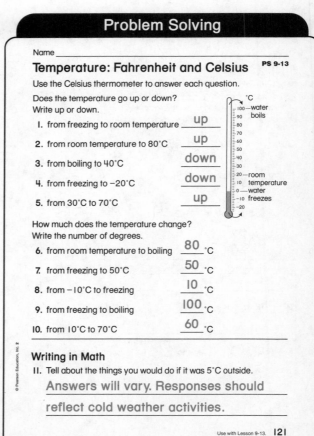

Does the temperature go up or down?
Write up or down.

1. from freezing to room temperature ___ up ___
2. from room temperature to 80°C ___ up ___
3. from boiling to 40°C ___ down ___
4. from freezing to −20°C ___ down ___
5. from 30°C to 70°C ___ up ___

How much does the temperature change?
Write the number of degrees.

6. from room temperature to boiling ___ 80 ___ °C
7. from freezing to 50°C ___ 50 ___ °C
8. from −10°C to freezing ___ 10 ___ °C
9. from freezing to boiling ___ 100 ___ °C
10. from 10°C to 70°C ___ 60 ___ °C

Writing in Math

11. Tell about the things you would do if it was 5°C outside.

Answers will vary. Responses should
reflect cold weather activities.

© Pearson Education, Inc. 2

Name _____

Understanding Probability

R 9-14

Probability is when you predict if something is **more likely** or **less likely** to happen.

 $\frac{4}{8}$ celery stalks
carrots

Since 8 is greater than 4, it is more likely that you will pick a carrot.

It is ⟨more⟩ likely that you will pick a carrot.

It is ⟨less⟩ likely that you will pick a celery stalk.

Write how many of each.
Then write more or less to complete the sentences.

1.

 $\frac{7}{2}$ apples
pears

It is _____less_____ likely that you will pick a pear.

2.

 $\frac{2}{5}$ almonds
peanuts

It is _____more_____ likely that you will pick a peanut.

Name _____

Understanding Probability

P 9-14

If you were to spin once, which color is the spinner most likely to land on?

1. black
⟨white⟩

2. black
⟨white⟩

3. black
white
⟨gray⟩

4. black
white
⟨gray⟩

If you were to spin once, which color is the spinner least likely to land on?

5. black
⟨white⟩

6. black
white

7. black
white
⟨gray⟩

8. ⟨black⟩
white
gray

Problem Solving *Reasoning*

Write more likely, less likely, or equally likely to answer the question.

9. Will the spinner land on black?

_____less likely_____

Name _____

Spinner Fun

E 9-14
DECISION MAKING

Pick 2 colors. Color the spinner. You must use 1 color **Answers** more than once. Then answer the questions. **will vary.**

Tell which colors the spinner is least likely and most likely to land on.

1. least likely _____

2. most likely _____

Color 1 section of the spinner yellow. Color 2 sections of the spinner blue. Color 3 sections of the spinner red. Then answer the questions.

Tell which colors the spinner is least likely and most likely to land on.

3. least likely _____yellow_____

4. most likely _____red_____

Name _____

Understanding Probability

PS 9-14

Robin puts different colors of cubes in a bag. He picks 10 cubes. For each exercise tell which color Robin is more likely and less likely to pick.

	More Likely	Less Likely
1. 2 yellow cubes 5 green cubes 10 blue cubes	blue	yellow
2. 8 yellow cubes 12 green cubes 5 blue cubes	green	blue
3. 10 yellow cubes 3 green cubes 5 blue cubes	yellow	green

4. Choose one exercise from Robin's activity to do yourself. Record the results in the chart. **Answers will vary.**

Yellow								
Green								
Blue								

5. Which color did you pick the most? _____

6. Which color did you pick the least? _____

7. Do your results match your answers for Robin's activity? _____

Using Probability

R 9-15

Name _____

Words like **certain**, **probable**, and **impossible**
tell about probability.

You pick one button from the jar.

It is certain that you
will pick a black or a gray button.

> **Certain** means
> it will happen.

There are more black buttons.

It is probable that
you will pick a black button.

> **Probable** means
> it is most likely
> to happen.

There are not any white buttons.

It is impossible
that you will pick a white button.

> **Impossible**
> means that it will
> not happen.

Look at the number of buttons in the jar.
Circle the button or buttons that tell about each probability.

You pick one button from the jar.

1. It is **certain** that you will pick

2. It is **probable** that you will pick

3. It is **impossible** that you will pick

Use with Lesson 9-15. **123**

Using Probability

P 9-15

Name _____

Use the tally chart to help you answer the questions.
Circle the missing word to complete the sentence.

Blue	ЖНТ ЖНТ I
Yellow	ЖНТ ЖНТ ЖНТ IIII

1. There are fewer _____ marbles in the jar.

(blue)
yellow

2. It is _____ that you will pick a red marble.

certain
(impossible)

3. It is _____ that you will pick a blue or
yellow marble.

probable
(certain)

4. You can pick one marble. It is _____ that
you will pick a yellow marble.

(probable)
impossible

Problem Solving *Reasoning*

5. There are red or yellow marbles in each jar.
Color the marbles to match each description below each jar.

It is certain to pick   It is impossible to pick
a red marble.   a red marble.

Use with Lesson 9-15. **123**

Mostly Marbles

E 9-15
DATA

Name _____

Count the number of marbles in each bag. Use tally marks.
Then circle the missing word to complete the sentence.

White Marbles	Black Marbles
ЖНТ III	ЖНТ III

1. You pick 4 marbles out of the bag.
It is _____ that you will
pick a white marble.

impossible   (possible)   certain

White Marbles	Black Marbles
II	ЖНТ ЖНТ

2. You pick 10 marbles out of the bag.
It is _____ that you will
pick some black marbles.

impossible   possible   (certain)

Try the exercises above using red and blue cubes.
Do your results match? Write about what you found.

Yes, results will match.

Color assignments may vary.

Use with Lesson 9-15. **123**

Using Probability

PS 9-15

Name _____

Complete the sentences.
Write **probable**, **certain**, or **impossible** for each.

1. Rickie has a bag with
8 red marbles and
3 green marbles.

It is probable
that he will pick
a red marble.

2. Marina has a bag with
11 yellow cubes
and 5 red cubes.

It is certain
that she will pick either
a yellow or a red cube.

3. Serena has a bag with
9 purple blocks and
6 pink blocks.

It is impossible
that she will pick
a green block.

4. Motar has a spinner with
1 red part and 4 blue parts.

It is probable
that he will spin blue.

5. Color the spinner so
it will be probable that
you will spin red.

Answers should
show more
sections colored
red than any
other color.

6. Color the spinner so
it will be impossible that
you will spin red.

No section is
colored red.

Use with Lesson 9-15. **123**

Name _____

Multiple-Step Problems

Sometimes it takes two steps to solve a problem.

Timmy has 7 red marbles and 8 blue marbles. He gives 6 marbles to his little brother. How many marbles does Timmy have left?

Think:
Do I have to add or subtract?

Step 1
Add to find out how many marbles Timmy has in all.

$7 + 8 = 15$

Step 2
Subtract to find how many marbles are left.

$15 - 6 = 9$

Timmy has ___9___ marbles left.

Write a number sentence for each part of the problem. Then write the answer.

1. Sandy picks 8 red flowers and 9 pink flowers.

She gives 3 flowers to Ben. How many flowers does Sandy have left?

Step 1
Add to find how many flowers she has in all.

$8 + 9 = 17$

Step 2
Subtract to find how many flowers Sandy has left.

$17 - 3 = 14$

Sandy has ___14___ flowers left.

Name _____

Multiple-Step Problems

Write a number sentence for each part of the problem.

1. Sam puts 8 cups of apple juice and 9 cups of grape juice in a party punch. How many cups are in the punch?

$8 + 9 = 17$ cups

People at the party drink 11 cups of punch. How many cups of punch are left?

$17 - 11 = 6$ cups

2. A basket holds 21 pounds of tomatoes. Another basket holds 14 pounds of tomatoes. How many pounds of tomatoes are there altogether?

$21 + 14 = 35$ pounds

Grandpa uses 16 pounds of tomatoes to make sauce. How many pounds of tomatoes are left?

$35 - 16 = 19$ pounds

Problem Solving *Mental Math*

Solve using mental math.

3. Beth has 20 red marbles and 15 blue marbles. Joyce has 40 yellow marbles. How many marbles do they have in all?

$20 + 15 + 40 = 75$ marbles

Name _____

At the Farm

Mr. and Mrs. Morley picked their crops. Use the data in the chart to answer each question.

Number of Pounds Picked

Apples	Peaches	Pumpkins	Corn	Squash
35	23	47	25	17

1. Mr. Morley took the apples and the peaches to the fruit stand. How many pounds of fruit did he take?

$35 + 23 = 58$ pounds

Then he sold 13 pounds of peaches. How many pounds of fruit does he have at the fruit stand now?

$58 - 13 = 45$ pounds

2. Mrs. Morley took the corn and the squash to the vegetable stand. How many pounds of vegetables did she take?

$25 + 17 = 42$ pounds

Then she took all the pumpkins to the stand. How many pounds of vegetables does she have at the stand now?

$42 + 47 = 89$ pounds

3. Write your own two-step problem. Use the data in the chart.

Problems will vary.

Name _____

Multiple-Step Problems

Peter has 28 apples. He uses 10 apples to make a pie.

Step 1: Subtract.

$28 - 10 = 18$

Then he gets 4 more apples. How many apples does he have now?

Step 2: Add.

$18 + 4 = 22$ apples

Solve.

1. Sasha has a string 35 inches long. She cuts off 16 inches to make a necklace.

Step 1: $35 - 16 = 19$

Then she cuts off 8 inches to make a bracelet. How many inches of string are left?

Step 2: $19 - 8 = 11$ inches

Mental Math

2. A tub contains 25 liters of water. José pours in 10 more liters. Ming adds another 10 liters. How many liters of water are in the tub now?

45 liters

Using the page Have students *look back* and identify the two steps for each problem. Then have them *check* to see that they solved both steps.

Name _____

PROBLEM-SOLVING APPLICATIONS   R 9-17

How Do You Measure Up?

You can use pounds to measure how
heavy or how light something is.

The box of blocks weighs more than the book.

The book weighs about 1 pound.

The eraser weighs less than the book.

The box of blocks is _____ 1 pound.   less than   (more than)

The eraser is _____ 1 pound.   (less than)   more than

Is it more or less than 1 pound?
Circle your estimate. Then measure.

Answers will vary.

	Estimate.	Measure.
1. soccer ball	less than	less than
	more than	more than
2. headphones	less than	less than
	more than	more than

Writing in Math

3. Choose an object in your classroom.
   Estimate and measure how much it weighs.
   Write about what you find.

   Answers will vary.

Use with Lesson 9-17.   125

© Pearson Education, Inc. 2

Name _____

PROBLEM-SOLVING APPLICATIONS   P 9-17

How Do You Measure Up?

Is each object **heavier than, lighter than,**
or **about** 1 pound?

Estimate. Then use a pound weight
and a balance scale to check.   Estimates will vary.

1. milk carton

   Estimate: _____ 1 pound

   Measure: lighter than 1 pound

2. dictionary

   Estimate: _____ 1 pound

   Measure: heavier than 1 pound

3. Some bananas weigh 3 pounds.
   A melon weighs 2 pounds.
   A bag of apples weighs 4 pounds.
   How much does the fruit weigh in all?   9 pounds

Writing in Math   Stories will vary.

4. Write a story about two pets you know.
   Then tell how much you think the animals weigh.

   _____

   _____

Use with Lesson 9-17.   125

© Pearson Education, Inc. 2

Name _____

Choose the Unit   E 9-17
                                          REASONABLENESS

Choose the best estimate of measure for each object.

1. Tracy wants to measure a
   ribbon to use as a necklace.

   About 2 centimeters

   (About 40 centimeters)

   About 500 centimeters

2. Jerome wants to measure
   some apples for a pie.

   (About 3 pounds)

   About 15 pounds

   About 25 pounds

3. Doreen measures fruit juice
   for her classroom party.

   About 1 liter

   (About 3 liters)

   About 75 liters

4. Roberto measures some
   fabric for a tablecloth.

   (About 2 yards)

   About 17 yards

   About 35 yards

5. Opal measures a board to
   cut for the roof of a birdhouse.

   About 2 inches

   About 83 inches

   (About 8 inches)

6. Jamal measures the length
   of a full basketball court.

   About 7 feet

   About 18 feet

   (About 94 feet)

Use with Lesson 9-17.   125

© Pearson Education, Inc. 2

Name _____

PROBLEM-SOLVING APPLICATIONS   PS 9-17

How Do You Measure Up?

Look at the pictures of the ribbons.
How much longer is the first ribbon?
Use a centimeter ruler to find out.

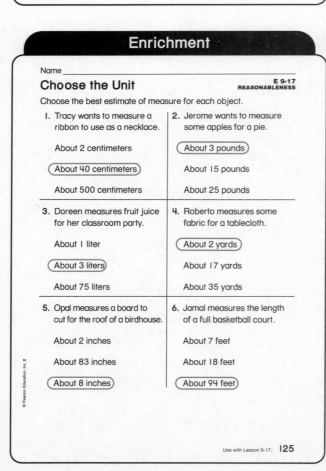

What is the problem asking?

How much longer the first ribbon is.

The first ribbon is _7_ cm longer.

Solve.

1. Estimate the length of the ribbon. Use an inch ruler to measure.

   Estimates will vary.
   Estimate. ____ inches   Measure. _5_ inches

Writing in Math

2. Describe an object you like. Tell about its length
   and weight. Use centimeters and kilograms.

   Stories will vary.

   _____

   _____

Using the page Have children *read* each problem. Then ask them what the problem is asking to make sure that
they *understand* the question.

Use with Lesson 9-17.   125

© Pearson Education, Inc. 2

Use with Chapter 9, Lesson 17.   **125**

Name _____

Building 1,000

R 10-1

Remember.

10 ones = __1__ ten   ========== = ▮

10 tens = __1__ hundred   ‖‖‖‖‖‖‖‖‖‖ = ▪

10 hundreds = __1__ thousand

(Count by 100s to count hundreds.)   ▪ ▪ ▪ ▪ ▪ ▪ = ◼

Color the models to show the hundreds.

1. 2 hundreds 200	▦ ▦ ▦ ▦ ▦
2. 3 hundreds 300	▦ ▦ ▦ ▦ ▦
3. 4 hundreds 400	▦ ▦ ▦ ▦ ▦
4. 5 hundreds 500	▦ ▦ ▦ ▦ ▦

Name _____

Building 1,000

P 10-1

Write how many. Use models if you need to.

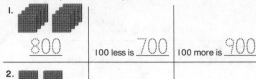
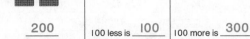

1. **800**   100 less is **700**   100 more is **900**

2. **200**   100 less is **100**   100 more is **300**

3. **700**   100 less is **600**   100 more is **800**

4. **500**   100 less is **400**   100 more is **600**

Problem Solving *Algebra*

Write the number.

5. How many more hundreds do you need to make 500?

▦ ▦ ▦ + **200** = 500

Name _____

A Secret Treasure

E 10-1
VISUAL THINKING

Help the children find the treasure.
Count by 100s to find the 1,000 gold coins.

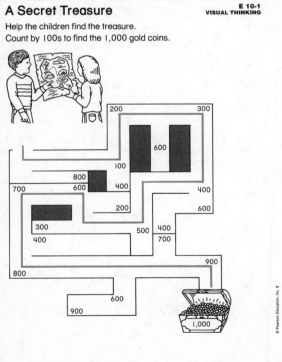

Name _____

Building 1,000

PS 10-1

Use the table to solve each problem.

There are 100 crayons in one box. Fill in the rest of the chart.

Boxes	1	2	3	4	5
Crayons	100	200	**300**	**400**	**500**

1. How many crayons are in 3 boxes?   **300** crayons

2. How many crayons are in all 5 boxes?   **500** crayons

3. Jack takes 1 box of crayons. How many crayons are left?   **400** crayons

There are 100 markers in one box. Fill in the rest of the chart.

Boxes	1	2	3	4	5	6	7	8
Markers	100	200	300	400	500	**600**	**700**	**800**

4. How many markers are in 6 boxes?   **600** markers

5. How many markers are in all 8 boxes?   **800** markers

6. Viola adds one more box of markers. How many markers are there now?   **900** markers

7. The school has 4 boxes of markers. They need 1,000 markers in all. How many more markers does the school need?

400 + **600** = 1,000   The school needs **600** more markers.

Name _____

Counting Hundreds, Tens, and Ones   R 10-2

You can write a 3-digit number counting hundreds, tens, and ones.

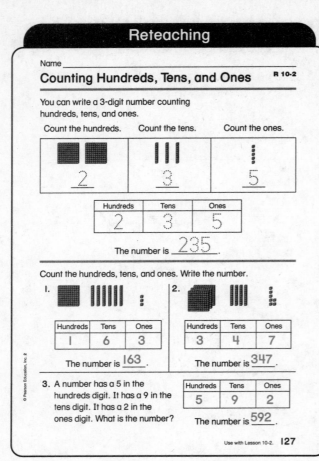

Count the hundreds.   Count the tens.   Count the ones.

2	3	5

Hundreds	Tens	Ones
2	3	5

The number is _235_.

Count the hundreds, tens, and ones. Write the number.

1.

Hundreds	Tens	Ones
1	6	3

The number is _163_.

2.

Hundreds	Tens	Ones
3	4	7

The number is _347_.

3. A number has a 5 in the hundreds digit. It has a 9 in the tens digit. It has a 2 in the ones digit. What is the number?

Hundreds	Tens	Ones
5	9	2

The number is _592_.

Use with Lesson 10-2. **127**

Name _____

Counting Hundreds, Tens, and Ones   P 10-2

Write the numbers.
Use models and Workmat 5 if you need to.

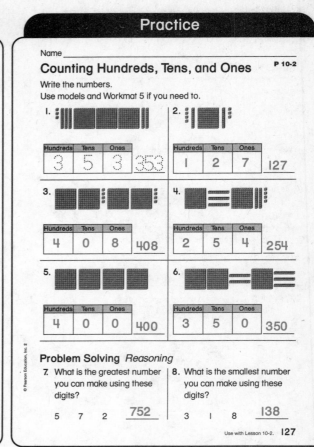

1.

Hundreds	Tens	Ones	
3	5	3	353

2.

Hundreds	Tens	Ones	
1	2	7	127

3.

Hundreds	Tens	Ones	
4	0	8	408

4.

Hundreds	Tens	Ones	
2	5	4	254

5.

Hundreds	Tens	Ones	
4	0	0	400

6.

Hundreds	Tens	Ones	
3	5	0	350

Problem Solving *Reasoning*

7. What is the greatest number you can make using these digits?

5   7   2   _752_

8. What is the smallest number you can make using these digits?

3   1   8   _138_

Use with Lesson 10-2. **127**

Name _____

Mail Match   E 10-2   NUMBER SENSE

Use the jumbled clues to find each person's mailbox.
Then draw a line from each person to the correct mailbox.

Clues   Mailboxes

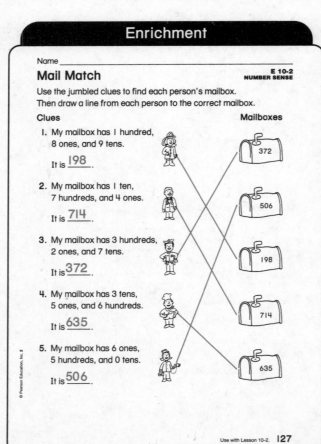

1. My mailbox has 1 hundred, 8 ones, and 9 tens.

It is _198_.

2. My mailbox has 1 ten, 7 hundreds, and 4 ones.

It is _714_.

3. My mailbox has 3 hundreds, 2 ones, and 7 tens.

It is _372_.

4. My mailbox has 3 tens, 5 ones, and 6 hundreds.

It is _635_.

5. My mailbox has 6 ones, 5 hundreds, and 0 tens.

It is _506_.

Use with Lesson 10-2. **127**

Name _____

Counting Hundreds, Tens, and Ones   PS 10-2

Use the clues to write the number.

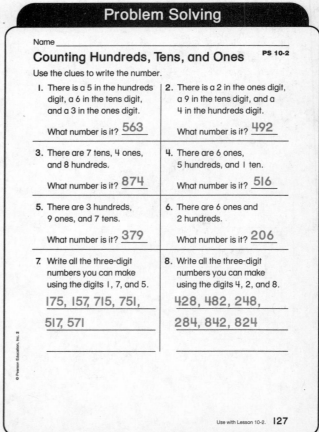

1. There is a 5 in the hundreds digit, a 6 in the tens digit, and a 3 in the ones digit.

What number is it? _563_

2. There is a 2 in the ones digit, a 9 in the tens digit, and a 4 in the hundreds digit.

What number is it? _492_

3. There are 7 tens, 4 ones, and 8 hundreds.

What number is it? _874_

4. There are 6 ones, 5 hundreds, and 1 ten.

What number is it? _516_

5. There are 3 hundreds, 9 ones, and 7 tens.

What number is it? _379_

6. There are 6 ones and 2 hundreds.

What number is it? _206_

7. Write all the three-digit numbers you can make using the digits 1, 7, and 5.

175, 157, 715, 751, 517, 571

8. Write all the three-digit numbers you can make using the digits 4, 2, and 8.

428, 482, 248, 284, 842, 824

Use with Lesson 10-2. **127**

Name _____

Writing Numbers to 1,000
R 10-3

| **Expanded form** uses plus signs to show hundreds, tens, and ones.
$200 + 60 + 4$ | The **number word** is two hundred sixty-four.
_____ |
| You can draw models to show expanded form.
 | The **standard form** is
264. |

Draw models to show the expanded form.
Write the number in standard form.

1. $400 + 30 + 8$ four hundred thirty-eight

 **438**

2. $300 + 70 + 2$ three hundred seventy-two

 **372**

3. $500 + 10 + 4$ five hundred fourteen

514

128 Use with Lesson 10-3.

© Pearson Education, Inc. 2

Name _____

Writing Numbers to 1,000
P 10-3

Circle the models to match the expanded form.
Write the number in standard form.

1. $200 + 70 + 5$ **275**

2. $100 + 40 + 8$ **148**

3. $300 + 30 + 2$ **332**

Circle the models to match the standard form.
Write the number in expanded form.

4. 571   **500** + **70** + **1**

5. 407   **400** + **0** + **7**

Problem Solving *Mental Math*

Write the total.

6. Crayons come in boxes of 10.
How many boxes do you
need for 100 crayons? **10** boxes

 10 crayons = 1 box

128 Use with Lesson 10-3.

© Pearson Education, Inc. 2

Name _____

A Number Crossword
E 10-3
NUMBER SENSE

Use the clues to fill in the number puzzle.

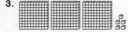

¹5	2	²3		³3	0	⁴5
		⁵4	2	9		6
⁶2	1	7		7	⁸4	9
	8				3	
	⁹2	6	9		8	

Across

1. $500 + 20 + 3$
3. [models]
5. $400 + 20 + 9$
6. [models]

Down

2. $300 + 40 + 7$
3. Three hundred ninety-seven
4. $500 + 60 + 9$
7. [models]
8. Four hundred thirty-eight
9. Two hundred sixty-nine

128 Use with Lesson 10-3.

© Pearson Education, Inc. 2

Name _____

Writing Numbers to 1,000
PS 10-3

Use the chart to answer each question.

Number of Pages in Each School Book

Math	Science	Social Studies	Reading	Music
608	365	214	390	198

Write the name of the book with the following
number of pages.

1. $200 + 10 + 4$ Social Studies

2. $100 + 90 + 8$ Music

3. $600 + 8$ Math

4. $300 + 60 + 5$ Science

5. Look at the number of pages in your math book.
Write the number in expanded form.   Check children's answers.

___ + ___ + ___

6. Eight books each have 100 pages.
How many pages is that in all?

800 pages

128 Use with Lesson 10-3.

© Pearson Education, Inc. 2

© Pearson Education, Inc. 2

Reteaching

Name _____

Changing Numbers by Hundreds and Tens

R 10-4

When you change a number by adding or subtracting tens, only the tens digit changes.

$100 + 30 + 6 = 136$

Think: 10 more

$136 + 10 = 146$

Think: 20 less

$136 - 20 = 116$

When you change a number by adding or subtracting hundreds, only the hundreds digit changes.

$300 + 50 + 3 = 353$

Think: 100 more

$353 + 100 = 453$

Think: 200 less

$353 - 200 = 153$

Underline the digits that change. Then solve the problem.

1.

$446 + 20 = 466$

$446 + 200 = 646$

$400 + 40 + 6 = 446$

2.

$538 - 30 = 508$

$538 - 300 = 238$

$500 + 30 + 8 = 538$

Practice

Name _____

Changing Numbers by Hundreds and Tens

P 10-4

Use models, drawings, or mental math to solve the problem.

1.

$362 - 10 = 352$

$362 - 100 = 262$

2.

$148 + 40 = 188$

$148 + 400 = 548$

3.

$594 - 30 = 564$

$594 - 300 = 294$

4.

$433 + 20 = 453$

$433 + 200 = 633$

Problem Solving *Number Sense*

Solve.

5. Mickey has 234 baseball cards. He gets 50 more cards. How many cards does he have now?

____284____ cards

6. Dixie has 426 baseball cards. She gives away 200 cards. How many cards does she have now?

____226____ cards

Enrichment

Name _____

Trick Hats

E 10-4
ALGEBRA

What number is hidden inside the hat?
Use mental math to solve. Write the missing number.

1. $381 + \boxed{100} = 481$

2. $521 - \boxed{10} = 511$

3. $738 - \boxed{200} = 538$

4. $361 + \boxed{300} = 661$

5. $499 - \boxed{40} = 459$

6. $287 + \boxed{200} = 487$

7. $127 + \boxed{400} = 527$

8. $629 - \boxed{20} = 609$

9. $859 - \boxed{30} = 829$

10. $515 + \boxed{40} = 555$

Problem Solving

Name _____

Changing Numbers by Hundreds and Tens

PS 10-4

Solve each problem.

1. Roy drives 382 miles. Then he drives another 100 miles. How many miles does Roy drive altogether?

____482____ miles

2. 165 people are in line. 20 more people get in line. How many people are in line now?

____185____ people

3. 279 people go on a train trip. 30 people get off the train. How many people are still on the train?

____249____ people

4. 314 people are on an airplane. At the first stop, 100 people get off. How many people are still on the airplane?

____214____ people

5. Tasia drives 478 miles to the beach. Then she drives another 200 miles. How many miles does she drive altogether?

____678____ miles

6. A boat travels 641 miles to one port. Then it travels another 300 miles to another port. How many miles does the boat travel in all?

____941____ miles

7. 485 people are on a ship. At one stop, 50 people get off the ship. How many people are still on the ship?

____435____ people

Name _____

Comparing Numbers

To compare two numbers with unequal hundreds, compare the hundreds first.

Remember:
< is less than

125   243

Think: 1 hundred is less than 2 hundreds. So, 125 < 243.

To compare two numbers with equal hundreds, compare the tens first.

Remember:
> is greater than

243   217

Think: 4 tens is greater than 1 ten. So, 243 > 217.

Write the number in standard form.
Then compare. Write > or <.

1.

455   >   326

2.

313   <   323

Name _____

Comparing Numbers

Compare. Write >, <, or =. Use models if you need to.

1. 157 < 214   361 < 378   419 < 516

2. 600 > 598   771 = 771   645 > 546

3. 197 < 217   505 < 550   987 > 978

4. 384 < 478   727 > 582   408 < 804

Problem Solving *Visual Thinking*

5. Draw lines to match the clues with the correct model.

My number is less than 5 hundreds. The ones digit is less than 7.

My number is greater than 3 hundreds. The tens digit is greater than 5.

My number has more than 3 hundreds. There are 0 tens in the number.

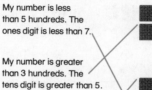

Name _____

Number Triangles

Use the numbers in the triangles.
Write a number that will make each sentence true.

Answers will vary.
Possible answers are given.

1. 537 > 487

2. 416 > 187

3. 231 < 512

4. 243 < 318

5. 634 > 138

6. 463 < 804

7. 492 < 717

8. 792 > 782

9. 591 > 572

Name _____

Comparing Numbers

Compare. Write >, <, or =.
Then answer the questions.

1. Doug has 125 pennies in his piggy bank.
   Amy has 458 pennies in her piggy bank.
   Whose piggy bank has more pennies?

   125 < 458   _____ Amy's _____

2. Mom's book has 215 pages.
   Dad's book has 680 pages.
   Whose book has fewer pages?

   215 < 680   _____ Mom's _____

3. Ellie's album has 409 pictures.
   Derek's album has 229 pictures.
   Derek adds 180 more pictures to his album.
   Whose album has more pictures?

   409 = 409   They both have the same amount.

4. Use numbers to compare how many children
   the buses can hold. Write >, <, or =.

   ____ > ____

© Pearson Education, Inc. 2

Name _____

Parts of 1,000

R 10-6

There are different ways to make 1,000.
You can count on by 100s and by 10s to make 1,000.

Start with 650.   Count on by 100s.   Count on by 10s.

100   200   300   10 20 30 40 50
750, 850, 950   960, 970, 980, 990, 1,000

650   +   __300__   +   __50__   = 1,000

650 + __350__ = 1,000

Find the parts for 1,000.
Count on by 100s. Then count on by 10s.

1. Start with 750.

100 → 200   10 20 30 40 50

750   +   __200__   +   __50__   = 1,000

750 + __250__ = 1,000

2. Start with 500.

100 200 300 400 500

500   +   __500__   = 1,000

Name _____

Parts of 1,000

P 10-6

Count on to solve each problem.

1. Kayla has 850 points. How many more points does she need to get to 1,000?

850 + __150__ = 1,000

__150__ points

2. Abdul has 550 points. If he needs 1,000 points to win, how many more points does he need?

550 + __450__ = 1,000

__450__ points

3. Monty has 700 points. He needs 1,000 points to win. How many more points does he need?

700 + __300__ = 1,000

__300__ points

4. Suki has 350 points. How many more points does she need to get to 1,000?

350 + __650__ = 1,000

__650__ points

Problem Solving *Number Sense*

Find the missing number.

5. Misha has 250 points. Tasia has 300 points. They need 1,000 points to win. How many more points do they need?

250 + 300 + __?__ = 1,000   __450__ points

Name _____

Bean Bag Toss

E 10-6
ALGEBRA

Four children play bean bag toss.
They already have some points.
Color the 2 numbers they must hit to make 1,000.
Then complete each number sentence.

1. Vanessa has 300 points.

200	500
600	300

300 + __200__ + __500__ = 1,000

2. Leroy has 250 points.

150	250
600	550

250 + __150__ + __600__ = 1,000

3. Maya has 450 points.

450	300
150	400

450 + __150__ + __400__ = 1,000

4. Chin has 200 points.

200	550
250	400

200 + __250__ + __550__ = 1,000

Name _____

Parts of 1,000

PS 10-6

Use the chart to solve each problem.

Sewing Supplies

Sewing Needles	Safety Pins	Spools of Thread	Straight Pins	Buttons
250	400	150	550	300

Mr. Wing needs 1,000 of each item in the chart.
Write a number sentence to find how many more of each item Mr. Wing needs.

1. Sewing needles __250__ + __750__ = 1,000

__750__ more sewing needles

2. Buttons __300__ + __700__ = 1,000

__700__ more buttons

3. Spools of thread __150__ + __850__ = 1,000

__850__ more spools of thread

4. Straight pins __550__ + __450__ = 1,000

__450__ more straight pins

5. How many more safety pins are needed to make 1,000? Skip count by 100s to find the answer.

400, __500, 600, 700, 800, 900__, 1,000

__600__ more safety pins are needed.

Name _____

Use Data from a Chart

You can use a chart to solve problems. This chart shows the points scored on a video game.

Points Scored	
Dan	356
Naomi	617
Philip	582
Lucy	298

Who scored more points, Dan or Naomi?

Look at the chart for the points that Dan and Naomi scored.

Dan scored __356__ points.

Naomi scored __617__ points.

356 (<) 617   __Naomi__ scored more points.

Use the chart to answer the questions.

1. Who scored more points, Philip or Lucy?

   Philip scored __582__ points.   582 (>) 298

   Lucy scored __298__ points.   __Philip__ scored more points.

2. Who scored more points, Lucy or Naomi?

   Lucy scored __298__ points.   298 (<) 617

   Naomi scored __617__ points.   __Naomi__ scored more points.

3. Who scored $300 + 50 + 6$ points? __Dan__

Name _____

Use Data from a Chart

Use data from the chart to answer the questions.

Number of People at the Games	
Basketball	465
Baseball	390
Soccer	288
Hockey	432

1. Did more people come to the baseball game or the hockey game?   __the hockey game__

2. Which game did $400 + 60 + 5$ people come to watch?   __the basketball game__

3. 2 hundreds, 8 tens, and 8 ones tells how many people came to which game?   __the soccer game__

Problem Solving *Reasonableness*

Circle the number that makes the most sense.

4. About 50 / (500) people are watching basketball.

5. About (300) / 30 people are watching soccer.

Circle the words that make more sense.

6. The number of people at a basketball game is less than / (greater than) the number of people at a hockey game.

Name _____

Choose five different numbers that have 3 digits.
Write the numbers in the chart.
Then use the numbers to answer the questions.

Movie Tickets Sold

Monday	Tuesday	Wednesday	Thursday	Friday
Answers will vary. Check children's answers.				

1. Were more tickets sold on Wednesday or Thursday? _____

2. How many tickets were sold on Monday? _____

3. On what day were the most tickets sold? _____

4. Were more tickets sold on Thursday or Friday? _____

5. Write the expanded number for the number of tickets sold on Tuesday. ____ + ____ + ____

6. Write your own problem. Have a friend solve it.

   __Answers will vary.__
   _____

Name _____

Use Data from a Chart

You can use a chart to solve problems.

Grade 1 collected 100 more cans.
They forgot to add this to their total.
How many cans did they collect altogether?

Cans Collected on Recycling Day	
Grade 1	267
Grade 2	430
Grade 3	290
Grade 4	378

What is the problem asking you to do?

__Add 100 to the total for Grade 1 to find how many cans they collected in all.__

What numbers will you use? __100 and 267__

What is the answer? __367 cans__

Use the chart to solve.

1. On the next day, Grade 2 collects two hundred more cans. Now how many cans do they have?

   __630__ cans

2. Grade 3 collects $50 + 4$ more cans on the next day. How many cans did they collect for both days?

   __344__ cans

3. Grade 4 cannot recycle 100 cans. The remaining cans are recycled. How many cans did Grade 4 recycle? Write the answer in expanded form.

   __$200 + 70 + 8$__ cans

Using the page After children *read* the problem, have them explain the problem in their own words to help them *understand* what is being asked.

Name _____

Before, After, and Between

R 10-8

Think about the order of numbers.

| 150 | 151 | 152 | 153 | 154 | 155 | 156 | 157 | 158 | 159 |
| 160 | 161 | 162 | 163 | 164 | 165 | 166 | 167 | 168 | 169 |

__152__ is **before** 153.   __168__ is **after** 167.

__161__ is **between** 160 and 162.

Write the numbers that are before, after, and between.

1.

| 300 | 301 | 302 | 303 | 304 | 305 | 306 | 307 | 308 | 309 |
| 310 | 311 | 312 | 313 | 314 | 315 | 316 | 317 | 318 | 319 |

__313__ is **before** 314.   __305__ is **after** 304.

__304__ is **between** 303 and 305.

2.

| 750 | 751 | 752 | 753 | 754 | 755 | 756 | 757 | 758 | 759 |
| 760 | 761 | 762 | 763 | 764 | 765 | 766 | 767 | 768 | 769 |

__764__ is **before** 765.   __759__ is **after** 758.

__753__ is **between** 752 and 754.

3.

| 530 | 531 | 532 | 533 | 534 | 535 | 536 | 537 | 538 | 539 |
| 540 | 541 | 542 | 543 | 544 | 545 | 546 | 547 | 548 | 549 |

__548__ is **before** 549.   __531__ is **after** 530.

__542__ is **between** 541 and 543.

Name _____

Before, After, and Between

P 10-8

Write the number that comes after.

1. 235, __236__   489, __490__   600, __601__

2. 319, __320__   899, __900__   534, __535__

Write the number that comes before.

3. __729__, 730   __404__, 405   __336__, 337

4. __799__, 800   __178__, 179   __297__, 298

Write the number that comes between.

5. 375, __376__, 377   819, __820__, 821   197, __198__, 199

6. 199, __200__, 201   450, __451__, 452   834, __835__, 836

Write the number.

7. What is one before 278? __277__

8. What is one after 743? __744__

9. What number is between 681 and 683? __682__

Problem Solving Reasoning
Circle the numbers.

10. Which two numbers come after 297?   213 (307) (299)

11. Which two numbers come before 810?   (775) (801) 811

12. Which two numbers come between 400 and 450?   (425) 465 (419)

Name _____

Team Shirts

E 10-8
REASONING

Five players came to play soccer.
Look at the clues and the numbers in the box.
Match the players with their team number.
Write the number on the shirt.

| 192 | 319 | 198 | 435 | 420 |

1. My number is between 197 and 199.

2. My number comes before Tom's number.

3. My number is between 419 and 421.

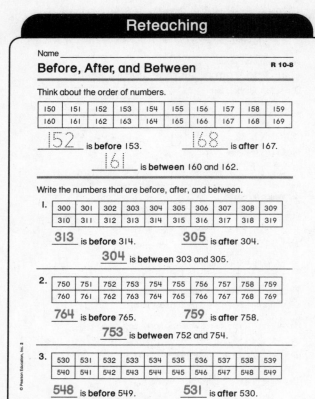

198
Tom

192
Adam

420
Sari

4. My number comes after Sari's number.

5. My number is between Tom's and Sari's number.

435
Ming

319
Carlos

Name _____

Before, After, and Between

PS 10-8

Use the clues to find each number.
Write the numbers on the doors.

180	368	222	817	540	614
Mott	Baldwin	Santos	Green	Summers	Tabriz

1. The number on Miss Baldwin's door is before 370 and after 359. It has 8 ones. What number is it?

2. The number on Mr. Green's door is between 813 and 823. It has 7 ones. What number is it?

3. The number on Ms. Summers's door is after 500 and before 600. The number has 4 tens and 0 ones. What number is it?

4. The number on Mrs. Santos's door is between 200 and 230. It has the same number of hundreds, tens, and ones. What number is it?

5. The number on Miss Tabriz's door is between 600 and 650. The number has 4 ones and 1 ten. What number is it?

6. The number on Mr. Mott's door is after 100. If you count by 20s four times, you will get the number. What number is it?

Name_____

Ordering Numbers

R 10-9

These numbers are in order from least to greatest.

$\boxed{167} < \boxed{270} < \boxed{273} < \boxed{499}$ *Each number is less than (<) the number after it.*

These numbers are in order from greatest to least.

$\boxed{684} > \boxed{680} > \boxed{371} > \boxed{262}$ *Each number is greater than (>) the number after it.*

Order the numbers from least to greatest.

$\boxed{275}$ $\boxed{543}$ $\boxed{110}$ $\boxed{212}$

$\underline{110} < \underline{212} < \underline{275} < \underline{543}$

Order the numbers from greatest to least.

$\boxed{616}$ $\boxed{583}$ $\boxed{775}$ $\boxed{102}$

$\underline{775} > \underline{616} > \underline{583} > \underline{102}$

Write the numbers in order from least to greatest.

1. $\boxed{187}$ $\boxed{126}$ $\boxed{219}$ $\boxed{267}$ 126, 187, 219, 267

2. $\boxed{341}$ $\boxed{489}$ $\boxed{452}$ $\boxed{317}$ 317, 341, 452, 489

Write the numbers in order from greatest to least.

3. $\boxed{419}$ $\boxed{578}$ $\boxed{535}$ $\boxed{487}$ 578, 535, 487, 419

4. $\boxed{682}$ $\boxed{734}$ $\boxed{546}$ $\boxed{650}$ 734, 682, 650, 546

134 Use with Lesson 10-9.

© Pearson Education, Inc. 2

Name_____

Ordering Numbers

P 10-9

Write the numbers in order from least to greatest.

1. 673, 628, 515, 437, 321

   321, 437, 515, 628, 673

2. 423, 409, 457, 524, 582

   409, 423, 457, 524, 582

3. 507, 387, 652, 481, 658

   387, 481, 507, 652, 658

4. 198, 277, 156, 287, 192

   156, 192, 198, 277, 287

Write the numbers in order from greatest to least.

5. 731, 682, 432, 819, 688

   819, 731, 688, 682, 432

6. 331, 287, 207, 432, 211

   432, 331, 287, 211, 207

Problem Solving *Writing in Math*

Use the space on the right to solve the problems.

7. In the numbers 572 to 592, are there more even or odd numbers? How do you know?

   There are more even numbers. There are 10 odd numbers and 11 even numbers.

134 Use with Lesson 10-9.

© Pearson Education, Inc. 2

Name_____

What Is Missing?

E 10-9
REASONING

Fill in the missing numbers.
Use the numbers in the box.

| 362 | 240 | 429 | 719 | 885 | 226 |

These numbers are in order from greatest to least.

1. 562, 467, 431, 429, 387, 362, 341

2. 973, 960, 885, 841, 769, 719, 700

3. 437, 411, 365, 271, 240, 226, 199

| 321 | 478 | 625 | 415 | 701 | 589 |

These numbers are in order from least to greatest.

4. 215, 297, 321, 341, 402, 415, 437

5. 482, 521, 618, 625, 701, 750

6. 389, 413, 459, 478, 532, 589, 599

134 Use with Lesson 10-9.

© Pearson Education, Inc. 2

Name_____

Ordering Numbers

PS 10-9

This chart tells how many miles each town is from Centerville. Use the numbers in the chart to answer the questions.

Distance from Centerville

Town	Miles
Hopetown	128
Beach Point	416
Port Smith	390
Pearl River	672
Ellenville	302

1. Which town is the farthest from Centerville?

   Pearl River

2. Which town is the closest to Centerville?

   Hopetown

3. Write the number of miles in order from least to greatest.

   128, 302, 390, 416, 672

4. Write the little towns in order from the farthest from Centerville to the nearest to Centerville.

   Pearl River, Beach Point, Port Smith, Ellenville, Hopetown

Writing in Math

5. Write a question about ordering using the map.

   Check children's answers.

134 Use with Lesson 10-9.

© Pearson Education, Inc. 2

© Pearson Education, Inc. 2

Name _____

Look for a Pattern

A pattern is something that repeats.

| Read and Understand |

Look for a pattern rule to find what number comes next.
What number comes next? 280, 270, 260, 250, 240, __?__

| Plan and Solve |

Think. What digit changes?   280, 270, 260, 250, 240 ___10s___

Think. Does it increase or decrease?   280, 270, 260, 250, 240 ___decrease___

Think. By how much?   280, 270, 260, 250, 240 ___by 10___

The pattern rule is ___The numbers decrease by 10.___

The next number is ___230___.

| Look Back and Check |

Does your answer fit the pattern rule?

Write the numbers that come next. Describe the pattern rule.

1. 285, 385, 485, 585, 685, __785__, __885__, __985__
The pattern rule is: ___The numbers increase by 100.___

2. 340, 360, 380, 400, 420, __440__, __460__, __480__
The pattern rule is: ___The numbers increase by 20.___

Name _____

Look for a Pattern

Write the missing numbers. Describe the pattern.

1. 185, 195, 205, 215, __225__, __235__, __245__
___The numbers increase by 10, or the tens digits increase by 1.___

Write the number that is 50 less.

2.
778	690	187	958
728	640	137	908

What pattern do you see? ___The tens digits decrease by 5.___

Write the number that is 300 more.

3.
205	537	169	649
505	837	469	949

What pattern do you see? ___The hundreds digits increase by 3.___

Problem Solving *Reasoning*

Find the pattern. Circle the number that comes next.

4. 105, 125, 145, 165   166   (185)   175

5. 300, 325, 350, 375   500   476   (400)

6. 550, 600, 650, 700   725   (750)   800

Name _____

Pattern Addition and Subtraction

Write the number in the pattern.
Then describe the pattern rule.
Then write the next number in the pattern.

1. $203 + \boxed{?} = 223, 223 + \boxed{?} = 243, 243 + \boxed{?} = 263$
The numbers (increase)/decrease by __20__. The next number is __283__.

2. $530 - \boxed{?} = 430, 430 - \boxed{?} = 330, 330 - \boxed{?} = 230$
The numbers increase/(decrease) by __100__. The next number is __130__.

3. $720 + \boxed{?} = 730, 730 + \boxed{?} = 740, 740 + \boxed{?} = 750$
The numbers (increase)/decrease by __10__. The next number is __760__.

4. $305 + \boxed{?} = 405, 405 + \boxed{?} = 505, 505 + \boxed{?} = 605$
The numbers (increase)/decrease by __100__. The next number is __705__.

5. $852 - \boxed{?} = 752, 752 - \boxed{?} = 652, 652 - \boxed{?} = 552$
The numbers increase/(decrease) by __100__. The next number is __452__.

6. $785 - \boxed{?} = 765, 765 - \boxed{?} = 745, 745 - \boxed{?} = 725$
The numbers increase/(decrease) by __20__. The next number is __705__.

Name _____

Look for a Pattern

| Read and Understand |

Find the number that comes next.

215, 315, 415, 515, 615, __?__

| Plan and Solve |

Look for a pattern rule. What is different about each number?

___The hundreds digit changes each time.___

How does the number change? ___It increases by 100.___

So, the next number in the pattern will follow the same rule.

The next number in the pattern is ___715___.

| Look Back and Check |

In your own words, what is the pattern rule?
Does your answer match the pattern rule?

Describe the pattern rule. Write the numbers that come next.

1. 400, 375, 350, 325, 300, __?__, __?__, __?__

Pattern rule ___The numbers decrease by 25.___

Next numbers __275__, __250__, __225__

Using the page To help children *plan and solve,* have them decide how the numbers in the pattern change. Then have them determine if the numbers increase or decrease by the amount they change.

Reteaching

PROBLEM-SOLVING APPLICATIONS   R 10-11

Rescue Vehicles

Fire truck A has 600 gallons of water. Fire truck B has 100 more gallons.	Fire truck C has 500 gallons of water. It uses 100 gallons to put out a fire.
Fire truck A: ⬛⬛⬛⬛⬛⬛	Fire truck C: ⬛ ⬛ ⬛ ⬛ ⬛
Fire truck B: ⬛⬛⬛⬛⬛⬛+⬛	Gallons used: ⬛ ⬛ ⬛ ⬛ ⬛̶
$600 + 100 = 700$	$500 - 100 = 400$
100 more than 600 is	100 less than 500 is
_700_ gallons.	_400_ gallons.

Solve.

1. A firefighter goes on 30 calls in one month.
   How much is 10 calls less than that?

   $30 - 10 = \underline{20}$ calls

   How much is 10 calls more than that?

   $30 + 10 = \underline{40}$ calls

2. A fire truck travels 400 miles in one month.
   How much is 100 miles more than that? _500_ miles

   How much is 100 miles less than that? _300_ miles

Practice

PROBLEM-SOLVING APPLICATIONS   P 10-11

Rescue Vehicles

1. A fire truck traveled 267 miles in one month to put out fires. Record the number of hundreds, tens, and ones in 267.

   _2_ hundreds   _6_ tens   _7_ ones

2. A fire boat had 215 calls in one year.
   It had 198 calls the next year.
   Compare these two numbers. Write >, <, or =.

   215 ⊙> 198

3. A fire truck responded to an alarm at quarter past 10. What is another way to write this time?

   _10:15_

Writing in Math

4. Write a number story about an ambulance. Use four numbers between 200 and 300. At the end of your story, list the numbers in order from greatest to least.

   Check children's math.

Enrichment

Let's Roll!

E 10-11
DATA

The table shows how many miles these rescue vehicles drove in one month. Use the data in the chart to answer each question.

Rescue Vehicles	
Fire Engine 1	386
Fire Engine 2	571
Ambulance	489
Fireboat	214

1. The ambulance rides another 100 miles. How many miles is that in all? _589_ miles

2. What is the number of hundreds, tens, and ones that the fireboat drove?

   _2_ hundreds

   _1_ tens

   _4_ ones

3. Compare the number of miles driven by Fire Engine 1 and Fire Engine 2.

   Write >, <, or =.   386 ⊙< 571

4. Fire Engine 3 drove 10 miles less than Fire Engine 1. How many miles did it drive? _376_ miles

5. Write your own problem about the numbers in the chart. Give your problem to a classmate to solve.

   Answers will vary.

Problem Solving

PROBLEM-SOLVING APPLICATIONS   PS 10-11

Rescue Vehicles

A lifeboat traveled 137 miles to a rescue.
Then it traveled another 100 miles to a larger boat.
How many miles did the lifeboat travel?

$137 + 100 = \underline{237}$

Check your answer. What did the problem ask you to do?

Find how many miles the lifeboat traveled in all.

Does your answer solve the problem? _yes_

Solve.

1. There were 156 firefighters at a fire.
   How many is 10 firefighters less? _146_ firefighters
   How many is 10 firefighters more? _166_ firefighters

2. Firehouse A responded to 187 alarms.
   Firehouse B responded to 215 alarms.
   Compare these two numbers. 187 ⊙< 215

Writing in Math

3. Write a number story about a rescue. Use two 3-digit numbers. Compare the numbers.

   Stories will vary.

Using the page Ask children to *look back* and reread the problem. Then have them *check* that they solved the problem correctly.

© Pearson Education, Inc. **2**

---

136   Use with Chapter 10, Lesson 11.

Using Mental Math

R 11-1

Add 315 + 264. Use mental math.

To add using mental math, begin with the expanded form of each number. Then add each place value.

315 ➜ 300 + 10 + 5   500 + 70 + 9 = 579
264 ➜ + 200 + 60 + 4
         500 + 70 + 9   So, 315 + 264 = 579

Add.

1. 523 + 172 = __?__

523 ➜ 500 + 20 + 3
172 ➜ + 100 + 70 + 2
         600 + 90 + 5
600 + 90 + 5 = 695

So, 523 + 172 = 695

2. 281 + 716 = __?__

281 ➜ 200 + 80 + 1
716 ➜ + 700 + 10 + 6
         900 + 90 + 7
900 + 90 + 7 = 997

So, 281 + 716 = 997

3. 193 + 605 = __?__

193 ➜ 100 + 90 + 3
605 ➜ + 600 + 0 + 5
         700 + 90 + 8
700 + 90 + 8 = 798

So, 193 + 605 = 798

Using Mental Math

P 11-1

Add. Use mental math.

1. 306 + 213 = 519   515 + 262 = 777

2. 164 + 311 = 475   623 + 123 = 746

3. 412 + 250 = 662   322 + 146 = 468

4. 707 = 303 + 404   711 + 105 = 816

5. 271 + 320 = 591   439 = 319 + 120

6. 409 + 230 = 639   725 + 114 = 839

Problem Solving Algebra

Write the missing number that makes the number sentence true.

7. 400 + 500 = 600 + 300   8. 200 + 700 = 700 + 200

9. 300 + 200 = 0 + 500   10. 500 + 400 = 900 + 0

11. 100 + 700 = 400 + 400   12. 600 + 300 = 800 + 100

Missing Numbers

E 11-1
ALGEBRA

Use mental math to find the missing digit of each number. Then write the number.

1. 236 + 1■2 = 378
142

2. 314 + ■23 = 537
223

3. 524 + 15■ = 675
151

4. 3■2 + 442 = 794
352

5. ■35 + 402 = 837
435

6. ■48 + 140 = 888
748

7. 15■ + 126 = 279
153

8. 251 + ■35 = 486
235

9. 305 + 3■2 = 607
302

10. ■21 + 344 = 565
221

Using Mental Math

PS 11-1

Points Scored at Pinball

Nina	Kobe	Marsha	Anna	Sulu	Roberto
436	234	412	341	617	563

Use mental math to solve.

1. Nina and Marsha are on one team. How many points do they score?
436 + 412 = 848

2. Kobe and Roberto are on one team. How many points do they score?
234 + 563 = 797

3. Anna and Sulu are on one team. How many points do they score?
341 + 617 = 958

4. Two players from different teams score a total of 575 points. One of the players is Kobe. Who is the other player?
Anna

5. Which team scored the most points?
Anna and Sulu

6. Which team scored the least points?
Kobe and Roberto

Name _____

Estimating Sums   R 11-2

You can estimate to find an answer that is close
to the exact sum. To estimate, find the closest hundred.

Estimate 185 + 437. Is it more than or less than 500?

Is 185 closer to 100 or 200? $\underline{200}$

Is 437 closer to 400 or 500? $\underline{400}$

$\underline{200} + \underline{400} = \underline{600}$

So, 185 + 437 is $\underline{\text{more than}}$ 500.

Is the sum more or less than the number?
Estimate the sum. Write **more than** or **less than**.

I. Is 179 + 267 more than or less than 600?

179 is close to $\underline{200}$.   267 is close to $\underline{300}$.

$\underline{200} + \underline{300} = \underline{500}$.

179 + 267 is $\underline{\text{less than}}$ 600.

2. Is 327 + 417 more than or less than 600?

327 is close to $\underline{300}$.   417 is close to $\underline{400}$.

$\underline{300} + \underline{400} = \underline{700}$.

327 + 417 is $\underline{\text{more than}}$ 600.

© Pearson Education, Inc. 2

Name _____

Estimating Sums   P 11-2

Is the sum more or less than the number?
Estimate the sum. Then write **more than** or **less than**.

I. Is 283 + 250 more than
or less than 500? $\underline{\text{more than}}$ 500

2. Is 415 + 403 more than
or less than 850? $\underline{\text{less than}}$ 850

3. Is 367 + 298 more than
or less than 650? $\underline{\text{more than}}$ 650

4. Is 454 + 432 more than
or less than 900? $\underline{\text{less than}}$ 900

5. Is 277 + 519 more than
or less than 750? $\underline{\text{more than}}$ 750

Problem Solving *Number Sense*
Look at the cards. Choose a number that
will make each sentence true.

6. 382 + $\underline{224}$ is about 600.

7. 378 + $\underline{101}$ is less than 600.

8. 211 + $\underline{440}$ is more than 600.

224	440
101	

© Pearson Education, Inc. 2

Name _____

The Raffle   E 11-2
                                  ESTIMATION

Use the data in the table to record how many
tickets each child sold. Then estimate the sums
to answer the questions.

Raffle Tickets Sold

Marissa	Benji	Amita	Steven	Nicky
127	415	378	292	134

I. Amita sold $\underline{378}$ tickets.

Steven sold $\underline{292}$ tickets.

Did they sell more than
600 tickets together?

(yes)   no

2. Marissa sold $\underline{127}$ tickets.

Nicky sold $\underline{134}$ tickets.

Did they sell more than
400 tickets together?

yes   (no)

3. Benji sold $\underline{415}$ tickets.

Marissa sold $\underline{127}$ tickets.

Did they sell more than
500 tickets together?

(yes)   no

4. Amita sold $\underline{378}$ tickets.

Benji sold $\underline{415}$ tickets.

Did they sell more than
700 tickets together?

(yes)   no

5. Nicky sold $\underline{134}$ tickets.

Benji sold $\underline{415}$ tickets.

Did they sell less than
500 tickets together?

yes   (no)

6. Steven sold $\underline{292}$ tickets.

Marissa sold $\underline{127}$ tickets.

Did they sell less than
400 tickets together?

yes   (no)

© Pearson Education, Inc. 2

Name _____

Estimating Sums   PS 11-2

Estimate to solve.

I. Mindy's Vegetable Stand has 213 red tomatoes
and 323 green tomatoes. Does she have
more than or less than 500 tomatoes?

$\underline{\text{more than}}$ 500 tomatoes

2. Sue's Sewing Store has 185 large buttons and
201 small buttons. Does Sue's shop have
more than or less than 300 buttons?

$\underline{\text{more than}}$ 300 buttons

3. Rob's Art Shop has 328 water color paints
and 215 oil paints: Does Rob's shop have
more than or less than 600 paints?

$\underline{\text{less than}}$ 600 paints

Circle the correct answer.

4. Ms. Walsh's Health Food Bar has 425 boxes
of hot cereal and some boxes of cold cereal.
In all, there are about 500 boxes of cereal.
How many boxes of cold cereal are there?

150   200   (100)

© Pearson Education, Inc. **2**

Name _____

Adding with Models

135 + 248 = _____

Step 1: Add the ones. Regroup if you need to.
Step 2: Add the tens. Regroup if you need to.
Step 3: Add the hundreds.

	Hundreds	Tens	Ones
135			
248			

5 + 8 = 13 ones. Regroup 10 ones for 1 ten.

135 + 248 = 383

Add to find the sum. Use models and Workmat 5.
Show each number.

1.

Hundreds	Tens	Ones

341 + 127 = 468

2.

Hundreds	Tens	Ones

524 + 249 = 773

Name _____

Adding with Models

Use models and Workmat 5. Show each number.
Add to find the sum.

1. 407 + 188 = 595   2. 182 + 253 = 435

3. 270 + 319 = 589   4. 685 = 558 + 127

5. 376 + 508 = 884   6. 427 = 194 + 233

Problem Solving *Estimation*

Circle the best estimate.

7.

Grade	Number of Children
1	235
2	189

About how many children are in both grades?

300   (400)   500

8.

Grade	Number of Children
3	429
4	311

About how many children are in both grades?

600   (700)   800

9. Each floor of the school holds 145 children. About how many children can the school hold if there are 2 floors?

150   250   (300)

Name _____

Around the Playground

Use the map and models to find the sums.

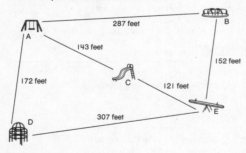

Find the distances.

1. From A to B to E.

287 + 152 = 439 feet

2. From D to A to C.

172 + 143 = 315 feet

3. From D to E to C.

307 + 121 = 428 feet

4. From C to E to B.

121 + 152 = 273 feet

Name _____

Adding with Models

Solve. Use models to find each sum.

1. Leo drives 415 miles to Oakland, then another 231 miles to Fairview. How many miles does he drive?

415 + 231 = 646 miles

2. Olivia flies 516 miles to Greenville, then drives another 148 miles. How many miles does she travel in all?

516 + 148 = 664 miles

3. A train travels 221 miles by day and 347 miles at night. How many miles does the train travel in all?

221 + 347 = 568 miles

4. A bus tour travels 472 miles on Thursday and 283 miles on Friday. How far does the bus travel in two days?

472 + 283 = 755 miles

Circle the best estimate.

5. Mrs. Pinky sails 256 miles on her boat to an island. Then she sails 139 miles to another island. About how many miles does she sail in all?

300   (400)   500

6. Mr. DeLuca hikes 192 miles in one week. Then he hikes 173 miles the next week. About how many miles does Mr. DeLuca hike in two weeks?

200   300   (400)

Name _____

Adding Three-Digit Numbers

R 11-4

Step 1: Add the ones. Regroup if you need to.
Step 2: Add the tens. Regroup if you need to.
Step 3: Add the hundreds.

Think:
Regroup 10 tens
for 1 hundred.

$163 + 174 = $ ___?___

Hundreds	Tens	Ones
1	6	3
+ 1	7	4
3	3	7

Draw to regroup. Add.

1. $218 + 136 = $ ___?___

Hundreds	Tens	Ones
	1	
2	1	8
+ 1	3	6
3	5	4

Add. Use models and Workmat 5 if you need to.

2.
Hundreds	Tens	Ones
1	2	5
+ 2	4	2
3	6	7

3.
Hundreds	Tens	Ones
	1	
4	1	9
+ 2	5	6
6	7	5

140 Use with Lesson 11-4.

Name _____

Adding Three-Digit Numbers

P 11-4

Add. Use models and Workmat 5 if you need to.

1.
Hundreds	Tens	Ones
	1	
6	3	4
+ 1	5	9
7	9	3

Hundreds	Tens	Ones
1		
1	2	9
+ 4	9	0
6	1	9

2.
457	219	405	286	124
+ 138	+ 390	+ 263	+ 491	+ 209
595	609	668	777	333

Problem Solving *Number Sense*

3. For the problems, use each number for only one digit.

3 5 6 2 4 1

Make the greatest sum.

2	7	2
+ 6	5	4
9	2	6

Make the least sum.

2	7	2
+ 1	2	3
3	9	5

140 Use with Lesson 11-4.

Name _____

Add Over Again

E 11-4
PATTERNS

Add. Look for the pattern.
Write the last addition problem in the pattern.

1.
209	309	409
+ 123	+ 223	+ 323
332	532	732

5	0	9
+ 4	2	3
9	3	2

2.
134	154	174
+ 252	+ 254	+ 256
386	408	430

1	9	4
+ 2	5	8
4	5	2

3.
315	415	515
+ 427	+ 327	+ 227
742	742	742

6	1	5
+ 1	2	7
7	4	2

4.
570	560	550
+ 118	+ 218	+ 318
688	778	868

5	4	0
+ 4	1	8
9	5	8

140 Use with Lesson 11-4.

Name _____

Adding Three-Digit Numbers

PS 11-4

Add.

1.
362	418	167	237	643
+ 143	+ 290	+ 482	+ 156	+ 215
505	708	649	393	858

2.
167	451	347	266	128
+ 131	+ 62	+ 112	+ 324	+ 205
298	513	459	590	333

Circle the numbers on the tic-tac-toe boards
that match the sums from Exercises 1 and 2.
The player that gets 3 in a row or in a diagonal, wins.

Player A

(708)	(649)	127
316	291	(858)
(513)	483	(590)

Player B

(333)	678	411
176	(505)	(393)
(298)	843	(459)

3. Which player wins tic-tac-toe? ___Player B___

4. Look at the board of the winning player.
   Which two circled numbers will make
   the greatest sum when added together?

   $505 + 459 = 964$

140 Use with Lesson 11-4.

---

140 Use with Chapter 11, Lesson 4.

© Pearson Education, Inc. **2**

Reteaching

Name _____

Practice with Three-Digit Addition

R 11-5

$417 + 163 = ?$

Rewrite the problem using the workmat.

Line up the hundreds, tens, and ones.
1. Add the ones. Regroup if you need to.
2. Add the tens. Regroup if you need to.
3. Add the hundreds.

Hundreds	Tens	Ones
☐	1	
4	1	7
+ 1	6	3
5	8	0

Write the addition problem. Find the sum.

1.

$152 + 341$

Hundreds	Tens	Ones
☐	☐	
1	5	2
+ 3	4	1
4	9	3

$374 + 183$

Hundreds	Tens	Ones
1		
3	7	4
+ 1	8	3
5	5	7

$560 + 278$

Hundreds	Tens	Ones
1		
5	6	0
+ 2	7	8
8	3	8

2.

$415 + 142$

Hundreds	Tens	Ones
☐	☐	
4	1	5
+ 1	4	2
5	5	7

$192 + 173$

Hundreds	Tens	Ones
1	☐	
1	9	2
+ 1	7	3
3	6	5

$307 + 378$

Hundreds	Tens	Ones
☐	1	
3	0	7
+ 3	7	8
6	8	5

Use with Lesson 11-5. **141**

Practice

Name _____

Practice with Three-Digit Addition

P 11-5

Write the addition problem. Find the sum.

1.

$291 + 105$

$$\begin{array}{r} 291 \\ + 105 \\ \hline 396 \end{array}$$

$315 + 482$

$$\begin{array}{r} 315 \\ + 482 \\ \hline 797 \end{array}$$

$158 + 771$

$$\begin{array}{r} 1 \\ 158 \\ + 771 \\ \hline 929 \end{array}$$

2.

$463 + 142$

$$\begin{array}{r} 463 \\ + 142 \\ \hline 605 \end{array}$$

$37 + 517$

$$\begin{array}{r} 1 \\ 37 \\ + 517 \\ \hline 554 \end{array}$$

$428 + 149$

$$\begin{array}{r} 428 \\ + 149 \\ \hline 577 \end{array}$$

3.

$219 + 168$

$$\begin{array}{r} 1 \\ 219 \\ + 168 \\ \hline 387 \end{array}$$

$537 + 92$

$$\begin{array}{r} 1 \\ 537 \\ + 92 \\ \hline 629 \end{array}$$

$502 + 238$

$$\begin{array}{r} 1 \\ 502 \\ + 238 \\ \hline 740 \end{array}$$

Problem Solving *Number Sense*

Solve the number riddles.

4. When I am added to 210, the sum is 864. What number am I? **654**

5. When I am added to 103, the sum is 333. What number am I? **230**

Use with Lesson 11-5. **141**

Enrichment

Name _____

Going Up

E 11-5
DECISION MAKING

This elevator holds up to 300 pounds.

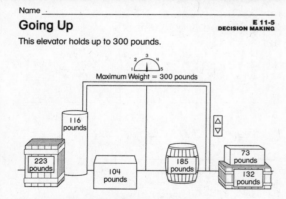

Maximum Weight = 300 pounds

116 pounds

223 pounds

104 pounds

185 pounds

73 pounds

132 pounds

All of these containers need to get to the top floor. What combinations of two containers can ride in the elevator? Write some addition problems to find out.

Trip 1	Trip 2	Trip 3
Possible answer:	Possible answer:	Possible answer:
$\begin{array}{r} 185 \\ + 104 \\ \hline 289 \end{array}$	$\begin{array}{r} 116 \\ + 132 \\ \hline 248 \end{array}$	$\begin{array}{r} 223 \\ + 73 \\ \hline 296 \end{array}$

Use with Lesson 11-5. **141**

Problem Solving

Name _____

Practice with Three-Digit Addition

PS 11-5

The table shows how many miles there are between cities. Use the table to solve each problem below.

	Port Smith	Lakeside	Greenville	New Hope
Port Smith		414	291	365
Lakeside	414		529	152
Greenville	291	529		327
New Hope	365	152	327	

1. Jenny goes from Port Smith to Greenville, then from Greenville to New Hope. How far does she travel?

618 miles

$$\begin{array}{r} 1 \\ 291 \\ + 327 \\ \hline 618 \end{array}$$

2. Miguel goes from New Hope to Lakeside, then from Lakeside to Port Smith. How far does he travel?

566 miles

$$\begin{array}{r} 152 \\ + 414 \\ \hline 566 \end{array}$$

3. Ben goes from Greenville to New Hope, then from New Hope to Port Smith. How far does he go?

692 miles

$$\begin{array}{r} 1 \\ 327 \\ + 365 \\ \hline 692 \end{array}$$

4. Shi-Ann goes from Lakeside to Greenville. Then she travels to another city. She travels a total of 856 miles. Where does she go to from Greenville?

New Hope

Use with Lesson 11-5. **141**

Reteaching

Name _____

PROBLEM-SOLVING STRATEGY   R 11-6

Make a Graph

How many second graders ride the bus?

200 second graders from Willow Town ride the bus.
250 second graders from Dandy Creek ride the bus.

Read and Understand

Find out how many second graders in all ride the bus.

Plan and Solve

First, add the number of second graders from both towns.

```
  200
+ 250
  450
```

450 second graders ride the bus.

Then, add this information to the graph.

Look Back and Check

Does the bar above second graders stop at 450?

Children Riding the Bus

(bar graph: First Graders, Second Graders at 450, Third Graders at 600; y-axis 0–650 by 50)

Read the problems. Add to find how many in all.
Then complete the graph.

1. 150 first graders from Willow Town ride the bus.
   200 first graders from Dandy Creek ride the bus.

   __350__ first graders in all.

2. 350 third graders from Willow Town ride the bus.
   250 third graders from Dandy Creek ride the bus.

   __600__ third graders in all.

142   Use with Lesson 11-6.

Practice

Name _____

PROBLEM-SOLVING STRATEGY   P 11-6

Make a Graph

Use the chart to answer the questions.

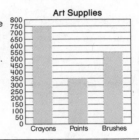

Art Supplies			
	Crayons	Paints	Brushes
Art Room 1	350	200	300
Art Room 2	400	150	250

1. How many crayons are there in all?

   __750__ crayons

2. How many paints are there in all? __350__ paints

3. How many brushes are there in all? __550__ brushes

4. Use your answers from Exercises 1–3 to complete the graph. Color to show how many of each of the art supplies there are in all.

Art Supplies

(bar graph: Crayons 750, Paints 350, Brushes 550; y-axis 0–800 by 50)

Problem Solving *Writing in Math*

5. How is a bar graph different from a chart?

   Answers may vary. Possible response given.

   A bar graph uses bars to show numbers.

142   Use with Lesson 11-6.

Enrichment

Name _____

Come Fly with Me!

E 11-6
DATA

Sam, Josh, and Mary are pilots. Use the chart to answer the questions.

Number of Miles Flown

	Friday	Saturday	Sunday
Sam	350	250	100
Josh	100	150	100
Mary	400	100	50

1. Use the data from the chart to complete the graph.

Number of Miles Flown

(horizontal bar graph: Sam, Josh, Mary; x-axis 0 50 100 150 200 250 300 350 400 450 500 550 600 650 700 750)

2. The next Monday, Josh flew 150 miles. He flew 200 miles on Tuesday. How many miles did he fly on those two days? __350__

   Add the new information to the graph.

3. Mary flies 200 more miles. Use the graph to show how many miles Mary flew in all.

4. Write a problem using the information in the graph. Give your problem to a classmate to solve.

   __Problems will vary.__

142   Use with Lesson 11-6.

Problem Solving

Name _____

PROBLEM-SOLVING STRATEGY   PS 11-6

Make a Graph

How many tickets were sold on each day? Add the numbers for each day and write the totals in the chart.

Tickets Sold for the Movies			
	Friday	Saturday	Sunday
Booth A	150	300	200
Booth B	200	350	300
Total	350	650	500

Use the totals to make a graph.

Total Tickets Sold for the Movies

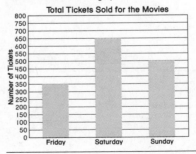

(bar graph: Number of Tickets y-axis 0–800 by 50; Friday 350, Saturday 650, Sunday 500)

Writing in Math

1. How can you use your graph to find out how many people went to the movies each day?

   Look at the bars and then the numbers next to each bar.

Using the page To help children *plan*, have them circle the numbers for each day, then add. Then have them *solve* by coloring in the bars on the graph.

142   Use with Lesson 11-6.

© Pearson Education, Inc. 2

Name _____

Ways to Find Missing Parts

R 11-7

Count on by hundreds and tens to find the parts of the whole.

$260 +$ _____ $= 700$

First, count on by hundreds.   4 hundreds

260 [360] [460] [560] [660]
       100   200   300   400

Next, count on by tens.   4 tens

660 [670] [680] [690] [700]
        10   20   30   40

4 hundreds and 4 tens is 440.

700	
260	440

So, $260 + 440 = 700$

1. $350 + \underline{\;?\;} = 600$

   Count on by hundreds.   2 hundreds

   350, 450, 550

   Count on by tens.   5 tens

   550, 560, 570, 580, 590, 600

   2 hundreds and 5 tens is 250.

   So, $350 + 250 = 600$

Use with Lesson 11-7. 143

Name _____

Ways to Find Missing Parts

P 11-7

Count on or count back to find the missing part.

1. $360 + \underline{240} = 600$	2. $420 + \underline{280} = 700$
3. $180 + \underline{520} = 700$	4. $500 = 170 + \underline{330}$
5. $270 + \underline{630} = 900$	6. $420 + \underline{180} = 600$
7. $700 = 390 + \underline{310}$	8. $500 = \underline{360} + 140$

Problem Solving Algebra

Circle the weights you would need to balance each scale.

9.
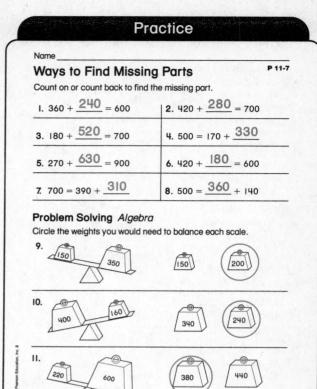

10.

11.

Use with Lesson 11-7. 143

Name _____

The Craft Store

E 11-7
NUMBER SENSE

Use the pictures to answer the questions.
Count on or count back to solve.

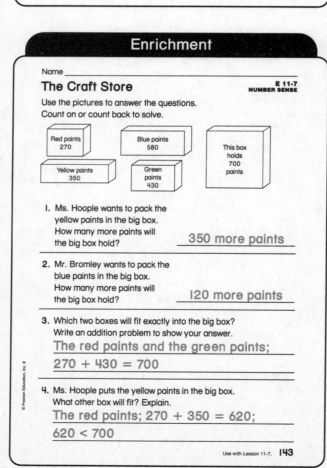

Red paints 270
Yellow paints 350
Blue paints 580
Green paints 430
This box holds 700 paints

1. Ms. Hoople wants to pack the yellow paints in the big box. How many more paints will the big box hold?

   350 more paints

2. Mr. Bromley wants to pack the blue paints in the big box. How many more paints will the big box hold?

   120 more paints

3. Which two boxes will fit exactly into the big box? Write an addition problem to show your answer.

   The red paints and the green paints; 270 + 430 = 700

4. Ms. Hoople puts the yellow paints in the big box. What other box will fit? Explain.

   The red paints; 270 + 350 = 620; 620 < 700

Use with Lesson 11-7. 143

Name _____

Ways to Find Missing Parts

PS 11-7

Ms. Murple needs to buy more items for her craft store. She wants to have a certain number of each item in the store. Count on or count back to find how many of each item she needs to buy.

Complete the chart.

1.

Ms. Murple's Craft Supplies

	Pipe Cleaners	Craft Paper	Colored Pencils	Boxes of Beads	Silk Flowers
Number in the Store	140	270	350	180	430
Number Needed	360	530	250	120	470
Number Wanted	500	800	600	300	900

Use the pictures to solve.

2. Ms. Murple needs to fill a carton with 500 paint jars. She only has four small boxes that hold 50 paint jars each. How many more small boxes of paint jars does she need to fill the carton?

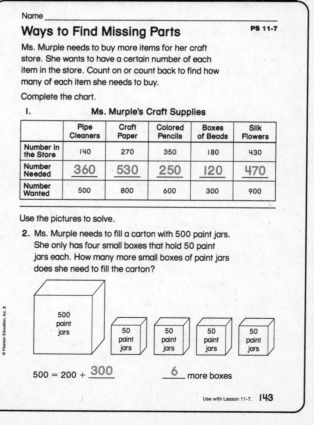

500 paint jars
50 paint jars
50 paint jars
50 paint jars
50 paint jars

$500 = 200 + 300$ 6 more boxes

Use with Lesson 11-7. 143

© Pearson Education, Inc. 2

Name _____

Estimating Differences

R 11-8

You can estimate to find an answer that is close to
the exact difference. To estimate, find the closest hundred.

Estimate 596 − 221.

Is 596 closer to 500 or 600?   *600*

Is 221 closer to 200 or 300?   *200*

600 − *200* = *400*

So, 596 − 221 is about _400_.

Circle the estimate that best matches each problem.

1. 502 − 105	is about	200	300	(400)
2. 909 − 403	is about	(500)	600	700
3. 615 − 412	is about	100	(200)	300
4. 511 − 298	is about	(200)	300	400
5. 881 − 500	is about	300	(400)	500
6. 231 − 108	is about	(100)	200	300
7. 799 − 182	is about	400	500	(600)
8. 627 − 275	is about	200	(300)	400

© Pearson Education, Inc. 2

144 Use with Lesson 11-8.

Name _____

Estimating Differences

P 11-8

Circle the problem that matches the estimate.

1. about 400	718 − 487	or	(921 − 513)
2. about 200	933 − 567	or	(478 − 301)
3. about 100	(684 − 572)	or	376 − 123
4. about 500	(834 − 311)	or	769 − 487
5. about 300	659 − 147	or	(801 − 490)
6. about 600	714 − 588	or	(899 − 312)

Problem Solving *Number Sense*

For the problems, choose a set of 3 numbers.
Use each number one time. Subtract to solve.

2   5   7   1   4   6

7. Make the greatest difference.   8. Make the least difference.

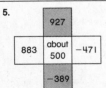

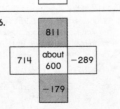

© Pearson Education, Inc. 2

144 Use with Lesson 11-8.

Name _____

Puzzle Boxes

E 11-8
ESTIMATION

Estimate down or across the boxes.
Color the outside boxes that match
the estimate in the center box.

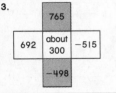

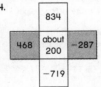

© Pearson Education, Inc. 2

144 Use with Lesson 11-8.

Name _____

Estimating Differences

PS 11-8

Match the number sentence with the estimate.

1. Sue and Roger collect coins.
   Sue has about 300 more coins
   than Roger.

2. Beth and David collect baseball
   cards. David has about 400 more
   cards than Beth.

3. Raif and Andrea collect marbles.
   Andrea has about 100 more
   marbles than Raif.

4. Suey and Ahmad collect seashells.
   Ahmad has about 200 more shells
   than Suey.

5. Greta and Zack collect postcards.
   Greta has about 500 more
   postcards than Zack.

591 − 482

623 − 198

743 − 416

932 − 387

417 − 226

Circle the correct answers.

6. Mickey and Dixie have about 400 comic books
   altogether. Which numbers tell how many comic
   books each one has?

 127   374   266

© Pearson Education, Inc. 2

144 Use with Lesson 11-8.

© Pearson Education, Inc. **2**

144   Use with Chapter 11, Lesson 8.

Reteaching

Name _____

Subtracting with Models

R 11-9

327 − 164 = __?__

Step 1: Subtract the ones. Regroup if you need to.
Step 2: Subtract the tens. Regroup if you need to.
Step 3: Subtract the hundreds.

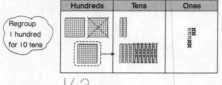

Hundreds	Tens	Ones

Regroup
1 hundred
for 10 tens

327 − 164 = _163_

Subtract to find the difference. Use models and Workmat 5.
Show each number.

1.
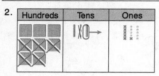

Hundreds	Tens	Ones

549 − 295 = _254_

2.

Hundreds	Tens	Ones

835 − 516 = _319_

Use with Lesson 11-9. **145**

Practice

Name _____

Subtracting with Models

P 11-9

Subtract. Use models and Workmat 5.

1. 476 − 321 = _155_	2. 659 − 372 = _287_
3. 953 − 209 = _744_	4. _119_ = 561 − 442
5. 390 − 126 = _264_	6. 732 − 121 = _611_
7. _286_ = 578 − 292	8. 818 − 409 = _409_

Problem Solving *Reasoning*

9. Write the name of each child below
the cards he or she collects.

Sports Card Collection

• Jake has about 300 more cards than Cindi.
• Melba has the most cards.
• William has about 100 less cards than Melba.

600 cards	200 cards	705 cards	510 cards
William	Cindi	Melba	Jake

Use with Lesson 11-9. **145**

Enrichment

Name _____

The Toy Store

E 11-9
DATA

Use the data in the chart to help Mr. Mickle find out
how many toys were sold. Use models and Workmat 5
to help you subtract. Then answer the questions below.

Toys	Started With	Left	Sold
Train Sets	532	215	317
Dolls	674	429	245
Games	427	119	308
Puzzles	387	215	172
Building Blocks	259	163	96

1. Which toy sold the most? _train sets_

2. Which toy sold the least? _building blocks_

3. How many more games than puzzles were sold?
Use models to subtract. _136_

Use with Lesson 11-9. **145**

Problem Solving

Name _____

Subtracting with Models

PS 11-9

Solve. Use models and Workmat 5 to find
each difference.

1. A truck carries 578 boxes. It takes
243 boxes to a store. How many
boxes are still on the truck? _578_ − _243_ = _335_

2. A train carries 635 pounds of hay.
It unloads 214 pounds. How many
pounds of hay are still on the train? _635_ − _214_ = _421_

3. A barge carries 792 cartons. It unloads
350 cartons at the dock. How many
cartons are still on the barge? _792_ − _350_ = _442_

4. A plane carries 469 pounds
of cargo. It unloads 325 pounds
at the first stop. How many pounds
of cargo are still on the plane? _469_ − _325_ = _144_

Find the answer.

5. A plane, a train, and a truck each carry cartons.
The plane carries about 500 more cartons than
the train. The train carries the least number of
cartons. How many cartons does each one carry?

295
450
780

_780_ _295_ _450_

Use with Lesson 11-9. **145**

Reteaching

Name _____

Subtracting Three-Digit Numbers
R 11-10

Step 1: Subtract the ones. Regroup if you need to.
Step 2: Subtract the tens. Regroup if you need to.
Step 3: Subtract the hundreds.

Think: Regroup 1 ten for 10 ones.

$362 - 125 = $ _?_

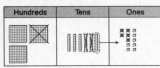

Hundreds	Tens	Ones
	5	12
3	6̸	2̸
1	2	5
2	3	7

Draw to regroup. Subtract.

1. $429 - 174 = $ _?_

Hundreds	Tens	Ones
3	12	
4̸	2̸	9
1	7	4
2	5	5

Subtract. Use models and Workmat 5 if you need to.

2.
Hundreds	Tens	Ones
5	7	4
2	1	3
3	6	1

3.
Hundreds	Tens	Ones
	7	18
7	8̸	8̸
2	6	9
5	1	9

146 Use with Lesson 11-10.

Practice

Name _____

Subtracting Three-Digit Numbers
P 11-10

Subtract. Use models and Workmat 5 if you need to.

1.
Hundreds	Tens	Ones
7	8	4
2	5	1
5	3	3

Hundreds	Tens	Ones
	7	15
4	8̸	5̸
1	3	9
3	4	6

2.
Hundreds	Tens	Ones
4	17	
5̸	7̸	8
2	9	7
2	8	1

Hundreds	Tens	Ones
5	12	
6̸	2̸	4
3	3	2
2	9	2

3.
4 1 7	4 1 6	7 1 0	6 1 4	
6 5̸ 7̸	5̸ 4̸ 1	8̸ 0̸ 9	7̸ 4̸ 2	9 2 7
− 1 2 8	− 3 9 0	− 2 6 3	− 4 5 0	− 3 0 4
529	171	546	292	623

Problem Solving *Visual Thinking*

Circle the weight you need to remove to balance the scale.

4.

350 (150) 225 125

146 Use with Lesson 11-10.

Enrichment

Name _____

Tic-Tac Subtract
E 11-10
NUMBER SENSE

1. Subtract to find the differences.

Hundreds	Tens	Ones
3		
4	3	7
1	6	4
2	7	3

Hundreds	Tens	Ones
5	7	8
2	6	4
3	1	4

Hundreds	Tens	Ones
5		
6	2	3
3	7	1
2	5	2

Hundreds	Tens	Ones
8		
9	1	7
2	3	2
6	8	5

354

Hundreds	Tens	Ones
	4	
7	5	3
2	4	9
5	0	4

Hundreds	Tens	Ones
2		
3	8	1
1	9	0
1	9	1

Hundreds	Tens	Ones
	3	
8	4	3
4	2	8
4	1	5

Hundreds	Tens	Ones
9	8	9
3	6	2
6	2	7

2. Look at the differences in each problem above.
   Find two that you can subtract to make a difference
   of 354. Draw a line to connect the problems.

146 Use with Lesson 11-10.

Problem Solving

Name _____

Subtracting Three-Digit Numbers
PS 11-10

Subtract. Write the letter for each difference
on the lines below to solve the riddle.

1.
4 6 2	9 2 5	7 7 6	3 8 7	5 9 1
− 1 3 6	− 1 8 4	− 2 3 6	− 1 4 9	− 2 0 4
326	741	540	238	387
R	E	C	D	F

2.
6 5 7	8 2 4	4 7 5	6 5 6	9 2 7
− 4 8 2	− 1 9 3	− 2 9 3	− 2 4 3	− 3 7 1
175	631	182	413	556
N	A	L	O	I

3. What has ears but cannot hear?

A	C	O	R	N	F	I	E	L	D
631	540	413	326	175	387	556	741	182	238

Solve.

4. The bags below are filled with jellybeans.
   Allie uses 245 jellybeans.
   How many jellybeans are left?

100 100 100   10 10 10
              10 10

_107_ jellybeans

146 Use with Lesson 11-10.

Name _____

Practice with Three-Digit Subtraction   R 11-11

528 − 143 = ___?___

Rewrite the problem using the workmat.

Line up the hundreds, tens, and ones.
Subtract the ones. Regroup if you need to.
Subtract the tens. Regroup if you need to.
Subtract the hundreds.

Hundreds	Tens	Ones
4	12	
5	2	8
1	4	3
3	8	5

Write the subtraction problem. Find the difference.

1.
648 − 217

Hundreds	Tens	Ones
		8
6	4	8
2	1	7
4	3	1

593 − 264

Hundreds	Tens	Ones
	8	13
5	9	3
2	6	4
3	2	9

435 − 192

Hundreds	Tens	Ones
3	13	
4	3	5
1	9	2
2	4	3

2.
328 − 114

Hundreds	Tens	Ones
3	2	8
1	1	4
2	1	4

782 − 329

Hundreds	Tens	Ones
	7	12
7	8	2
3	2	9
4	5	3

957 − 173

Hundreds	Tens	Ones
8	15	
9	5	7
1	7	3
7	8	4

Name _____

Practice with Three-Digit Subtraction   P 11-11

Write the subtraction problem. Find the difference.

1.
639 − 218
```
  639
− 218
  421
```

562 − 129
```
  512
  562
− 129
  433
```

947 − 351
```
  814
  947
− 351
  596
```

2.
817 − 253
```
  711
  817
− 253
  564
```

707 − 95
```
  610
  707
−  95
  612
```

478 − 321
```
  478
− 321
  157
```

3.
589 − 193
```
  418
  589
− 193
  396
```

643 − 228
```
  313
  643
− 228
  415
```

850 − 49
```
  410
  850
−  49
  801
```

Problem Solving *Estimation*

Circle the best estimate.

4. 624 − 410
100 (200) 300

5. 934 − 411
(500) 600 700

6. 776 − 187
400 500 (600)

Name _____

Teamwork   E 11-11
DECISION MAKING

Choose one player from each team. Write
a subtraction problem using their scores.
Then write how many more points the player
from the A Team scored.

Answers will vary.

A Team Score	
Marco	745
Elena	916
Dekembi	692
Linda	885

B Team Score	
Jackie	452
Kalisha	325
Dante	581
Akmad	263

Subtraction Problems

1. A Team Player _____

   B Team Player _____

   A Team scored _____ more points.

2. A Team Player _____

   B Team Player _____

   A Team scored _____ more points.

3. A Team Player _____

   B Team Player _____

   A Team scored _____ more points.

Name _____

Practice with Three-Digit Subtraction   PS 11-11

The table shows how many books
of each kind are at the town library.
Use the table to solve the problems.

Number of Books	
Fiction	672
Places	328
People	576
Science	441
Art	255

1. How many more books about people
   are there than books about places?

   __248__ more books
```
  616
  576
− 328
  248
```

2. How many more fiction books
   are there than art books?

   __417__ more books
```
  612
  672
− 255
  417
```

3. 170 of the science books are about
   animals. How many science books
   are not about animals?

   __271__ books
```
  314
  441
− 170
  271
```

4. 192 of the fiction books are about people
   from other countries. How many fiction
   books are about people from our country?

   __480__ books
```
  517
  672
− 192
  480
```

5. The library gets another 135 books about science.
   Are there more than or less than
   500 books about science now?   __more than__ 500 books

© Pearson Education, Inc. 2

Name _____

PROBLEM-SOLVING SKILL   R 11-12

Exact Answer or Estimate

James collects 321 cans for recycling day. He needs 550 cans to win a prize. How many more cans does James need?

Subtract to find the **exact** amount of cans James needs.

$$\begin{array}{r} 5\,5\,0 \\ -\,3\,2\,1 \\ \hline 229 \end{array}$$

_229_ cans

Genie collects 387 cans. Sandra collects 134 cans. About how many more cans does Genie collect than Sandra?

To find out **about** how many more cans, use an estimate.

387 is about 400
134 is about 100

$$\begin{array}{r} 4\,0\,0 \\ -\,1\,0\,0 \\ \hline 300 \end{array}$$

about _300_ more

Circle **estimate** or **exact answer**. Solve.

1. Aleesha collects 327 newspapers. She needs 650 to fill a carton. How many more papers does she need?

(exact answer)   estimate

Subtract to find the answer.

$$\begin{array}{r} \boxed{}\;\boxed{4}\;\boxed{10} \\ 6\;\;5\;\;0 \\ -\,3\;\;2\;\;7 \\ \hline 3\;\;2\;\;3 \end{array}$$ more

2. Nan collects 167 plastic bottles. She collects 219 glass bottles. About how many bottles does she collect in all?

exact answer   (estimate)

Add to find the answer.

$$\begin{array}{r} 200 \\ +200 \\ \hline \end{array}$$

about _400_ bottles

Name _____

PROBLEM-SOLVING SKILL   P 11-12

Exact Answer or Estimate

Circle **estimate** or **exact answer**. Answer the question.

1. A train travels 312 miles on Monday and 478 miles on Tuesday. About how many miles did the train travel on both days?

(estimate)   exact answer

Sample estimate is given.

$$\begin{array}{r} 300 \\ +\,500 \\ \hline 800 \end{array}$$

about 800 miles

2. There are 517 children at the Elm Street school. 325 children take the bus to school. How many children do not take the bus to school?

estimate   (exact answer)

$$\begin{array}{r} 4\;1\;1 \\ 5\not{1}7 \\ -\,3\;2\;5 \\ \hline 1\;9\;2 \end{array}$$

192 children

3. Mrs. Cook reads a book with 572 pages. She has read about 300 pages. About how many pages does she have left to read?

(estimate)   exact answer

Sample estimate is given.

$$\begin{array}{r} 600 \\ -\,300 \\ \hline 300 \end{array}$$

about 300 pages

Problem Solving *Writing in Math*

4. Write a math problem in which an exact answer is needed.

Problems will vary.

Name _____

The Play's the Thing

E 11-12
REASONING

The chart shows how many people came to the school play on each day.

People at the School Play	
Thursday	135
Friday	213
Saturday	167
Sunday	152

1. Use the information in the chart to write a problem that has an exact answer. Solve the problem.

Possible answer: How many people came to the play on Saturday and Sunday? 167 + 152 = 319 people

2. Use the information in the chart to write a problem that can be answered with an estimate. Solve the problem.

Possible answer: About how many people came to the play on Thursday and Friday? 100 + 200 = 300; about 300 people

---

Name _____

PROBLEM-SOLVING SKILL   PS 11-12

Exact Answer or Estimate

Riuchi has 573 newspapers. She delivers 128 newspapers on her paper route. How many newspapers does Riuchi have left?

Do you need an exact answer? Can you estimate?

You need to find how many newspapers are left. You need an exact answer.

Think: Riuchi takes away 128 newspapers from 573 newspapers. This is a subtraction problem.

573 newspapers
− 128 are taken away.
445 newspapers are left.

Circle **estimate** or **exact answer**. Answer the questions. Show your work.

Sample estimate is given.

1. 423 people work at the newspaper company. About 200 people take the bus to work. About how many people do not take the bus to work?

(estimate)

$$\begin{array}{r} 400 \\ -\,200 \\ \hline 200 \end{array}$$

exact answer

about 200 people

2. A reporter travels 249 miles to cover a story. Then the reporter travels another 135 miles. How many miles does the reporter travel in all?

estimate   (exact answer)

$$\begin{array}{r} 1 \\ 249 \\ +\,135 \\ \hline 384 \end{array}$$

384 miles

Reteaching

Name _____

PROBLEM-SOLVING APPLICATIONS   R 11-13

Amazing Animals

You can add to solve problems with three-digit numbers.	You can subtract to solve problems with three-digit numbers.
A tree frog lays 134 eggs. Another tree frog lays 182 eggs. How many eggs did they lay in all?	A male lion weighs 475 pounds. A female lion weighs 384 pounds. How many more pounds does the male weigh?
Add to find how many in all.	Subtract to find how many more.

$$\begin{array}{r} 1\ \ \ \\ 1\,3\,4 \\ +1\,8\,2 \\ \hline 3\,1\,6\ \text{eggs} \end{array}$$

$$\begin{array}{r} 3\,1\,7 \\ \cancel{4}\,\cancel{7}\,5 \\ -3\,8\,4 \\ \hline 9\,1\ \text{more pounds} \end{array}$$

Solve.

1. A rain forest tree is 238 feet tall. Another tree is 172 feet tall. How much taller is the first tree?

   Subtract to find the answer.

   __66__ feet taller

$$\begin{array}{r} 1\ |13|\ \ \\ \cancel{2}\,\cancel{3}\,8 \\ -1\,7\,2 \\ \hline 6\,6 \end{array}$$

2. A group of tourists travels 387 miles to a rain forest. Then they travel 152 miles through the rain forest. How many miles did they travel in all?

   Add to find the answer.

   __539__ miles

$$\begin{array}{r} 1\ \ \ \\ 3\,8\,7 \\ +1\,5\,2 \\ \hline 5\,3\,9 \end{array}$$

Practice

Name _____

PROBLEM-SOLVING APPLICATIONS   P 11-13

Amazing Animals

Solve.

1. A monkey sits on a tree that is 115 feet high. The monkey climbs 60 feet. Then it climbs another 50 feet. How high is the monkey now?

   __225__ feet

2. One week, a group of chimpanzees ate 500 bananas. The next week, they ate 300 bananas. How many more bananas did the chimpanzees eat in the first week?

   __200__ more bananas

3. A toucan sits on a branch that is 212 feet high. Another toucan sits on a branch that is 108 feet high. How much higher is the first toucan?

   __104__ feet higher

Writing in Math

4. Write a subtraction story about your favorite rain forest animal. Use three-digit numbers in your story.

   Stories will vary.

Enrichment

Name _____

Rain Forest Animals   E 11-13
REASONABLENESS

Circle the most reasonable answer.

1. A toucan flies 250 yards. Then it flies some more. About how many yards does the toucan fly?

   (about 350 yards)

   about 250 yards

   about 150 feet

2. A mother tree sloth climbs 560 feet. A baby tree sloth climbs less than the mother. About how many feet does the baby tree sloth climb?

   about 560 feet

   about 560 yards

   (about 400 feet)

3. A monkey climbs 90 feet up a tree. Then the monkey climbs a little farther. About how high is the monkey?

   (about 125 feet)

   about 20 yards

   about 500 inches

4. A big tree is 235 feet tall. A smaller tree is next to the big tree. About how tall is the shorter tree?

   (about 150 feet)

   about 100 yards

   about 300 feet

5. A python snake is 396 inches long. An anaconda snake is 267 inches long. How much longer is the python snake?

   __129__ inches

Problem Solving

Name _____

PROBLEM-SOLVING APPLICATIONS   PS 11-13

Amazing Animals

A jaguar runs for 417 feet. A puma runs for 253 feet. How many more feet does the jaguar run?

What is the question asking?

How many more feet the jaguar runs than the puma.

Do you add or subtract? ___subtract___

$$\begin{array}{r} 3\ 11 \\ \cancel{4}\,\cancel{1}\,7 \\ -2\,5\,3 \\ \hline 1\,6\,4 \end{array}$$

The jaguar runs __164__ more feet than a puma.

Solve.

1. There are 563 ants in a colony. 246 ants leave to look for food. How many ants are still in the colony?   __317__ ants

Writing in Math

2. A baby gorilla weighs 87 pounds. Another baby gorilla weighs 62 pounds. The mother gorilla weighs 295 pounds. Do the baby gorillas together weigh more than the mother? How do you know?

   No, the baby gorillas weigh 87 + 62 = 149 pounds; 149 < 295.

Name _____

Skip Counting Equal Groups

R 12-1

You can skip count **equal groups**
to find how many there are in all.

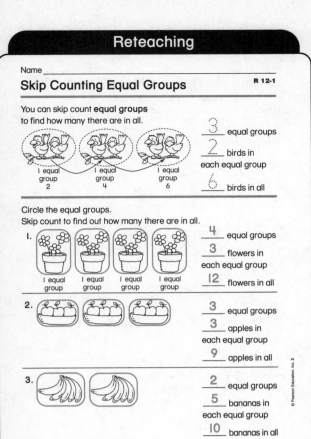

3 equal groups

2 birds in
each equal group

6 birds in all

Circle the equal groups.
Skip count to find out how many there are in all.

1.
4 equal groups

3 flowers in
each equal group

12 flowers in all

2.
3 equal groups

3 apples in
each equal group

9 apples in all

3.
2 equal groups

5 bananas in
each equal group

10 bananas in all

Name _____

Skip Counting Equal Groups

P 12-1

Draw to show equal groups. Skip count to find how
many there are in all. Use counters if you need to.

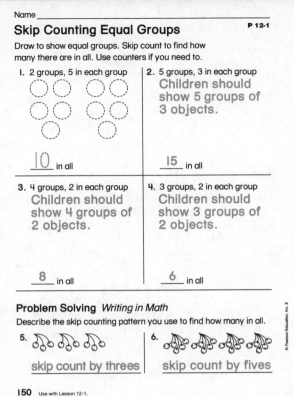

1. 2 groups, 5 in each group

10 in all

2. 5 groups, 3 in each group

Children should
show 5 groups of
3 objects.

15 in all

3. 4 groups, 2 in each group

Children should
show 4 groups of
2 objects.

8 in all

4. 3 groups, 2 in each group

Children should
show 3 groups of
2 objects.

6 in all

Problem Solving *Writing in Math*

Describe the skip counting pattern you use to find how many in all.

5.

skip count by threes

6.

skip count by fives

Name _____

Puppies and Kittens

E 12-1
NUMBER SENSE

Look at the pictures. Write how many in all.

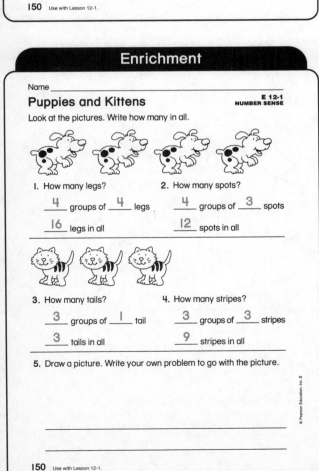

1. How many legs?

4 groups of 4 legs

16 legs in all

2. How many spots?

4 groups of 3 spots

12 spots in all

3. How many tails?

3 groups of 1 tail

3 tails in all

4. How many stripes?

3 groups of 3 stripes

9 stripes in all

5. Draw a picture. Write your own problem to go with the picture.

_____

_____

Name _____

Skip Counting Equal Groups

PS 12-1

Draw a picture to solve. Write how many in all.

1. Hannah has 3 groups of
2 balloons. How many
balloons does she have
in all?

Children should
draw 3 groups of
2 balloons.

6 balloons in all

2. Jed has 4 groups of
4 party hats. How many
party hats does he
have in all?

Children should
draw 4 groups of
4 party hats.

16 party hats in all

3. Latrell has 2 groups of
5 stickers. How many
stickers does he have in all?

Children should
draw 2 groups of
5 stickers.

10 stickers in all

4. Aliza has 5 groups of
3 cups. How many cups
does she have in all?

Children should
draw 5 groups of
3 cups.

15 cups in all

Writing in Math

5. Write a word problem about 3 groups
of 4. Solve the problem. Draw a
picture to show the groups.

Answers will vary.

_____

_____

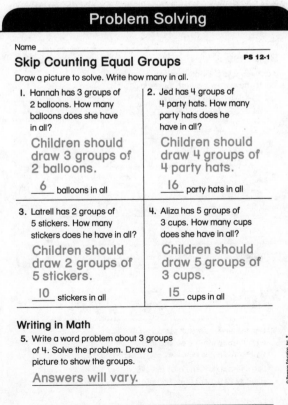

Reteaching

Name _____

Repeated Addition and Multiplication
R 12-2

You can write an addition sentence
to tell how many there are in all.
You can write a multiplication sentence
to tell how many there are in all.

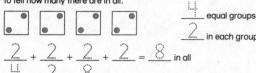

_4_ equal groups

_2_ in each group

_2_ + _2_ + _2_ + _2_ = _8_ in all

_4_ × _2_ = _8_ in all

Write the number of equal groups.
Write how many there are in each group. Then write
an addition sentence and a multiplication sentence.

1.

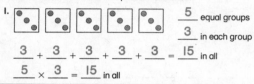

_5_ equal groups

_3_ in each group

_3_ + _3_ + _3_ + _3_ + _3_ = _15_ in all

_5_ × _3_ = _15_ in all

2.

_4_ equal groups

_4_ in each group

_4_ + _4_ + _4_ + _4_ = _16_ in all

_4_ × _4_ = _16_ in all

© Pearson Education, Inc. 2

Use with Lesson 12-2. 151

Practice

Name _____

Repeated Addition and Multiplication
P 12-2

Write an addition sentence and a multiplication
sentence that tell how many there are in all.

1.

_3_ + _3_ + _3_ = _9_   _3_ × _3_ = _9_

2.

_2_ + _2_ + _2_ + _2_ = _8_   _4_ × _2_ = _8_

3.

_4_ + _4_ + _4_ + _4_ + _4_ = _20_   _5_ × _4_ = _20_

4.

_6_ + _6_ + _6_ = _18_   _3_ × _6_ = _18_

5.

_6_ + _6_ = _12_   _2_ × _6_ = _12_

Problem Solving *Number Sense*

6. Find the sum. Write a multiplication sentence
that shows the same amount.

5 + 5 + 5 + 5 + 5 + 5 = _30_   _6_ × _5_ = _30_

© Pearson Education, Inc. 2

Use with Lesson 12-2. 151

Enrichment

Name _____

Ball Toss
E 12-2
REASONING

3 children toss balls into baskets. Write number sentences
that tell how many balls are tossed in all.

1.

_2_ + _2_ + _2_ + _2_ = _8_

_4_ × _2_ = _8_

2.

_2_ + _2_ + _2_ + _2_ + _2_ + _2_ = _12_

_6_ × _2_ = _12_

3.

_4_ + _4_ + _4_ = _12_

_3_ × _4_ = _12_

4. Use the clues to match the name of
each child to the correct ball toss above.
Write the number of tosses each child made.

Louis tosses as many balls as Rita.
Rita tosses 4 more balls than Bill.

Louis _12_   Rita _12_   Bill _8_

© Pearson Education, Inc. 2

Use with Lesson 12-2. 151

Problem Solving

Name _____

Repeated Addition and Multiplication
PS 12-2

Write an addition sentence and a multiplication sentence
for each part of the problem. Draw pictures if you need help.

1. Ms. Marple is making punch. She needs to mix 3 cups of cider,
2 cups of orange juice, and 5 cups of soda water to make one bowl.

If she makes 3 bowls of punch, how
many cups of cider does she need?

_3_ + _3_ + _3_ = _9_   _3_ × _3_ = _9_

How many cups of orange juice does
she need to make 3 bowls of punch?

_2_ + _2_ + _2_ = _6_   _3_ × _2_ = _6_

How many cups of soda water does
she need to make 3 bowls of punch?

_5_ + _5_ + _5_ = _15_   _3_ × _5_ = _15_

2. Mr. Marple mixes 3 cups of flour with granola
and milk to make one loaf of bread. How many
cups of flour does he need to make 4 loaves?

_3_ + _3_ + _3_ + _3_ = _12_

_4_ × _3_ = _12_

3. Mr. Marple uses 2 cups of milk to make one loaf of bread.
Circle the number sentence that shows how many cups
of milk he would need to make 5 loaves of bread.

5 × 1 = 5   (5 × 2 = 10)   5 × 3 = 15

© Pearson Education, Inc. 2

Use with Lesson 12-2. 151

© Pearson Education, Inc. 2

Building Arrays

Name _____

R 12-3

A collection of objects arranged in equal rows and columns is an **array**. You can use an **array** to show equal groups.

Array

Circle each row. Count the number of rows.

There are _4_ rows.

Count the number of dots in each row.

There are _3_ dots in each row.

Write the multiplication sentence.

_4_ × _3_ = _12_ in all

Circle each row. Count the number of rows.
Count the number of dots in each row.
Write the multiplication sentence.

1.

There are _3_ rows.

There are _5_ dots in each row.

_3_ × _5_ = _15_ in all.

2.

There are _5_ rows.

There are _5_ dots in each row.

_5_ × _5_ = _25_ in all.

152   Use with Lesson 12-3.

Building Arrays

Name _____

P 12-3

Write a multiplication sentence to describe each array.

1.

_3_ × _4_ = _12_

rows   in each   in all
        row

2.

_5_ × _2_ = _10_

3.

_4_ × _4_ = _16_

4.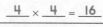

_1_ × _5_ = _5_

5.

_3_ × _5_ = _15_

6.

_3_ × _3_ = _9_

Problem Solving *Visual Thinking*

7. Write the multiplication sentence for the shaded squares.

_4_ × _5_ = _20_

152   Use with Lesson 12-3.

An Array of Arrays

Name _____

E 12-3
VISUAL THINKING

Color an array for each product below.
Write the multiplication sentence.

1. Red: Color an array for 8 in all.   _____ × _____ = 8

2. Blue: Color an array for 10 in all.   _____ × _____ = 10

3. Green: Color an array for 12 in all.   _____ × _____ = 12

4. Yellow: Color an array for 15 in all.   _____ × _____ = 15

5. Orange: Color an array for 16 in all.   _____ × _____ = 16

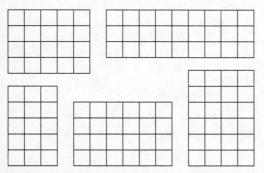

Answers will vary. Check student's arrays.

152   Use with Lesson 12-3.

Building Arrays

Name _____

PS 12-3

This is what the windows in Billy's Sports Shop look like.

Write a multiplication sentence to answer each question.

1. How many baseball mitts are there in all?

_2_ × _4_ = _8_

2. How many balls are there in all?

_4_ × _3_ = _12_

3. Billy adds 2 more baseball caps to each row. Draw what the display looks like now. Write a multiplication sentence.

Children should draw 3 groups of 5.

_3_ × _5_ = _15_

4. Billy adds another row of baseball mitts. Draw what the display looks like now. Write a multiplication sentence.

Children should draw 3 groups of 4.

_3_ × _4_ = _12_

152   Use with Lesson 12-3.

Name _____

Multiplying in Any Order
R 12-4

You can multiply numbers in any order and get the same product.

Color 3 rows
with 2 in each row.

Color 2 rows
with 3 in each row.

$\underline{3} \times \underline{2} = \underline{6}$
rows   in each row   in all

$\underline{2} \times \underline{3} = \underline{6}$
rows   in each row   in all

So, $\underline{3} \times \underline{2}$ is the same as $\underline{2} \times \underline{3}$.

Color the rows. Write the numbers.
Multiply to find the product.

1. Color 5 rows
with 3 in each row.

Color 3 rows
with 5 in each row.

$\underline{5} \times \underline{3} = \underline{15}$
rows   in each row   in all

$\underline{3} \times \underline{5} = \underline{15}$
rows   in each row   in all

So, $\underline{5} \times \underline{3}$ is the same as $\underline{3} \times \underline{5}$.

Name _____

Multiplying in Any Order
P 12-4

Write the numbers. Multiply to find the product.

1. $\underline{2}$ rows
$\underline{4}$ in each row

$\underline{4}$ rows
$\underline{2}$ in each row

$\underline{2} \times \underline{4} = \underline{8}$

$\underline{4} \times \underline{2} = \underline{8}$

2. $\underline{2}$ rows
$\underline{5}$ in each row

$\underline{5}$ rows
$\underline{2}$ in each row

$\underline{2} \times \underline{5} = \underline{10}$

$\underline{5} \times \underline{2} = \underline{10}$

Problem Solving *Algebra*
Complete the number sentences.

3.

$3 \times \underline{5} = 15$

$5 \times \underline{5} = 25$

Name _____

Multiplication Match
E 12-4
ALGEBRA

Complete each number sentence. Then draw a line from the number sentence in Column A to the matching number sentence in Column B.

Column A

1. $4 \times 1 = \underline{4}$
2. $3 \times 6 = \underline{18}$
3. $2 \times 5 = \underline{10}$
4. $7 \times 2 = \underline{14}$
5. $6 \times 2 = \underline{12}$
6. $4 \times 2 = \underline{8}$
7. $3 \times 5 = \underline{15}$
8. $6 \times 4 = \underline{24}$
9. $1 \times 7 = \underline{7}$

Column B

$5 \times 2 = \underline{10}$
$2 \times 4 = \underline{8}$
$1 \times 4 = \underline{4}$
$6 \times 3 = \underline{18}$
$5 \times 3 = \underline{15}$
$2 \times 7 = \underline{14}$
$2 \times 6 = \underline{12}$
$7 \times 1 = \underline{7}$
$4 \times 6 = \underline{24}$

Name _____

Multiplying in Any Order
PS 12-4

Draw 2 pictures showing different ways to group.
Write the multiplication sentences.

1. Gabby has 6 pictures.
Show two ways
she can arrange
the pictures in
an array.

Answers may vary. Sample answers given.

Children's drawings should match sentences.

$\underline{2} \times \underline{3} = \underline{6}$ | $\underline{3} \times \underline{2} = \underline{6}$

2. Jacob has 10 stamps
to put in a stamp album.
Show two ways
he can arrange
the stamps in an array.

$\underline{5} \times \underline{2} = \underline{10}$ | $\underline{2} \times \underline{5} = \underline{10}$

Use the array to complete the number sentences.
Write the missing numbers.

3.

$\triangle \times 3 = 12$

$\triangle = \underline{4}$

$4 \times \bigcirc = 20$

$\bigcirc = \underline{5}$

$\square \times 2 = 12$

$\square = \underline{6}$

Name _____

Vertical Form

R 12-5

You can write multiplication facts in two ways.

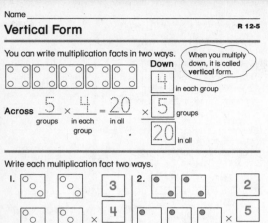

When you multiply down, it is called **vertical** form.

Down

4 in each group
× 5 groups
20 in all

Across 5 × 4 = 20
groups in each group in all

Write each multiplication fact two ways.

1.
3
× 4
12

4 × 3 = 12
groups in each group in all

2.
2
× 5
10

5 × 2 = 10
groups in each group in all

3.
6
× 2
12

2 × 6 = 12

4.
5
× 3
15

3 × 5 = 15

154 Use with Lesson 12-5.

Name _____

Vertical Form

P 12-5

Multiply across and down.

1.
3
× 4
12

4 × 3 = 12

2.
2
× 3
6

3 × 2 = 6

3.
5
× 2
10

2 × 5 = 10

4.
6
× 1
6

1 × 6 = 6

Problem Solving *Reasoning*

5. Beth has 8 stickers.
Write 2 multiplication sentences
that tell different ways to group them.

8 × 1 = 8   Answers will vary.
2 × 4 = 8   Possible answers given.

154 Use with Lesson 12-5.

Name _____

At the Bakery

E 12-5
VISUAL THINKING

Multiply. Then draw lines to match
each picture with 2 different multiplication facts.

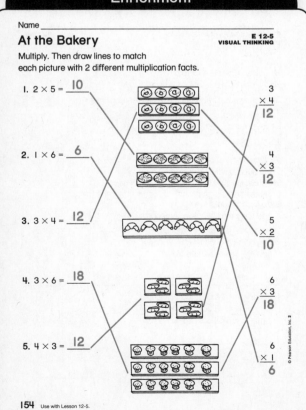

1. 2 × 5 = 10

2. 1 × 6 = 6

3. 3 × 4 = 12

4. 3 × 6 = 18

5. 4 × 3 = 12

3
× 4
12

4
× 3
12

5
× 2
10

6
× 3
18

6
× 1
6

154 Use with Lesson 12-5.

Name _____

Vertical Form

PS 12-5

Draw a picture to solve. Multiply across and down.

1. There are 3 pencil holders
with 3 pencils in each holder.
How many pencils are
there in all?

Children should draw
3 pencils in
each holder.

3
3
9

3 × 3 = 9

2. There are 2 tanks with
5 fish in each tank. How
many fish are there in all?

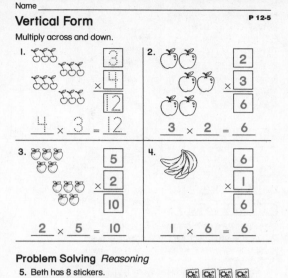

5
× 2
10

Children should draw
5 fish in each tank.

2 × 5 = 10

3. There are 2 baskets with
6 apples in each basket.
How many apples are
there in all?

6
× 2
12

Children should draw
6 apples in each basket.

2 × 6 = 12

4. There are 3 vases with
4 flowers in each vase.
If Tricia puts one more flower
in each vase, how many
flowers are there in all?

Children should
draw 5 flowers
in each vase.

5
× 3
15

3 × 5 = 15

154 Use with Lesson 12-5.

---

154 Use with Chapter 12, Lesson 5.

© Pearson Education, Inc. **2**

Reteaching

Name _____

PROBLEM-SOLVING STRATEGY   R 12-6
Draw a Picture

You can draw a picture to solve a problem.

> **Read and Understand**

Francis knits 4 mittens. Each mitten has 5 buttons.
How many buttons are there in all?

What does the problem ask you to do?

Find how many buttons in all.

> **Plan and Solve**

There are 4 mittens. Draw 5 buttons on each mitten.

     $\underline{4} \times \underline{5} = \underline{20}$ buttons in all

> **Look Back and Check**

Did you draw the correct number of groups?
Did you use the correct number to show how many
in each group? Does the answer make sense?

Draw a picture to solve. Then write a multiplication sentence.

1. There are 6 vases. Each vase has 3 flowers.
   How many flowers are there in all?

   What does the problem ask you to do?

   Find how many flowers in all.

   $\underline{6} \times \underline{3} = \underline{18}$ flowers in all

   Children's drawings should show 3 flowers in each vase.

Practice

Name _____

PROBLEM-SOLVING STRATEGY   P 12-6
Draw a Picture

Draw a picture to solve each problem.
Then write a multiplication sentence.

1. Margot has 4 pencil holders.
   Each one holds 3 pencils.
   How many pencils does Margot have?

   Children's drawings should show 4 groups of 3.

   $\underline{4} \times \underline{3} = \underline{12}$ pencils

2. Ramona has 5 dolls.
   Each doll has 3 buttons.
   How many buttons are there in all?

   Children's drawings should show 5 groups of 3.

   $\underline{5} \times \underline{3} = \underline{15}$ buttons

3. Ben has 6 toy cars.
   Each car has 4 wheels.
   How many wheels are there in all?

   Children's drawings should show 6 groups of 4.

   $\underline{6} \times \underline{4} = \underline{24}$ wheels

Problem Solving *Estimation*

4. Jeb has 3 boxes with 7 crayons in each box.
   Does he have more or less than 18 crayons?
   Explain your answer.

   Sample answer is given. He has more
   than 18 crayons. $3 \times 6 = 18$, so 3×7
   must be more than 18.

Enrichment

Name _____

At the Hobby Store   E 12-6   **DECISION MAKING**

Draw 4 window displays for Mr. Morgan's Hobby Store.
Choose a group of items to draw in each window.
Write a multiplication sentence for each. **Answers will vary.**

balls: 4 rows, 3 balls in each	crayon boxes: 3 rows, 3 crayon boxes in each	paint jars: 4 rows, 4 paint jars in each
blocks: 5 rows, 3 blocks in each	rolls of ribbon: 2 rows, 3 rolls of ribbon in each	spools of thread: 2 rows, 4 spools of thread in each

1. _____
   ___ × ___ = ___

2. _____
   ___ × ___ = ___

3. _____
   ___ × ___ = ___

4. _____
   ___ × ___ = ___

Problem Solving

Name _____

PROBLEM-SOLVING STRATEGY   PS 12-6
Draw a Picture

Dexter has 5 boxes.
He packs 3 balls in each box.
How many balls does he pack in all?

Draw a picture. Then write a number sentence to solve.

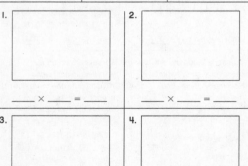

$\underline{5} \times \underline{3} = \underline{15}$

Did you draw a picture of 3 balls in each box?

Draw a picture to solve each problem.
Then write a multiplication sentence.

1. Lucy has 4 boxes. She packs
   5 yo-yos in each box. How many
   yo-yos does she pack in all?

   Children should draw 4 groups of 5.

   $\underline{4} \times \underline{5} = \underline{20}$

2. Yancy has 3 boxes. He packs
   3 tops in each box. How many
   tops does he pack in all?

   Children should draw 3 groups of 3.

   $\underline{3} \times \underline{3} = \underline{9}$

Using the page To help children *look back*, have them reread each problem, then *check* their pictures to see if they match the numbers in the problem.

Reteaching

Name _____

Making Equal Groups

R 12-7

You can share equally by making equal groups.

There are 9 counters in all.
There are 3 children. Draw equal shares.
How many counters does each child get?

> To make an **equal share**, give each child the same amount.

Matthew   Aliki   Hannah

Each child gets __3__ counters.

Draw counters to show equal shares.
Write how many each child gets.

1. 4 children want to share 16 counters equally.

Philip   Elizabeth   Beto   Helen

Each child gets __4__ counters.

2. 3 children want to share 15 counters equally.

Sabrina   Moesha   Kyle

Each child gets __5__ counters.

156 Use with Lesson 12-7.

Practice

Name _____

Making Equal Groups

P 12-7

How many coins will each child get?
Write the answer. Use coins if you need to.

1. 15 pennies, 5 children — Each child gets __3__ pennies.

2. 20 nickels, 4 children — Each child gets __5__ nickels.

3. 12 quarters, 3 children — Each child gets __4__ quarters.

Complete the table.

	Number of coins	Number of children	How many coins does each child get?
4.	16	2	8
5.	9	3	3
6.	16	4	4
7.	14	7	2

Problem Solving *Number Sense*

8. You have 18 plums. Can you find 6 different ways to show equal groups?

__1__ group of __18__   __6__ groups of __3__

__2__ groups of __9__   __9__ groups of __2__

__3__ groups of __6__   __18__ groups of __1__

156 Use with Lesson 12-7.

Enrichment

Name _____

Party Time

E 12-7
VISUAL THINKING

Sue is putting these toys into bags. She wants to make equal shares. Draw the equal shares. Write how many toys go in each bag.

1. Sue puts the jacks in 3 bags.
How many jacks are in each bag? __4__ jacks

Drawings should show 4 in each bag.

2. Sue puts the tops in 4 bags.
How many are in each bag? __2__ tops

Drawings should show 2 in each bag.

3. Sue puts the whistles in 3 bags.
How many are in each bag? __3__ whistles

Drawings should show 3 in each bag.

156 Use with Lesson 12-7.

Problem Solving

Name _____

Making Equal Groups

PS 12-7

Count the coins.
Use the number of coins to solve each problem.

Quarters   Dimes

Nickels   Pennies

1. How many quarters in all? __10__
How can 2 children equally share the quarters?

Each child gets __5__ quarters.

2. How many nickels in all? __8__
How can 4 children equally share the nickels?

Each child gets __2__ nickels.

3. Write 2 ways you can equally share the pennies.

__3__ groups of __4__

__6__ groups of __2__   **Answers may vary.**

4. Write 2 ways you can equally share the dimes.

__2__ groups of __8__

__4__ groups of __4__   **Answers may vary.**

156 Use with Lesson 12-7.

© Pearson Education, Inc. 2

Reteaching

Name _____

Writing Division Sentences

R 12-8

When you share equally, you **divide**.

5 children want to share 10 counters equally. Draw 1 counter for each child. Keep drawing 1 counter for each child until you have drawn 10 counters in all.

Brandon   Melissa   Joaquin   Dorothea   Janet

There are __10__ counters to share equally.

There are __5__ groups of counters.

There are __2__ counters in each group.

Each child gets __2__ counters.   So, 10 ÷ 5 = __2__.

Draw to show equal groups.
Write how many each child gets.
Then write the division sentence.

   1. 4 children want to share 12 counters.

Gabriel   Talia   Shane   Natanya

Each child gets __3__ counters.   12 ÷ 4 = __3__

Use with Lesson 12-8. **157**

Practice

Name _____

Writing Division Sentences

P 12-8

Draw to show equal groups. Write the division sentence.

1. 9 markers divided among 3 boxes.

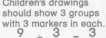

Children's drawings should show 3 groups with 3 markers in each.

__9__ ÷ __3__ = __3__

2. 12 buttons divided among 4 cups.

Children's drawings should show 4 groups with 3 buttons in each.

__12__ ÷ __4__ = __3__

3. 15 flowers divided among 5 vases.

Children's drawings should show 5 groups with 3 flowers in each.

__15__ ÷ __5__ = __3__

4. 8 balls divided among 2 cartons.

Children's drawings should show 2 groups with 4 balls in each.

__8__ ÷ __2__ = __4__

Problem Solving *Reasonableness*

Draw a picture to help answer the question.

5. Rita has 14 cat treats.
She has 3 cats.
How many treats will each cat get?
Are there any treats left over?

Children's drawings should show 3 groups of 4 cat treats, with 2 left over.

Each cat will get 4 treats and there will be 2 treats left over.

Use with Lesson 12-8. **157**

Enrichment

Name _____

At the Farmer's Market

E 12-8
DECISION MAKING

Draw the fruit in boxes to show equal groups.
Then write a division sentence.

1. There are 12 oranges in all. | 2. There are 8 apples in all.

Answers may vary.
Check children's drawings.

____ ÷ ____ = ____ | ____ ÷ ____ = ____

3. There are 9 tomatoes in all. | 4. There are 6 watermelons in all.

____ ÷ ____ = ____ | ____ ÷ ____ = ____

Use with Lesson 12-8. **157**

Problem Solving

Name _____

Writing Division Sentences

PS 12-8

Count how many there are of each fruit.
Write division sentences to show equal shares.
Draw circles around equal groups of fruit if you need help.

Strawberries   Pears   Lemons   Apples

1. Karen puts the pears into 6 boxes.
How many pears go in each box?

__12__ ÷ __6__ = __2__   Children may draw 6 groups of 2.

2. Wendall puts the strawberries in 4 cartons.
How many strawberries go in each carton?

__16__ ÷ __4__ = __4__   Children may draw 4 groups of 4.

3. Anna puts the apples in 3 baskets.
How many apples go in each basket?

__9__ ÷ __3__ = __3__   Children may draw 3 groups of 3.

4. Willy gets 3 more lemons. Can he put an
equal number of lemons in 2 boxes? Explain.

No, now there are 13 lemons. If he puts 6 lemons in each box, 1 will be left over.

Use with Lesson 12-8. **157**

© Pearson Education, Inc. 2

Name _____

PROBLEM-SOLVING SKILL   R 12-9

Choose an Operation

Different operations solve different problems.
Write the sign that shows the operation you will
use to solve the problem; $+$, $-$, $\times$, or $\div$.

There are 5 cages at the pet store. 4 puppies are in
each cage. How many puppies are at the pet store?

Think about what the problem tells you.

There are __5__ cages. There are __4__ puppies in each cage.
What does the problem want you to find?

How many puppies there are at the pet store.

What operation do you need to use? __×__

Circle the number sentence that solves the problem.

($5 \times 4 = 20$) $5 + 4 = 9$ $5 - 4 = 1$

So, there are __20__ puppies at the pet store.

Write the sign that shows the operation you need to use.
Circle the number sentence that solves the problem.

1. A cage has 9 birds. Jack buys 3 birds.
   How many birds are left?

   What operation do you need to use? _____

   $9 + 3 = 12$ ($9 - 3 = 6$) $9 \times 3 = 27$

   There are __6__ birds left at the pet store.

158 Use with Lesson 12-9.

Name _____

PROBLEM-SOLVING SKILL   P 12-9

Choose an Operation

Circle the number sentence that solves the problem.

1. Sara makes 6 bracelets. She puts 3 beads on each
   bracelet. How many beads does she use in all?

   $6 - 3 = 3$ $6 + 3 = 9$ ($6 \times 3 = 18$)

   Sara uses __18__ beads.

2. Monty builds a birdhouse. He uses 7 pieces of wood
   for the house and 3 pieces of wood for the roof.
   How many pieces of wood does he use in all?

   ($7 + 3 = 10$) $7 \times 3 = 21$ $7 - 3 = 4$

   Monty uses __10__ pieces of wood.

3. Mr. Kaplan bakes 8 muffins. He eats 2 muffins
   for breakfast. How many muffins are left?

   $8 \times 2 = 16$ ($8 - 2 = 6$) $8 + 4 = 12$

   Mr. Kaplan has __6__ muffins left.

4. Miss Thomas sews 5 dolls. She has 15 buttons.
   She wants to sew the same number of buttons on
   each doll. How many buttons does each doll get?

   $5 + 3 = 8$ ($15 \div 5 = 3$) $5 - 3 = 2$

   Each doll gets __3__ buttons.

158 Use with Lesson 12-9.

Name _____

At the Supermarket

E 12-9
ALGEBRA

Decide if you will add, subtract, multiply, or
divide to solve each problem. Write the number
sentence to solve the problem.

1. Charlene has 5 rows of soup cans with 4 in each row.
   How many soup cans are there?

   | 5 | | 4 | = | 20 |

   __20__ soup cans

2. There are 12 boxes of cereal in
   one carton. Mr. Mooney puts
   6 boxes on a shelf. How many
   cereal boxes are still in the carton?

   | 12 | | 6 | = | 6 |

   __6__ cereal boxes

3. Will puts an equal number of steaks in
   2 bins. There are 10 steaks in all.
   How many steaks go in each bin?

   | 10 | | 2 | = | 5 |

   __5__ steaks

4. There are 16 loaves of bread in a box.
   Mrs. Melon buys 4 loaves. How many
   loaves of bread are left in the box?

   | 16 | | 4 | = | 12 |

   __12__ loaves of bread

158 Use with Lesson 12-9.

Name _____

PROBLEM-SOLVING SKILL   PS 12-9

Choose an Operation

Melly collects stickers. She puts 6 stickers
on each page in her book. She fills 4 pages
with stickers. How many stickers are there in all?

What operation will you use to solve this problem?

Will you add, subtract, or multiply? _multiply_

$6 + 4 = 12$ $6 - 4 = 2$ ($6 \times 4 = 24$)

Why do you think you will _multiply_?

Because each page is a group of stickers.

There are __24__ stickers in all.

Circle the number sentence that solves the problem.

1. Kareem collects 5 model cars.
   He gives 2 cars to his friend.
   How many cars does Kareem
   have now?   Kareem has __3__ cars.

   ($5 - 2 = 3$) $5 + 2 = 7$ $5 \times 2 = 10$

2. Nadia collects 20 finger puppets.
   She puts an equal number of
   puppets on 4 shelves. How many   There are __5__ puppets
   puppets are on each shelf?   on each shelf.

   ($20 \div 4 = 5$) $20 - 4 = 16$ $20 + 4 = 24$

Using the page To help children *plan* and *solve* each problem, ask them to estimate if their answer will be a small or large number.

158 Use with Lesson 12-9.

Name _____

PROBLEM-SOLVING APPLICATIONS   R 12-10

Up, Up, and Away!

Write a number sentence.
Decide what operation you
will use to solve the problem.

5 planes are ready for take-off.
There are 3 pilots on each plane.
How many pilots are on the planes altogether?

What numbers will you use? __5__ and __3__

What operation will you use? Write the sign. __X__

__5__ × __3__ = __15__   __15__ pilots are on the planes.

Solve.

1. There are 73 passengers.
   40 of them order chicken for dinner.
   How many passengers do not order chicken?

   __73__ − __40__ = __33__ passengers

2. A plane has 24 seats in one section.
   There are 3 seats in each row.
   How many rows of seats are there?

   __24__ ÷ __3__ = __8__ rows of seats

Use with Lesson 12-10. **159**

Name _____

PROBLEM-SOLVING APPLICATIONS   P 12-10

Up, Up, and Away!

Solve.

1. A plane has 6 rows of seats in one part of the cabin.
   Each row has 3 seats. How many seats are there in all?

   __6__ rows × __3__ seats in each row = __18__ seats in all

2. Javier brought magazines to read on the plane.
   It took Javier 2 hours to read each magazine.
   The flight lasted 6 hours. How many magazines
   did Javier read during the flight?

   __6__ ÷ __2__ = __3__ magazines

3. A passenger has two suitcases. One suitcase weighs
   27 pounds. The other suitcase weighs 56 pounds.
   How many pounds do the two suitcases weigh in all?

   __27__ + __56__ = __83__ pounds in all

Writing in Math

4. Write a multiplication story about a trip
   you would like to take on an airplane.

   Stories will vary.

   _____

   _____

Use with Lesson 12-10. **159**

Name _____

Arithmetic Airport   E 12-10
                                               MENTAL MATH

Use mental math to solve.

1. Christy has 20 pounds of luggage.
   Martin has twice as many pounds of
   luggage as she does. How many pounds
   does Martin have?   __40__ pounds

2. The waiting area has 3 rows of seats.
   There are 6 seats in each row. How many
   seats are there in all?   __18__ seats

3. Glen waits in line to board the plane.
   There are 25 people in the line.
   Glen is fourth in line. How many people
   are behind him?   __21__ people

4. There are 16 sandwiches and 4 trays
   at the snack bar. Ms. Marshall puts an
   equal number of sandwiches on each tray.
   How many sandwiches go on each tray?   __4__ sandwiches

5. Write your own math problem about the airport.
   Give it to a friend to solve.

   Problems will vary.

   _____

   _____

   _____

Use with Lesson 12-10. **159**

Name _____

PROBLEM-SOLVING APPLICATIONS   PS 12-10

Up, Up, and Away!

A plane has 127 passengers.
At one stop, 82 more passengers get on the plane.
How many passengers are on the plane now?

What numbers will you use?

127 and 82

127 + 82 = __209__   __209__ passengers in all

Solve.

1. There are 65 suitcases on a
   baggage cart. 25 suitcases
   are loaded onto a plane.
   How many suitcases are
   still on the cart?

   __65__ − __25__ = __40__

2. A plane makes 3 trips in
   one day. How many trips
   does the plane make
   in one week?

   __7__ × __3__ = __21__

Writing in Math

3. Write a division story about airplanes.

   Stories will vary.

   _____

   _____

Using the page To help children *read and understand*, ask them to tell the numbers they will use to write each
number sentence.

Use with Lesson 12-10. **159**